THE NEW NATURALIST

A SURVEY OF BRITISH NATURAL HISTORY

NATURAL HISTORY IN THE HIGHLANDS & ISLANDS

The aim of this series is to interest the general reader in the wild life of Britain by recapturing the inquiring spirit of the old naturalists. The Editors believe that the natural pride of the British public in the native fauna and flora, to which must be added concern for their conservation, is best fostered by maintaining a high standard of accuracy combined with clarity of exposition in presenting the results of modern scientific research. The plants and animals are described in relation to their homes and habitats and are portrayed in the full beauty of their natural colours, by the latest methods of colour photography and reproduction.

THE NEW NATURALIST

NATURAL HISTORY IN THE HIGHLANDS & ISLANDS

BY

F. FRASER DARLING

D.Sc. F.R.S.E.

WITH 46 COLOUR PHOTOGRAPHS
BY F. FRASER DARLING, JOHN MARKHAM AND OTHERS
55 BLACK-AND-WHITE PHOTOGRAPHS
AND 24 MAPS AND DIAGRAMS

COLLINS ST. JAMES'S PLACE LONDON

First published in 1947 by
Collins 14 St. James's Place London
Produced in conjunction with Adprint
and printed in Great Britain
by Collins Clear-Type Press
London and Glasgow

TO THE MEMORY OF

WILLIAM ORR, F.R.C.V.S.

† *Singapore, December 1945*

KENNETH McDOUGALL, M.Sc., M.R.C.V.S.

† *Normandy, August 1944*

WHO KNEW AND LOVED THE HIGHLANDS AND ISLANDS
AND THE WILD LIFE THEREIN

CONTENTS

COLOUR PLATES

COLOUR PLATES

It should be noted that throughout this book Plate numbers in arabic figures refer to Colour Plates, while roman numerals are used for Black-and-White Plates

PLATES IN BLACK AND WHITE

LIST OF MAPS AND DIAGRAMS

EDITORS' PREFACE

FOR MANY years Dr. F. Fraser Darling has found his field of work in the Highlands and Islands of Scotland. One of his pioneer researches was into the social behaviour of a herd of red deer, in an area of Wester Ross dominated by the massif of An Teallach. In 1936 he began the first of two seasons' work on Priest Island of the Summer Isles, studying the social structure of gull colonies and of small flocks of grey lag geese and other gregarious birds. It was from this work that Dr. Darling was led to enunciate his theory connecting the size of a social group of gregarious animals, with its breeding-time, and breeding-success. Statistical analysis and further observation by other workers have confirmed this theory and shown it to be of wide biological importance. Darling then made protracted autumn and winter visits to Lunga of the Treshnish Isles, and to North Rona, in order to study a further type of animal sociality, that of the Atlantic grey seal, an animal of whose life history we knew surprisingly little. He also worked his small farm on Tanera in the Summer Isles in such fashion as to show that it was possible and reasonable to raise considerably the stock-carrying capacity of the West Highlands and to grow a large amount of human food under crofting conditions.

Fraser Darling is a born naturalist, was brought up to farming, and became a scientist as thoroughly and quickly as academic discipline permitted. His first researches (at the Institute of Animal Genetics, Edinburgh University) were on the Scottish Mountain Blackface breed of sheep. He combines the qualities of a trained biologist and practical farmer with those of a sensitive field observer. As a humanist he is considering the Highland problem with none of the peculiar obsessions with which it has so often been approached : some Highland countrymen believe only in sport, or stalking, or sheep : others believe that no problem is more important than crofting, or water power, or the tourist industry, or the collecting of rare alpine plants. Fraser Darling's sympathies are with *all* the interesting problems of living things in the Highlands, not least with the human species which —in this wild part of Britain where man is in such close contact with the natural physical environment—must be regarded in relation to the others. It is in this spirit that he is interpreting his present work as Director of the West Highland Survey.

In this book, which is the first effort, so far as we are aware, to give a picture of Highland natural history as a whole, Dr. Darling has, naturally, expanded on those subjects with which he is most familiar—the life histories of seals, deer and sea-birds, and the ecology of grazing and regeneration of forest growth. Nevertheless, he has a general view, derived from a wide and mature experience, tempered with homely wisdom, and illuminated by his genuine love for the Highlands. There is, in this book, no aura of bogus romance ; there are no purple passages or sporting reminiscences : instead, he has given us something of the *real* essence of Scotland's land and sea.

THE EDITORS

Every care has been taken by the Editors to ensure the scientific accuracy of factual statements in these volumes, but the sole responsibility for the interpretation of facts rests with the Authors

AUTHOR'S PREFACE

A MAN does not write a book like this one without a good deal of help. First, there is that host of observers and seekers after knowledge whose works have been scanned for their contribution to this attempted synthesis. Then there is the good criticism given by the Editors, James Fisher in particular, for his friendship has been sorely tried. Charles Elton was good enough to spend part of his first holiday in seven years reading the draft, and his suggestions have been invaluable. Averil Morley has helped me throughout in gathering data and as a constant kindly critic. I am grateful to them all, but would not like to unload on to them any of the responsibility for this book. After all, I have not always taken their advice and must stand or fall alone in what seems to me something of a tight-rope act. This work is not a handbook of natural history ; that is why I have refused to call it *The Natural History of the Highlands and Islands* ; that would have been too presumptuous a title. Whole orders of animals and plants escape any mention, partly for want of space but mainly, perhaps, because one man is not omniscient. The aim has been to tell a plain tale of a remarkable region and of some of the causes, interactions and consequences which confront the inquiring mind. One thing I would say : I know more now about natural history in the Highlands and Islands than when I began this book three years ago, and writing it has set me thinking. I want to get into the field again and look into new problems that have occurred to me. If the book has the same effect on anybody else, it will have served some good purpose.

F. D.

Strontian,
North Argyll.

CHAPTER I

GEOLOGY AND CLIMATE

IT MAY be truly said of the Highlands and Islands of Scotland that the geology of the country makes the scenery. The geology cannot be ignored in describing the area, as the subject might be if the rocks were overlaid with a great thickness of soil deposited by alluvial drift. Here in the Highlands there is often no soil at all, the bare rocks starkly showing to sun and tempest; or again, a thin layer of acid peat may be the only covering. Such true soils as exist on the hillsides and in the straths are usually of fairly local origin, reflecting the qualities of the rocks near at hand.

Geology, then, linked with climate, determines very largely the nature of the initial vegetation of the Highlands. Man himself determines the secondary vegetation to some extent through his management of animals and of fire, but there are decided limits to what he can do in the face of the geology. Vegetation in its turn, and again governed by climate, has a remarkable effect on the animal life of the region, both in variety and distribution. Geology, through the relief of the land to which it gives rise, also has a definite effect on climate—for example, the presence of mountains results in the condensation of the moisture of the air, hence the characteristic heavy rainfall in their vicinity. The vegetation influences slightly the immediate climate of a region, and the two together may have their effect on the superficial geology, as in woodlands preventing erosion and gullying of hillsides.

We should remember the constant interplay of these dynamic forces as well as life itself in studying the natural history of the Highlands and Islands. It is a noble drama of weather and mountain and sea and plant and animal, the *dramatis personae* of which may be given this diagrammatic form:

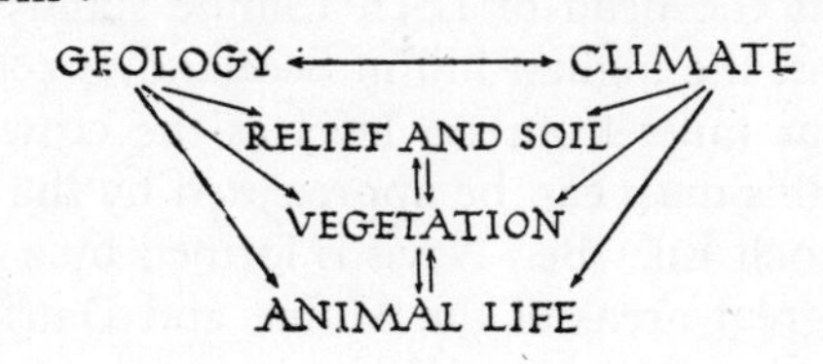

From almost every point of view of natural history, the Highland region of Scotland is demarcated by the sharp geological line known as The Highland Border Fault which runs north-east, south-west across Scotland from the mouth of the Clyde to Stonehaven. Although a good deal of Scotland's best agricultural land lies along the east coast north of this line, the great mass of the country to the north-west of the Fault (also known in history as the Highland line) is mountainous. The word mountainous does not, however, allow us properly to speak of *mountains* in Scotland. It is rather an inverted boast of the Scot, secure in his country's superiority of wild terrain, to inform the visitor that there are reputedly mountains in England and Wales and in Ireland, but in Scotland they are called hills.

The Highlands, also, are not necessarily high ground. The highest point of the Hebridean island of Benbecula is only 420 feet, but Benbecula is unquestionably as Highland in its natural history as in its human cultural relationships.

There is another major geological feature which plays a large part in the topography of the area, in the shape of the Great Glen of Scotland, a second big fault forming Glen Albyn (the English have an annoying habit of calling it the Caledonian Canal !). This great dividing line between the Northern and North-West Highlands on the one hand and the Central and South-West Highlands on the other is marked not only by the Great Glen itself, but by the chain of long freshwater lochs it contains, the most famous of which is Loch Ness, 21¾ miles long and of great depth. The loch drains north-eastwards to the short Ness River and the Moray Firth at Inverness. The very low watershed which crosses the Great Glen, in so far as the flow north-east or south-west is concerned, is above the head of Loch Oich and is no more than 115 feet above sea level. The next loch south-westwards is Loch Lochy, and the Lochy River which flows from it runs into the salt water of Loch Linnhe, which ultimately fans out after the Corran Narrows and becomes the Firth of Lorne which is such a distinctive feature of the western coastline. At the south-westward end of the Great Glen and at the head of Loch Linnhe stands the sentinel-like massif of Ben Nevis, the highest hill in Scotland, 4,406 feet high. The summit is only four miles from sea level as the crow flies, so the full sense of height of this mass can be appreciated by the traveller coming eastwards down Loch Eil. Ben Nevis is formed by a granite intrusion between the two great areas of the Moine and Dalriadan schists. It is a wide-topped hill of no particular beauty of shape, but its north corrie is undoubtedly impressive, for it contains the highest sheer cliff face in Britain of about 1,500 feet (Plate I, facing page 16) as well as one of the very few semi-permanent snow patches in Britain. This patch of snow is untouched by the sun's rays.

The actual summit of Ben Nevis is not of the granite rock of which the main mass of the hill is composed. The summit is the top of a gigantic cylinder of tertiary basalt. Presumably this volcano originally spread the basalt over the whole of the hill, but all except the protected summit has been eroded away.

It is worth noting that the two highest mountainous groups in Scotland are formed of granite—Ben Nevis, and the Cairngorm region, 4,296 feet, east of the Spey ; and east again, there is Lochnagar, on the eastern side of the Highland area, also granite and reaching 3,760 feet. The Cairngorms are of much greater extent than the Ben Nevis massif and, partly because of their considerable alpine plateaux at about the 4,000-foot contour, have a special place in Highland natural history. Topographically, the Cairngorms viewed from afar may seem as uninteresting as Ben Nevis, but the physical beauty of these hills is for intimate observation in the magnificent corries and on the high plateaux. It is possible to walk a pony on to these high ridges and plateaux without any trouble, the ground being good all the way.

There are two more striking geological phenomena which will be less obvious to the casual observer than those of the Highland Boundary Fault and the Great Glen. First, that definite line of tectonic tumult known as the Moine Overthrust which reaches from the south-west corner of Skye north-north-eastwards to the eastern shore of Loch Eriboll on the north coast. Here the older rocks of the Moine schists are thrust westwards over younger rocks along a hundred-mile line. Through the whole length, like a sandwich filling between archaean gneiss with the overlying Torridonian sandstone on the west side, and the Moine schists on the east, are beds of Cambrian age including an extremely hard and shiny metamorphosed quartzite which makes a barren strip of country. This rock is so hard and shiny that even the peat finds it difficult to keep a hold on slopes of any considerable inclination. There are many patches of acres of bare rock (e.g. Pl. 3a, p. 44) to be found on the passage of the quartzite from Eriboll to Skye, and it may be best described in the climber's graphic phrase of " boiler-plating."

Here and there along the line of this uninteresting sandwich filling there appears a geological titbit in the shape of an outcrop of limestone such as the famous Durness limestone of Cambrian age. The effect of this is to enliven the natural history and change the scenery of this vast geological sandwich. Instead of bareness and blackness of peat we get greenness and soil. It is this limestone which makes the Assynt district a place which no naturalist should ignore from the geological, entomological, conchological or botanical points of view. The effect is, perhaps, still more marked around Durness. Even the bird life has its particular interest in this area and so has the world of loch and river. A little farther south than Assynt, in a black area of bog to the east of Suilven and Canisp, there rises an island of limestone a few hundred acres in extent. The climber on these hills in spring or autumn will experience pleasure and something of a shock to see the townships of Elphin and Cnockan on their geological emerald. If he goes down to these thriving villages he will notice that the sheep are larger, the cattle better-looking, and there will be Highland pony mares and foals such as he will see nowhere else so commonly till he reaches the *machairs* of South Uist. The roadsides are like the verges of an English lane. All this is part of the paradox of the Highlands and of Highland life. They are full of surprises and facts which do not seem to fit in. No sooner does the theorizing type of mind construct a hypothesis which looks neat than some disconcerting fact will create paradox.

So much for the Moine Thrust and its consequences ; the second striking geological phenomenon is the mixture in the West Highlands of old rocks and new volcanic ones. From Cape Wrath to Applecross the West Coast is a wild jumble of the ancient Hebridean gneiss and that very old and barren sandstone known as Torridonian. These two formations make for scenery which is exceptionally wild in quite different ways. Then at the foot of Loch Linnhe is the Isle of Mull and, to the north of it, some similar tertiary volcanic rocks in Morvern and Ardnamurchan. Such volcanic rock is a dull grey in colour and amorphous in texture, except where there occur amygdaloid pockets of crystals of much beauty, but it makes some distinctive scenery. These tertiary rocks as we see them in Mull are the remains of immense beds of lava, possibly 50 million years of age as against the 1,500 million years or so of the gneiss farther north. The lava erodes into terrace-like formations which correspond to the actual flows, and on which terraces the soil is found to be brown and rich—a real soil without peat—and the grass grows thick in summer. The country of the tertiary terraces is cattle country and turns up again in the western part of Skye. Sometimes the terraced denudation gives way to a natural castellated architecture such as the Castle Rock of the Treshnish Isles (see also Pl. Va, p. 52), and further still to towers and spires like the Quirang and the Old Man of Storr in Skye (Pl. II, p. 17). This latter rock is like a natural Tower of Pisa and visible from many miles away. Sometimes, again, the tertiary basalt has solidified in a peculiar way to make those giant hexagonal columns much visited at Staffa, the small island between Iona and the Treshnish Isles. Such columns may also be found elsewhere, as in Mull, Canna and Oidhsgeir, on a much smaller scale, but probably the most impressive examples in Scotland are those of the northern face of Garbh Eilean of the Shiant Isles. Though the steamer from Kyle of Lochalsh to Stornoway passes within four miles of the Shiants, these islands are rarely visited, and the tremendous columnar architecture remains almost unknown. The Shiants are the northern outposts of Scotland's youngest rocks ; only four miles away to the west is the east coast of the Hebrides, composed of her oldest rock, the archaean gneiss. Geology is a hard subject to learn, but it helps one to understand scenery, and with a little knowledge it gives great sense of wonderment at the immensity of the movements of the earth's crust.

The Moine Thrust has been mentioned as one of the major geological features of the Highlands. The Moine schists which occur to the east of the Thrust are the most extensive group of rocks found in the Highlands as a whole. They are sometimes called the Undifferentiated Eastern Schist, and words such as gneissose and schistose crop up in a detailed geological description ; but whatever the names, the group of rocks reaches in a broad, roughly parallel-sided band, fifty miles wide, from the north coast of Scotland to the foot of the Great Glen where it comes up short against the tertiary basalt of Mull and western Morven. South of the Great Glen, similar schists and gneisses, the Dalriadan, underlie a large part of the Central Highlands and reach far into Aberdeenshire. Many of the high tops of the Highlands are on this formation—Ben Lawers 3,984 feet, Craig Meagaidh 3,700, Mam Soul 3,862 and Carn Eige 3,877 feet. The schists form a great plateau on the western side of the Spey opposite the Cairngorms. This schist plateau has the Gaelic name of Monaliadh

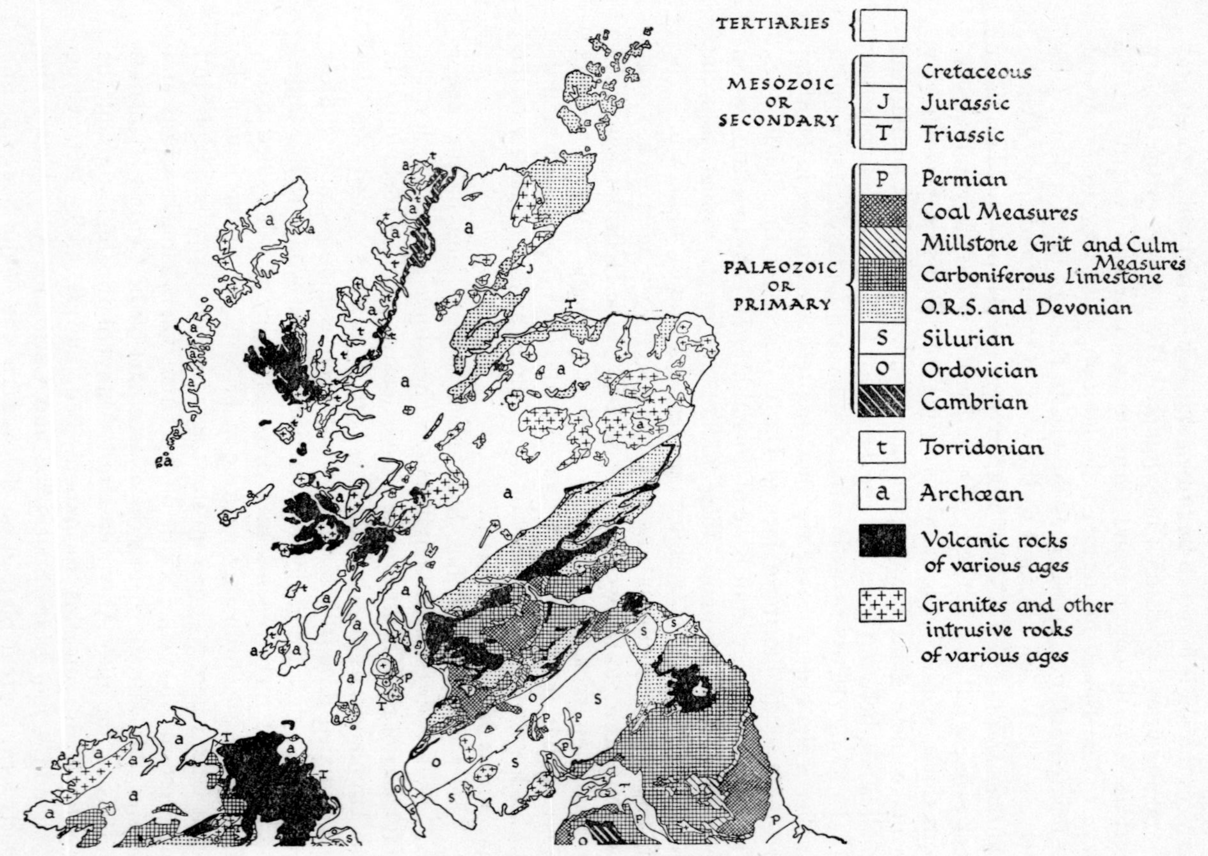

FIG 1.—Geology of the Highlands
The exposures of Tertiary and Cretaceous are not large enough to show on this scale

—the grey mountains—and the Cairngorms across the valley are called the Monaruadh—the red mountains. The grey is most obvious when it comes up against either the granite as on the east side of the Highlands, or against the reddish-purple Torridonian, as on the west. Though schists and gneisses are intimately associated and both very ancient, the schists break down more easily, and as they contain a fair quantity of alumina they often make good soil, and produce a different vegetational complex from the adjoining Torridonian, for example. The presence of overmuch peat, of course, may entirely cut out the influence of the slowly-disintegrating rock.

An igneous rock known as gabbro is of infrequent occurrence in the Highlands, but its appearances and the consequences of glacial action on the gabbro constitute some of the most spectacular scenery not only in the Highlands but in the whole world. The more important masses of gabbro are closely associated with the tertiary lava and are in fact intrusive masses of molten rock which solidified underground but have since been exposed by denudation. The small example of gabbro scenery in the shape of Ardnamurchan Point, the most westerly point of the mainland of Great Britain, is wild, but not high enough to be considered grand, but this rock in Skye is the stuff of the Cuillin hills (Pl. IIIa, p. 32) which rise to 3,309 feet. Gabbro is hard and knobbly, which makes it safe for the experienced climber, and by the coincidence of the Cuillin range being the centre of an ice cap in glacial times, the glaciers working outwards to the perimeter have carved the great corries and left the sharp ridges in which we delight to-day. With the retreat of the glaciers the shape of the moraines becomes obvious, and subsequent weathering of the hills has produced some great scree slopes.

South-west of Skye there is another fairly large island of nearly 30,000 acres, called Rum. Its highest hills do not go beyond 2,600 feet, but in beauty of line they are not less than the Cuillins ; and when we come to examine their geology, we find that nearly a third of the island, including these fine hills, is composed of gabbro.

Another mass of gabbro and allied rocks occurs over a hundred miles farther west to form the group of islands known as St. Kilda. They are unique in British scenery and in British natural history. Here, the Atlantic has not allowed the accumulation of the fragments which result from weathering and make the scree slopes seen in the Cuillins. Instead, the gabbro stands up out of the sea in naked pinnacles. The highest point of the largest island, Hirta, is 1,396·8 feet above sea level, from just below which is the highest sheer sea-cliff in Britain. (This is disputed by those who say the Kame of Foula, 1,220 feet, is the highest.) Even so, the island being three miles or so across, the height of this cliff is not so striking as the smaller island of Boreray on the north side of the group, which being roughly triangular and less than a mile across rises to 1,245 feet. Stac Lee and Stac an Armin are mere rocks in the sea, a furlong or less across at their foot, but they rise to 544 and 627 feet and make a difficult climb for a good man (see Pls. XXIb, p. 176, and XXIX, p. 228). It is on these stacks of gabbro in the western ocean that the largest gannet colonies in the world are found.

Finally, the 70-foot stack of Rockall (Pl. XXII, p. 177), 184 miles west of St. Kilda, is of a rock allied to gabbro though more acid in composition. The natural history of that rock, in so far as it is known, would not fill a volume. No birds breed on it regularly though guillemots do from time to time. Lichens there may be but no other vegetation. Gannets and other sea birds are often found resting there in summer. Near it is Leonidas or Hazelwood Rock, usually awash. Farther away Helen's reef, about a mile long comes to the surface only at spring tides in one place, so the geological nature of this submerged land is unknown to us. The naturalist, of all men, cannot resist the temptation sometimes to dream of what Rockall would have been had it thrust itself just another hundred feet through the waves and been able to withstand the wave action which has reduced it to its present proportions. We should have had a long low island with a hump and a few smaller eminences. What sort of a place would it have been botanically? What haven would it have made for nesting birds from the sea, and would the Atlantic seal have been an altogether more numerous species than it is, by having a North Atlantic sanctuary which would usually have been unapproachable during the autumn breeding season? James Fisher tells me that on an exceptionally calm day the Leonidas Rock may dry out and would provide the only possible hauling-out place for the seal; but in fact, the Atlantic seal has been seen only once in the vicinity.

I have very roughly indicated the geological character of the Highlands in so far as it affects the topography; there remains, however, the phenomenon of glaciation as the most tremendous carver of scenery from the matrix of rocks of one kind or another. I mentioned the effect of glaciation on the Cuillins, but that was a minor area of ice action compared with the Highlands as a whole. Glaciologists now appear to be agreed that there were four glacial periods in which the Highlands were involved, though it is improbable that the whole region was covered by the ice each time. There were certainly ice caps on the North-West Highlands and on the Grampians.

From these two or more central ice caps there are well-defined radial courses which have gouged out or deepened many of the glens and polished the summits of some of the lower hills. The country of the Hebridean gneiss in Sutherland and north-west Ross has been heavily scored by glaciers flowing westwards from the direction of the higher Torridonian sandstone hills inland and in the melting of the ice many boulders of this dark red rock have come to rest on the grey gneiss hills. Such erratic blocks are often well-worn and rounded: the stalker in this ground is sometimes tricked into putting his glass on them if he does not know it well, thinking such boulders are deer, seen from a mile away. And in the Torridonian area we see some fine hanging corries facing eastwards at about 1,750 feet, with a large area of boulder moraine below the lip of the corries. Where the boulders, long carried in the ice, have been open to the weather, only the deeper scorings and the rounding are obvious; but I have had occasion to move some of these boulders from their bed of fine glacial sand, their tops being in the way of my plough. The lower faces of such rocks, which had lain in their beds since the melting ice had lost momentum to carry them farther, were flat, scratched in some places but carrying quite a high polish on other parts of the sole. The coarser qualities of Torridonian sandstone do not take a smooth surface easily, but these surfaces gave the finger-tips a palpable sensation of polish.

The glaciers have not only carved and gouged the countryside but have had a profound effect on the subsequent natural history. The rock surfaces, shorn and left bare, have often remained bare or have gathered only a superficial layer of peat on which there grows but a poor vegetation. Again, some of the gougings have made saucer-like depressions which will not drain completely and either become lochs or peat-filled bogs with their own flora. The moraines are exceptionally well drained and the herbage grows in the rock detritus or on a very thin layer of peat. The best heather in the West Highlands—where heather does not normally grow well—is on the moraines.

The Spey Valley, and perhaps the Dee Valley also, is probably the best coniferous-tree-growing area in Scotland, a point to which return will be made later in the book: what is emphasized here is the comparative dryness of the ground of all this region, caused by the immense quantity of glacial drift (Pl. 1, p. 36) which drains readily and has only a thin layer of peat above it. The glacial drift of the Highlands is sandy and gravelly, not the boulder clay which is found in the north of England and in parts of the Central Plain of Scotland; for which fact we can be heartily glad, for to have boulder clay beneath our feet in a country of high rainfall would be unendurable.

Climate

The relation of geology and scenery we have taken for granted; that of geology, climate and vegetation we take almost for granted, and because of that we are too apt, perhaps, to generalize. Our old school geography books informed us that the climate of the British Isles was mild and humid and that the laving waters of the Gulf Stream (which we now call the Atlantic Drift) kept our insular climate an equable one. Though it is generally true that the south-eastern side of Britain is drier than the north-western, it is for the naturalist to inquire more deeply into such generalizations, for he knows that altitude, position and slope in relation to sun, nearness to sea and so on have considerable local effects on climate. At least, he is finding out that he must know local climates quite well if he is to be a good naturalist—for example, Loch Tay is 20 miles long; from east to west there is an increase of an inch per year of rainfall for every mile you go. We should rightly judge, therefore, that the more detailed natural history of Killin would show considerable differences from that of Aberfeldy on the score of rainfall alone. When I lived at Dundonnell at the head of Little Loch Broom I found the rainfall to be about 72 inches a year. Seven miles to the south in Strath na Sheallag beyond the Torridonian cones of An Teallach (Pl. IIIb, p. 32), the rainfall in my gauge there measured 100 inches. Seven miles north of Dundonnell lies Ullapool, which receives an average of 48 inches. Both snow and frost are more severe in Strath na Sheallag than in Ullapool. The differences in the vegetational complex of these two areas were marked, and so were those of the animal groupings, though of course it would be wrong to put it all down to the climate. If climates can alter so markedly within a few miles—and that is the rule rather than the exception in the Highlands—so can they alter within a few yards. The ecologist, the man who studies organisms in relation to their environment, is now giving more attention to what are called micro-climates. That gully in the north corrie of Ben Nevis which was mentioned on p. 3 as never getting the sun, and where the snow sometimes remains the year round, is an example of a distinct micro-climatic region. What is its annual mean temperature and its extremes? What does its relative-humidity chart look like? How much light gets in there? We do not know. And coming to its living things, what plants are found there? Perhaps the fauna would include a few spiders, some of which creatures have a habit of living in unlikely places on mountains. Again, knowledge remains incomplete. The distinctive natural history and weather data of that micro-climate remain to be discovered and set down, despite the fact that a meteorological station was maintained on the summit of Ben Nevis for twenty years from 1884 to 1903 and hourly records of all kinds taken.

The north side of a tree has a micro-climate quite distinct from that of the south side, and as a result of this there are definite zones of disposition of mosses and lichens. Similarly, the upper canopy of a tree has a different climate from that at its foot. The micro-climates of such a broken-up area as the Highlands are legion and beyond the scope of this book: attention will have to be confined to some of the variations likely to be met in our passage here and there through the hills, glens, lochs and islands.

Let us first of all realize the amount of indentation of the land of the West Highlands, which allows the sea to enter far into the countryside. That in itself, the western ocean being relatively warm for this latitude of 53–59° N., makes for mildness in the immediate neighbourhood of the sea lochs. It must be remembered, however, that altitude far outweighs latitude and distance from the sea in the matter of climate. West Highland hills tend to rise steeply from the sea, and as a great deal of ground lies above the 1,500-foot contour, the over-all temperature is low. The coasts, especially in favoured places, are exceptionally mild, and years may pass without more than 2° F. of frost being recorded. Only the coasts of western Wales and southern England can exceed the mean annual warmth of those of the West Highlands. The mean January temperatures of the West Highland coasts are between 40 and 42° F. compared with 38° and less on the

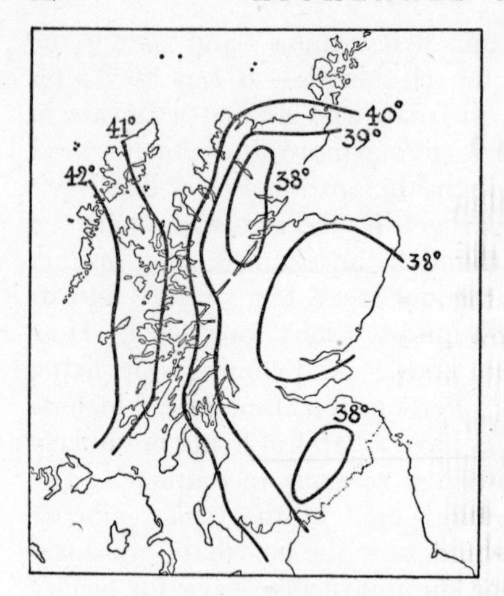

FIG. 2a.—January Isotherms
(reduced to sea level)

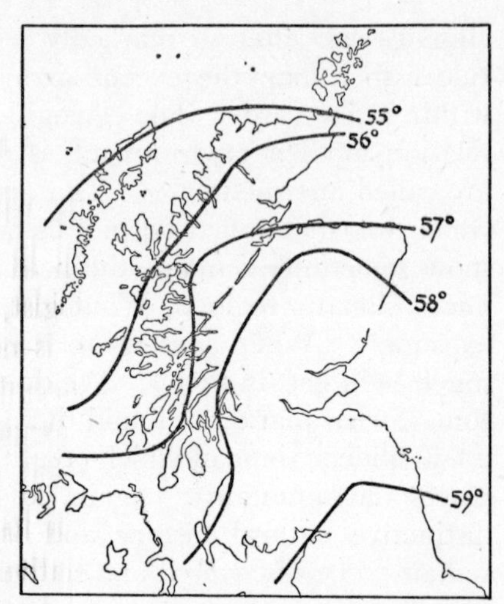

FIG. 2b.—July Isotherms
(reduced to sea level)

east coast of Scotland. The July isotherms tend to go east and west rather than north and south, but as the west coast of Scotland is reached they take a distinct dip south-westwards and show the West Highlands to have a mean summer temperature of 55–57° F. compared with 56–58° F. on the east coast. If we take the differences between annual mean summer and winter temperatures, there is only 14° F. of difference on the West Highland coast, compared with 20° F. at Dundee and 24° F. in London, Kent and East Anglia. These, of course, are sea-level temperatures. The Highlands show a completely different story as soon as you go uphill, and when you truly go inland into the Monaliadh or Cairngorm regions, conditions are much more extreme. Much work has been done on mountain climate in Britain by Dr. Gordon Manley, President of the Royal Meteorological Society. The twenty years' work on Ben Nevis is available to me in summary and I give these figures as a comparison with the sea-level conditions which pertain on the coast only a few miles away. The mean temperature of the hottest month, July, was 41·1° F., and of the coldest month, February, 23·8° F., a range of 17·3° F. The extreme records were, Maximum 66° F. (28 June 1902) and Minimum 1° F. (6 January 1894).

When we come to rainfall we see how easy it is to fall into a trap by generalizing that the west coast is wetter than the east. The belt

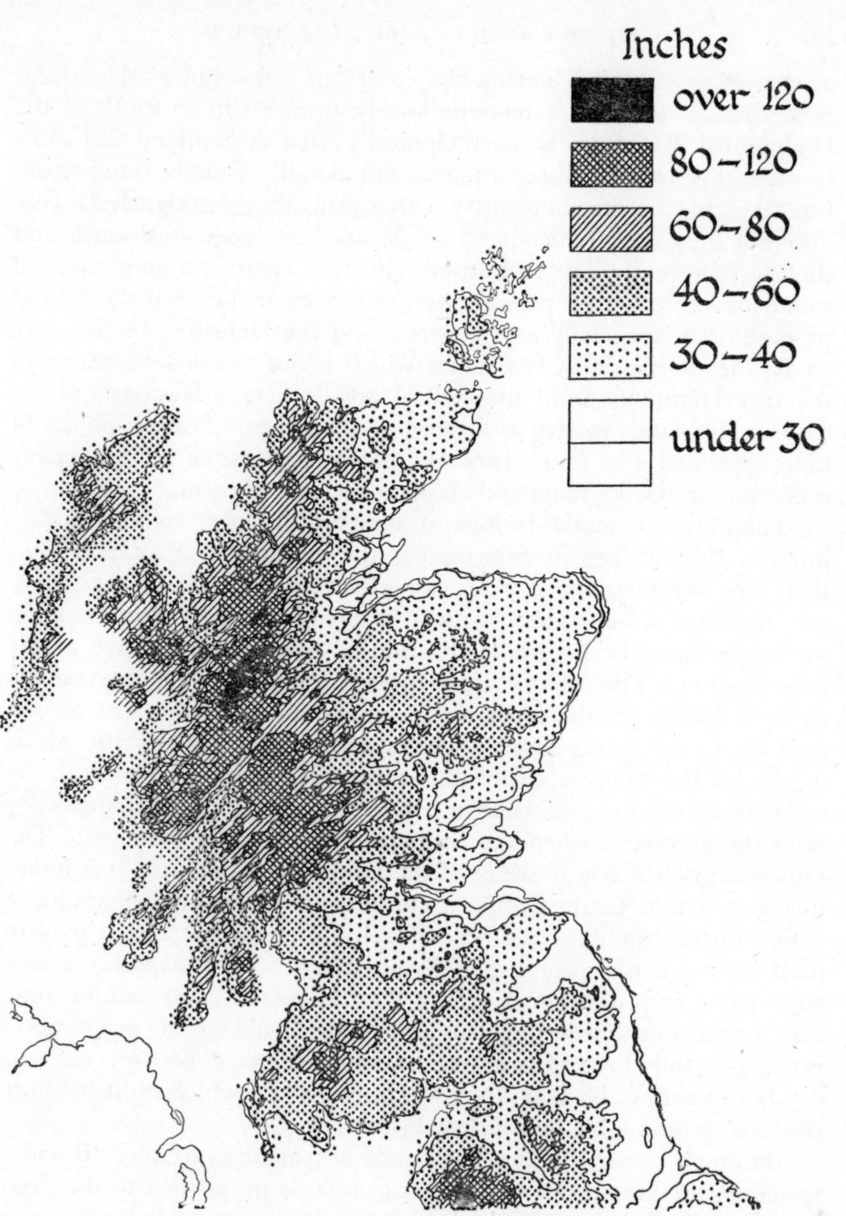

FIG. 3.—Average annual rainfall in the Highlands

Based on a map prepared in the Meteorological Office and reproduced by permission of His Majesty's Stationery Office

of very high rainfall is not on the coast but a few miles inland, and even then it does not extend uniformly from north to south of the Highlands. Reference to Bartholomew's Atlas of Scotland will show the monthly rainfall distribution in fair detail. Coming south from Cape Wrath, the strip of country with a rainfall over 100 inches a year does not start until Latitude 57·30° N. and then goes southwards and slightly south-eastwards to Latitude 56° N. There is a good area all round this strip with a precipitation of 60–100 inches, but the coastal promontories, especially in the north, and the Hebrides, receive only 40–60 inches of rain, a low figure which is not reached elsewhere in the true Highlands until the central area. A very few parts of the eastern Highlands receive as little as 30–40 inches. There is no doubt that Skye and the Inner Isles are partly responsible for the heavy precipitation on the mainland coast to the east of them.

These two climatic factors of temperature and rainfall are of immense importance in determining the vegetation of an area, but there are interrelations of these two which must always be taken into consideration when natural history is being studied. For example, something must be known of the rate of evaporation relative to the precipitation. The ratio between these two in any given situation has a big influence on the types of plants and to a lesser extent on the animals to be found there. The evaporating power of the air is measured by what is called the saturation deficit, which can be calculated from the difference in temperature between the wet and dry bulb thermometers when the temperature of the air is known. The saturation deficit is a measure of the humidity of the air. It is found in practice that there is often a constant variation in the saturation deficit during the day, and where such variation pertains, it may in itself influence the grouping of living things. The evaporation rate tends to be high in summer on the West Highland coast and for some way up the hills, but in the glens and on the high tops the evaporation rate is generally low. The annual average difference between wet and dry bulb readings on Ben Nevis was only 0·7° F., which must be quite the most humid climate in Great Britain.

Sunshine records in the Highlands are highly variable. Broadly speaking, the amount of sunshine is in inverse proportion to the rainfall, so the strip of the Highlands to which allusion has already been made as enduring 100 inches or more of rain enjoys least sun. It is also possible to draw a line bisecting the Outer Hebrides longitudinally, showing an annual total of sunshine of less than 1,200 hours on the west side and 1,200–1,300 hours on the east. I remember very well during several months on North Rona, equidistant 47 miles north of the Butt of Lewis and Cape Wrath, how much oftener it was possible to see Cape Wrath lighthouse quite clear than the north end of Lewis which would be shrouded in cloud. The resident in the Highlands knows well how much more sun there is on the little islands and promontories than on even the general run of coastal areas. The published figures probably do not show the true position because the number of sun gauges is few in the West Highlands. One of the surprises of the West is the local area of high sunshine records for the island of Tiree (Pl. 25, p. 212), the outermost of the Inner Hebrides. The island is low (beneath the waves, as Gaeldom described it in the old days) and has but little cloud-stopping or cloud-gathering power. The soil is mostly of shell sand or loam, so its moisture drains or evaporates quickly. It was not without good reason that in past days Tiree was known as the granary of the Isles. Only the south coast of England equals or exceeds Tiree's record. Grain needs sunshine to ripen it and fill it, but apart from that agricultural fact the plant ecologists say it is hard to demonstrate the precise effect of differing amounts of sunshine on vegetation. It remains probable, nevertheless, that actual lack of sunshine or a very low summer figure would inhibit the growth of such plants as broom and harebells, and encourage others such as the bryophytes (mosses and liverworts).

Tradition has it that the climate of the Highlands and Islands has deteriorated in living memory and in the fifty to seventy years before that. The meteorologists are always telling us we are wrong in thinking the weather was better in "our young days." All the same, in the North-West Highlands salt pans were in general use many years ago for evaporating sea water, but it is said the fall in the amount of sunshine—much more than the remission of the salt tax—was responsible for their use being discontinued.

It will be best for us to consider the climatic factor of snow when we come to note its effect in the higher mountainous regions. But let it be said that the Highlands as a whole do not suffer nearly so much snow as the Southern Uplands of Scotland or the Pennine Chain of England. Snow comes earlier and stays later on the tops of the hills because the factor of altitude is concerned, but the Atlantic mildness pervades much of the lower ground. Nearness to the sea is a considerable factor in determining how low the snow will come on a hill face and how long it will stay. This is brought home to anyone living offshore from the West Highland mainland and who has for a view a wide range of peaks stretching from three to twenty miles inland. Snow as a climatic factor can be of much importance in a region long after it has fallen if the catchment area of the snow is large. The Cairngorm hills provide an excellent example: their greatest accumulation of snow is at the end of April or even in early May, whereafter there is a steady melting which is not complete until August. It is in the dry month of June that the snow held on the spacious tops and plateaux of this region can maintain the water even in rapid-running rivers and affect the fish life down in the Spey and Dee Valleys. Obviously, snow has a great effect on plant and animal life in areas where it lies long, but we are here dealing with the general climate of the Highlands and must not be drawn away into discussion of local and micro-climates.

The shore line of the West Highland mainland is particularly free from snow. I have known years when the snow has not lain for more than a couple of hours in a whole winter—and then, like as not, it has been at the end of April or in the first week of May. That first week or so of May is regularly a wintry period, and is so well known in the North that it is called the Gab o' May. Taken all in all, it is remarkable how little is the effect of snow on vegetation in the Highlands except on the summits and in those places where it drifts and packs. Its influence on the behaviour of animals may be profound, but of that more later.

Frost has a distribution in the Highlands somewhat like that of snow, except for the peculiar conditions which will produce spring or autumn frosts on the floor of a glen and not at a few hundred feet up the hillsides. That is a phenomenon, of course, which is known all too well in the fruit-growing districts of England. The shore line of islands off the western seaboard may, as has been said, register no more than 2° F. of frost all winter, but occasional bad years such as the early 1940's may show up to 14° F. of frost. I remember seeing very thin pancake ice forming on the flat-calm sea of the Anchorage of Tanera in January 1941. Tanera is well out to the Minch and the sea is of fairly high salinity there.

Wind is a climatic factor of great variability and of exceedingly great importance in Highland natural history and the topography of the area. It would be entirely wrong to call the Highlands windswept;

PLATE I

G. P. Abraham

Ben Nevis, the north-east ridge and precipice
Inverness-shire

PLATE II

Robert M. Adam

OLD MAN OF STORR, Skye : tertiary basalt country

it cannot even be said truly that the coastal areas are windswept, for here on the shores of Loch Sunart where I am writing, the trees round the house are of beautiful symmetry and of great height, yet only 150 yards away on a shingle beach the wind blows much harder. The summits of the hills are windswept and the outer coasts are still more windswept, and it should be understood that the outer coasts of the North-West Highlands are the windiest part of Great Britain ; much windier, for example, than the Shetland Isles or the outer Norwegian coast, or Valencia Island off south-west Ireland. The gales above 4,000 feet are worse than on the coast ; the meteorological data from the Ben Nevis Observatory period gave an average of 261 gales a year of more than 50 m.p.h.

On the outer coasts of the Highlands gusts of 100 m.p.h. occur from time to time, and in certain places, where the configuration of the hills governs the play of wind, there are freak gusts and up and down draughts of excessive strength. In December 1938, I was going over the hill of North Rona during a three-day southerly gale to fetch water from the well on the southern cliff face. The wind was not so bad as it had been in the night, but I had to go on hands and knees over the ridge at 300 feet, from which there was an unbroken downward sweep to the sea on the south. When I reached the edge of the 70-foot cliffs which were at an angle of 30° from the vertical, I saw the turf at the edge of the cliff being lifted like the edge of a blanket, and the outer fringes of it were being torn off and flung inland just as a blanket would wear in a wind. All this is common enough in the islands ; I had seen it before. But a few yards inland I saw two bare patches in the turf where two boulders had rested for years ; the black surface of the bare patch was a good inch below the turf, and the boulders themselves—a foot to eighteen inches across and about eight inches high—were rolled uphill a distance of about three feet. The seals might well have shifted them had they been there, but no seals wandered in that part of the island. Only the force of the wind could have moved those stones, and as I still cannot believe that any wind we know could turn up the dead weight of a boulder well set with a flat bottom in the turf, presumably the cliff being set at that angle had the effect of multiplying the force of the wind at the upper edge ; and a fairly large area of turf must have been lifted and stretched in some of the gusts, with the result that the boulders would be thrown out of their sockets uphill.

The effect of wind is much less farther inland from the sea. The tree line on the coasts may be no more than 200 feet—assuming that trees will grow at all—whereas it is 1,800 feet on the western side of the Cairngorms. The prevailing wind in the Highlands is from the south-west. Such winds come off the relatively warm waters of the North Atlantic Drift and are laden with moisture. The weather is rarely cold during the time they blow. If the observer is far enough out from the high hills to see what is really happening in the sky, he will note that the south-westerly gales are predictable from the movements of the clouds before the wind is felt at sea level, or he may see a great bank of cloud out to the west in the Atlantic the night before. The south-westerly gales are gusty even out on the coasts, but they are so moisture-laden that one's sense of smell is heightened : earth and sea have a beauty of their own at such a time through the scents they convey. The observer is watching the sky for signs of the end of the gale and sees a break of blue sky for a moment ; then he notices that the clouds are no longer moving from the south-west but from the west. Soon he feels the wind to be coming from the west at sea level and the clouds are moving from north-west. Finally the wind veers farther to north-west and falls light in the north. That is the end of the gale.

The trough of low barometric pressure is left behind and the recording needle marks a steady rise and then levels off as the wind reaches the north. These gales have a closely similar pattern : in winter they may last several days ; or only twenty hours in summer, sometimes completing the pattern day after day, beginning in the early morning with short gusts which are the forerunners and falling light in the late evening. It is the West Highland coast which shows up these gales as if under a magnifying glass. They will be mere breezes a few miles inland or at the head of a sea loch. Only their raininess will be felt there. The barograph shows less pronounced movement also, back in from the coast.

It is obvious that the effect of wind on the outer coasts is very great, for there is not only the period of great gales in the winter, when there are no leaves on the shrubs and no leafy vegetation at ground level, but there is the continual wearing of the summer period. I have seen leaves die from shaking through three days of blowing. Such trees as exist take on a distorted appearance, not one branch or twig managing to survive on the windward side of the trunk. It is a remark commonly heard that a tree has been bent by the constant action of the wind, but this is not true. Distortion is brought about by the continual lack of survival of all growth on one side. The distal ends of twigs are killed and the tree develops more and more a fuzziness of short annual shoots from the main stem. The influence of wind on the coastal region is further complicated by the spray which it may carry, for most broad-leaved plants object to a deposition of salt on their foliage. This is a subject we shall touch on later in the book.

North winds are relatively uncommon in the Highlands, but are recognized as bringers of snow in winter, snow which sets up its own train of events in natural history. A north wind in June or July means the best of sunny weather, but in August the north wind brings rain. East winds blow most regularly in spring, but gales from the south-east occur as well in the West Highlands. They are very cold for the district, as the south wind can be as well, for the air has come over a mountainous region where it must become chilled. The south-easters are dry winds and have a desiccating effect on the autumn herbage, sufficient to curtail the grazing season in some years. The south winds of summer mean a leaden sky and rain.

To conclude, the climate of the Scottish Highlands and Islands is rapidly changeable and far from uniform. The coastal climate is maritime or oceanic, but in the Central and Eastern Highlands it is more continental—more extreme temperatures, less wind, less rain and drier air. The meteorological tendency to drier air in the central region and the Dee Valley is further added to by the capacity of the ground to drain rapidly.

RELIEF AND SCENERY

LET US look at a physical map of Scotland and allow ourselves to make a tour of the Highlands as observers of country rather than as naturalists making detailed studies of habitats. We shall then be able to see those habitats with eyes wider open for the comparative sense we shall have gained. It will be convenient to divide the Highlands into five zones to which we cannot fairly give definite boundaries, though the zones themselves are significant in natural history. The divisions are my own and do not carry the weight of the acceptance of a committee of biologists. I should call them :

a. The southern and eastern Highland fringe which is in effect a frontier zone.
b. The Central Highlands, which may be likened to a continental or alpine zone.
c. The Northern Highlands, a zone with sub-Arctic or boreal affinities.
d. The West Highlands south of Skye, which may be called the Atlantic or Lusitanian Zone.
e. The Outer Hebrides and islands of Canna, Coll, Tiree, and such small islands as the St. Kilda group, the Treshnish group, the Flannans, North Rona and Sula Sgeir ; an oceanic zone.

The Southern and Eastern Highland Fringe

This zone follows the line of the Highland Border Fault from Helensburgh almost to Stonehaven, and then turns at right angles north-westwards to include the middle Dee. The Lochnagar massif, 3,786 feet, may properly belong to the Central Highland zone, but it is a good pivotal point and its long southern slopes all drain into the eastern plain below the Highland Border Fault. From Lochnagar we can cross to Pitlochry and thence to Loch Tay and south-westwards to the head of Loch Lomond and to the sea at the head of Loch Fyne.

The land to the south and east of this zone is highly productive agricultural ground which shows some of the best farming in Scotland.

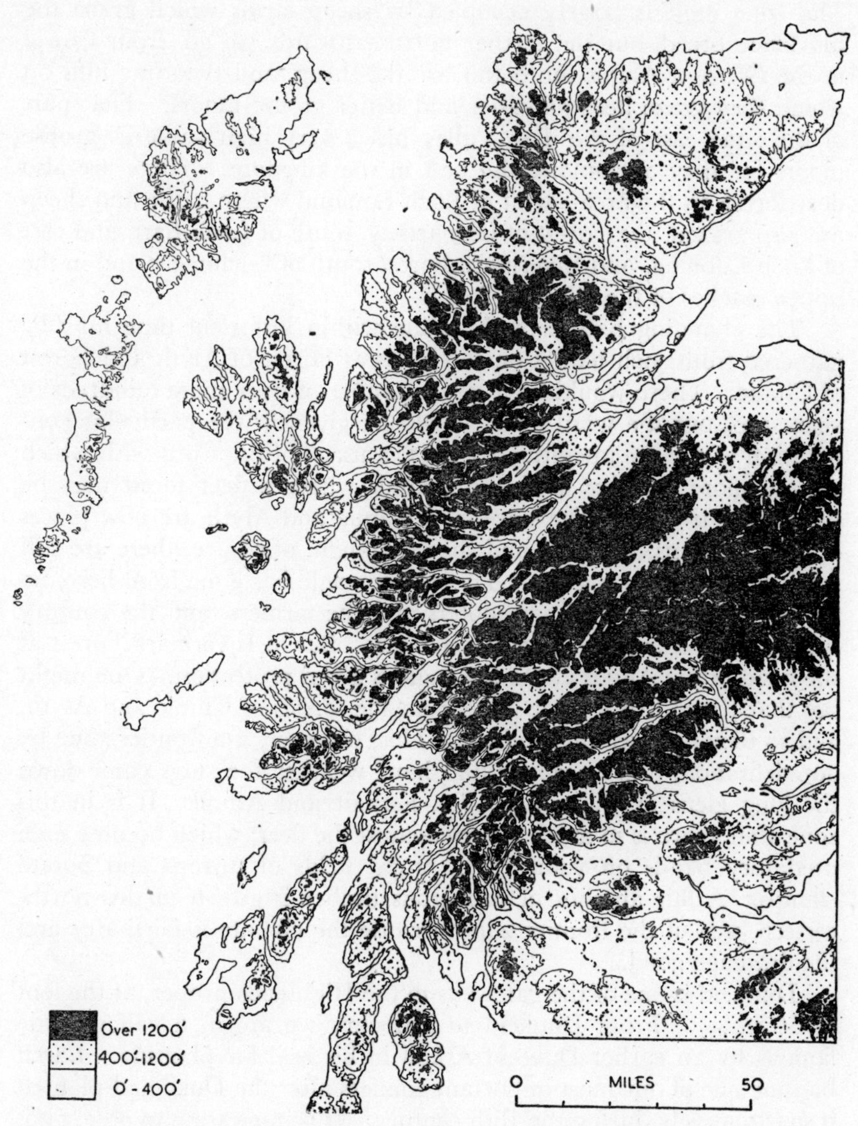

FIG. 4.—Generalized relief features of the Highlands

By courtesy of the Land Utilisation Survey of Great Britain

The zone itself is largely occupied by sheep farms which graze the Blackface breed, but the farther north-eastwards we go from Cowal to the Glens of Angus the better are the sheep, and the same hills on which they graze become easier and better grouse moors. That part of the zone east of the Tay Valley has a very high value as grouse moors for they are among the best in the kingdom. There are also deer forests in the area—west of Loch Lomond where cattle and sheep are also grazed, the Forest of Glenartney, south of Loch Earn and east of Loch Lubnaig, and Invermark Forest south of Lochnagar and in the upper reaches of the Glens of Angus.

The changing nature of this zone within historical time may be gathered from such names on the maps as Forest of Alyth and Forest of Clunie. There would be a large number of trees there hundreds of years ago, but the word forest would be given in the particular connotation of a large uncultivated tract, a usage of the word with which we are more familiar in the Highlands where a deer forest may be practically treeless. The Forests of Clunie and Alyth are now places of rearing farms for cattle and sheep, though, of course, there are still large areas of grouse moor. The golden eagle has gone from here, no longer tolerated by grouse-shooters and the farmers, and the country is not rough enough to give it sanctuary. But in Invermark Forest at the head of the Angus Glens the eagle is given protection. One might say that the red deer have gone from the forests of Clunie and Alyth, and so they have as full residents. This, however, is a frontier zone by our definition, and in winter and hard weather the stags come down the long glens of Glen Isla, Glen Fernait and Atholl. It is in this zone that there is so much outcry against the deer, which become such predatory bands on young corn crops, fields of turnips and potato clamps. A fair amount of coniferous timber is grown in this north-eastern area of the frontier zone because the climate is fairly dry and the drainage good.

Dunkeld is one of the gateways to the Highlands proper, at the foot of Strathtay. From Dunkeld to Pitlochry we are in a valley made famous by an earlier Duke of Atholl in his zeal for planting. Larch became one of our most important conifers after the Duke had planted it so extensively during the 18th century. It is interesting to note, also, that it is in this afforested country that the new hybrid between the European and Japanese larch has occurred by a fortunate accident. The hybrid, with its hardiness and immunities, is expected to be a notable forester's tree in the future. All this area and that already described carries a big stock of roe deer. Despite its unpopularity with the forester, the roe happily persists, apparently as strong as ever.

West of Dunkeld we are into Strath Bran, still timber country, grouse moors and rearing farms. The fauna of Highland hills are constantly pressing down into this zone and are as surely being scotched before the plain of Strathmore is reached. Peregrine falcons, wild cats, eagles, foxes, red deer—all these come through and rarely return. There are no high tops in this area until the head of Glen Almond where the summit of Ben Chonzie, 3,048 feet, dominates everything else in the district ; yet there is big country here which the relative smoothness of the hill faces tends to emphasize. The streams have good brown trout and the valleys are always well wooded among the numerous farms. The bird population is rich and varied.

West again, we come into the Forest of Glenartney with its two sharp peaks of Ben Vorlich, 3,224 feet, and Stuc a' Chroin, 3,189 feet, which are visible from Arthur's Seat, Edinburgh. Glenartney is the most southerly of the deer forests proper, and though the high country of the two peaks is very suitable for deer, the winter trek of the animals makes the forest harder and harder to maintain in an age when the voice of agriculture is clamant.

The country now is getting much wilder and the easily walked slopes of good heather are giving way to some bare rock faces, to wetter sedgy hills and birch woods rather than conifers. Such is the country either side of Loch Lubnaig where the Forestry Commission is changing the face of the hillsides. The varied scheme of plantings here can serve as a model to confound those who hold that forestry spoils scenery. The same kind of country exists in the Trossachs round Loch Katrine of tourist fame. A Highlander hesitates to call the Trossachs Highland but there is no doubt of the beauty of the scenery. Birch and oak woods line the shore of the loch and hold a good number of black grouse still.

We now come to Loch Lomond, beginning at the foot of Glen Falloch as a narrow and quite uninteresting loch. It becomes more impressive the farther south we go down its twenty-odd miles. The shores are fringed with birches and oaks, and on the west bank particularly there are some fine groups of deciduous trees. Spring and autumn in this region have a charm beyond that of many Highland areas—and autumn, be it known, is a time when Scotland is at her most magnificent. If Ben Lomond looks splendid seen across the loch from Tarbet or Luss, a still finer view can be obtained from the other side where there is no road except the transverse one from Loch Katrine to Inversnaid Lodge, which can be reached also from Aberfoyle. The view westwards from above Inversnaid includes a group of "Munros"[1] draining to Loch Sloy—Ben Vorlich (another of the name) with its two peaks, and Ben Vane and Ben Ime. This is the scene of a hydro-electric project and a road is to be made into the area which will certainly allow more people to see the fine scenery than have been able heretofore. This group of hills is in the West of Scotland fair and square and has a high rainfall. The most southerly of the group is Ben Arthur (the Cobbler), 2,891 feet, where there is much bare rock and excellent climbing. At the foot of the sedgy slopes of this hill we are on the west coast at the head of Loch Long. The role of frontier zone is practically lost here, for there is not the rich agricultural land immediately to the south. There is water, and, as the foot of Loch Lomond is reached, the industrial area which is but an extension of Glasgow.

Glasgow is fortunate in its landowners to the north. On both sides of Loch Lomond fair access is given to all, and every attempt is made to preserve the natural woodland and the forest fauna. The Loch Lomond-Trossachs area has priority as a projected national park area. The area would link up with the National Forest Park already established by the Forestry Commission west of Arrochar, and which now includes the privately-given peninsula between Loch Goil and Loch Long. This extremely broken stretch of Highland country, ironically called Argyll's Bowling Green, is within a few miles of the busy industrial Clyde. The establishment of a national park, and the faithful implementation of the Town and Country Planning Act which is now in force in Scotland, should ensure to Glasgow an area of pristine beauty with a rich natural history, much of which yet awaits patient investigation.

The Central Highland Zone

This area gives the nearest approach to continental and alpine conditions that we have in Scotland. The southern boundary may be made a line drawn from Lochnagar to the head of Loch Lomond,

[1] A Munro is a hill 3,000 feet or over, separated from another by a dip of 500 feet or more: from the Scottish mountaineer H. T. Munro, who first listed them. There are 543 of them.

including the high hills on the north side of Loch Tay. The western boundary would be a line from Loch Lomond through Ben Nevis to Carn Eige and Mam Soul, thence almost due east across the Great Glen at a point just south of Urquhart Castle. This northern line would continue from that point to Tomintoul, one of the highest inhabited villages in Scotland, at 1,280 feet ; and the line from Tomintoul to Lochnagar could well form the short eastern boundary. The south-western and north-western corners of this arbitrarily delimited zone are the least typical, in that they lose the plateau-like quality of the Central Highlands proper, but on reflection I should not like to include the peaks round the head of Glen Lyon in the West Highland zone, nor do I think the triangle of country north of the Great Glen may rightly be said to have the sub-arctic-heath complex of vegetation like that of the Northern Highlands. Between 80 and 90 per cent of the ground in this central zone is above the 1,000-foot contour. Arable farming is scarcely practised except in the narrow straths. The farms of Glen Moriston constitute one of the incongruities of the north-western corner of our area, much more so than those of Cromdale and Boat of Garten on the northern edge east of the Spey, for these latter are typical upland farms. The slopes of the hills are mainly of good heather and after 2,500 feet become alpine desert.

The Central Highland zone has its particular interest for naturalists who may be specialists in some branches. There is the botanical field of the high tops, among which Ben Lawers, 3,984 feet, has always held a special place. The schistose of which this hill is composed breaks down easily, and there are exposures of other rocks as well, providing soil which allows a greater variety of alpine plants to grow than on some other summits. The richness of Ben Lawers is also due, probably, to the likelihood of the summit escaping the last glaciation.

The Cairngorm region is of special interest to ornithologists wishing to study the snow bunting and dotterel. The ptarmigan (Pl. XVIIb, p. 148) is common there and the golden eagle (Pl. XIIIa, p. 100) enjoys practical sanctuary, for even sheep-farming is absent from much of the area. The Cairngorm tops are our most considerable arctic relic. The ancient pine forests at the eastern and north-western foot of the Cairngorms are also a relic of a past age and contain the Scottish crested tit (Pl. XV, p. 108) and the Scottish crossbill. The entomologist also finds these forests of special interest. The central Highland area contains some of the biggest deer forests in Scotland, such as Blackmount in Breadalbane of over 80,000 acres (Pl. XV, p. 108), the Forest of Mar, which is almost as large, and the wonderful deer country between Loch Ericht and Loch Laggan, which includes Ben Alder, 3,757 feet.

Our central zone holds the upper reaches of three large river systems—the Dee which flows eastwards from the Cairngorms and the Grampians ; the Spey which rises from tiny Loch Spey in the Corrieyairick Forest north of the high top of Creag Meagaidh above Loch Laggan ; and the Rivers Garry, Tummel and Tay flowing southwards, joining and continuing as the Tay outside the central alpine zone. The much shorter River Spean which flows westward from Loch Laggan has now disappeared because of the erection of a hydro-electric dam and aqueducts at the foot of Loch Laggan. The Spey, rising at 1,142 feet on the backbone of Scotland, runs 120 miles in a north-easterly direction to the sea in the Moray Firth. It gathers its waters from the Monaliadh hills, from the Grampians and the Cairngorms, the largest area of long-snow-lying country in the Highlands. The River Truim, the Spey's first large tributary, runs through Badenoch, one of the barest parts of the Highlands. It rises near the Pass of Drumochter, 1,500 feet, which takes the main road from Perth to Inverness. Badenoch has the appearance of a devastated countryside ; an appearance partly due to nature and partly to the destructive hand of man several hundred years ago. This area was fought over many a time and bands of broken men were burnt out of their retreats just as the last wolves were a century or two later. The rock is a dull grey and apt to break down into a shaley scree. To my mind, the Forests of Drumochter and Gaick, a little to the east, are the most depressing part of the Highlands. The hills are big humps without individuality, there are screes but not fine cliff faces, and trees are few and far between. Even the weather has a habit of being leaden. The practice of burning heather is always obvious in that no hill face seems to bear an unbroken dark green surface of untouched heather.

West of the road, in the upper Spey Valley region and south of Loch Laggan, the hills become sharper and more shapely and there is a good deal of natural birch, among which are many stands of coniferous timber which in no way spoil the landscape. The Spey and the Truim join above Newtonmore, and from there until the Spey leaves the central zone, the straths and the slopes to over 1,250 feet hold large stands of planted coniferous timbers. There is still plenty of natural birch and juniper scrub as far as Aviemore and beyond. We are in a very beautiful area which is one of the most popular holiday resorts in Scotland for those who like quiet, a mixture of woodland and high hill and a sharp healthy climate of low summer rainfall. At Aviemore the Valley of the Spey widens, and if the observer climbs the wooded hillock of Craigellachie south-west of the village, he will see the old Scots pine forests of Rothiemurchus (Pl. 16, p. 125) and Glenmore as the floor of a great basin formed by the Cairngorms and the little range of hills to the north which culminates in Meall a' Bhuachaille, 2,654 feet. Loch Morlich (Pl. 2, p. 37) lies in the middle of the basin and its bright sandy shores at the eastern end are visible. The dark green of the timber stretches through the pass or *bealach* at the foot of Meall a' Bhuachaille into the Forest of Abernethy (Pl. 17, p. 128). The old trees have suffered more heavily here and have been replaced by plantations of Scots pine, but Abernethy is still beautiful and the birch and juniper take away the grim formality of the solid stands of planted timber.

The Cairngorms, which form the heart and the most extreme alpine conditions of our central zone, are fairly easily reached from Aviemore by means of the track and the pass known as the Lairig Ghru. The Lairig splits the granite massif of the Cairngorms into two halves at a height of 2,750 feet, and is the most spectacular part of the Cairngorms seen from Aviemore or farther west of the Spey. Ben Macdhui, 4,296 feet (Pl. 20, p. 141), is on the east side and Braeriach and Cairntoul on the west side of the pass. The summit of the Lairig is also the county boundary between Inverness-shire and Aberdeenshire. Just south of the summit are the very small lochans known as the Pools of Dee. The water is extremely clear and probably originates from springs. This is the source of the Dee which in twelve miles becomes a considerable river at the Chest of Dee. By time the Linn of Dee is reached (the uppermost limit of salmon in the river) we are into forest again, mostly planted Scots pine until we get below Braemar, where Ballochbuie still holds a fine show of the old pines. These are part of the Royal property at Balmoral.

The Grampian Hills south of the Cairngorms give a sense of vastness. Ben Iurtharn, 3,424 feet ; Glas Thulachan, 3,445 feet ; and the tops of Beinn a' Ghlo, 3,671 feet ; all these and many another 3,000-footer can be easily climbed on a pony, and once on those clean, smooth summits the pony can be let out to a gallop, so different are they from the sharp peaks, the broken ground and the boggy approaches to the high hills of the West. This country is remote from everywhere and since, once there, it is difficult to get lower than 1,500 feet, there is a great exhilaration in movement through these hills. The snow lies long up here but in summer there is a wealth of excellent grazing for deer, sheep and cattle. I have found patches of beautiful brown soil as high as 1,800 feet. One of the best routes into the Cairngorms is up Glen Tilt from Blair Atholl, past the Falls of Tarf. It is a long and arduous defile or U-shaped glacial valley for most of the way until the Bynack Shieling is reached at 1,500 feet. After that there is the sense of height and space, and the high hills of the Cairngorms lie ahead in a much more picturesque group than when seen from the west. This time it is the noble Glen Dee which splits the massif rather than the sharp nick of the Lairig Ghru. Trees are few up here, though the narrow dens which cut down to the Tarf from Fealar and round about have plenty of small birches, and curiously enough there are a few well-grown spruces at the Bynack Shieling; out of which spruces one day I frightened a capercaillie (Pl. XIc, p. 96). He must have come out of the wooded area of the Dee below Derry Lodge, where this bird is relatively common. The Forest of Mar was one of the places where the caper was reintroduced (unsuccessfully) in the early 19th century.

The Northern Highlands, a Zone of Sub-arctic Affinities

The northern end of Drum Albyn and its coasts becomes definitely a harder country north of Loch Carron than the West Highland Atlantic zone. The large island of Skye, set athwart the Minch, has an undoubted effect of checking the flow of warm water of the North Atlantic Drift. The coasts of the North-West have several long sea lochs, but the coast as a whole is tighter-knit than the islands and coasts of the Atlantic zone which fans out from the Firth of Lorne into the Atlantic Ocean.

The rocks of the northern zone on the western side are mostly very hard, and poor in such minerals as make good soil; they are Lewisian gneiss, Torridonian sandstone and quartzite; these three have little either of calcium or of fine particles which will become clay and contribute to the soil picture. Furthermore, where the bed rock itself is not showing through (and often it is over 50 per cent of the landscape) the ground is covered with peat which has no bottom of shell sand or clay which, on disintegration or removal of the peat, might become productive soil. Sand dunes occur on the coast at only a few places such as Gairloch, Gruinard Bay, Achnahaird on the north coast of the Coigach peninsula, across Rhu Stoer and at Achmelvich, and at Sandwood Bay a few miles south of Cape Wrath. None of these are of shell sand.

It is a hard, rocky coast to which a multitude of short, rapid rivers run from Drum Albyn—the Laxford from Loch Stack and Loch Mor into Loch Laxford ; the Inver from Loch Assynt into Enard Bay ; the Kirkaig out of the lochs below Suilven ; the Polly, the Kannaird, the Broom and the Dundonnell Rivers ; the superb Gruinard River which is only six miles long on its run from Loch na Sheallag ; the Little Gruinard, even shorter, coming from the Fionn Loch which is one of the most famous trout lochs in the North ; and the River Ewe, only two miles long after it leaves Loch Maree, but very broad ; the Kerry River running into Gairloch, famed for its pearls ; and the Applecross River which drains much of the peninsula of that name. Most of these rivers are noted for salmon and sea trout, though some are curiously poor. As things stand at the moment the rivers of this region, so variable in their flow from day to day, make up in economic value for the poverty of the land for agricultural and pastoral purposes and for general lack of timber.

The boreal or sub-arctic affinities of the northern zone are most marked on the two geological formations already named, the gneiss and the sandstone. Each rock has its very distinctive form and each contributes to what is probably the wildest scenery in Scotland except for the small area of the Cuillin Hills of Skye (Pl. IIIa, p. 12). But here in the interplay of gneiss, sandstone and quartzite the naturalist may walk for a week or more and see no human habitation other than an occasional stalker's cottage. So rough and wild is the country that habitations unconnected with sport are difficult to find away from the sea's edge. The outcrop of limestone in the Assynt district allows the exception of the crofting townships of Elphin and Cnockan to which allusion was made in the first chapter (p. 4).

The Lewisian gneiss of the mainland rises to greater heights in the general run of the country than it does in the Hebrides, except in Harris and at one place in South Uist. Also, it is not hidden under such a blanket of peat as in Lewis. The gneiss country of Sutherland and Ross is one of a myriad little hills of great steepness, with little glens running hither and thither among them. The lochans are seemingly countless and most of them have a floor of peat. The gneiss hills themselves are like rock buns, looking as if they had risen in some giant oven and set into their rough shapes. This ground holds up the water in pockets in the rock and allows the formation of cotton sedge bogs and such very shallow lochans as grow water lobelia and water lilies. When these lochans are near the sea and grow reeds the bird life is rich. Greenshanks (Pl. XIIb, p. 97) are common in the gneiss country —say one pair to 3,000 acres, which is quite twice as many as may be found on the adjoining Torridonian sandstone. Heather (*Calluna*) is not common on the gneiss ; the complex is one of dwarf willow, sedge and poor grasses. Also, this type of vegetation does not appreciably alter in the altitudinal range of the gneiss. For example, I could find no major difference in sample patches in the Gruinard Forest at the foot of Carn nam Buailtean at 600 feet, and at the top of Creag Mheall Mor in the Fisherfield Forest at over 2,000 feet. The hills maintain over all their mottled pattern of green and grey, and when the snow is on the tops there is never the distinctive line at about 1,750 feet which is commonly seen on the Torridonian formation.

The gneiss is difficult country to walk through : by keeping to the little glens it is impossible to steer a straight course for any distance and no one would attempt to go in a straight line over the hills. On the upper gneiss country where many detours are necessary round rock faces and soft spots, a speed of one mile an hour is quite good going. It is also quite easy to lose one's self, for these little round hills are all very much alike.

The crofting townships on the gneiss are strictly coastal. Their arable grounds (Pl. 7b, p. 64) are usually tiny patches of an acre or less in the hollows or in the less steep faces of the rocks. Loch Laxford, a sea loch, shows some typical low gneiss country with crofts at Foindlemore and Fanagmore.

The gneiss tends to get higher the farther it goes inland. A' Mhaighdean (the maiden) reaches 2,850 feet above the Dubh Loch in Ross, 10–12 miles from the sea as the crow flies. It forms a high cliff face on this hill of exceptional grandeur, a rare thing for the formation on the mainland. Its sea cliffs are nowhere impressive here because they are never sheer or higher than a couple of hundred feet. Even the

Torridonian, a formation which one might expect to make magnificent cliffs, does not provide these in any quantity at the sea's edge. The island of Handa, near Scourie and opposite Fanagmore at the mouth of Loch Laxford, is a splendid exception. The Torridonian rock is stratified horizontally, so the vertical breaks make nesting ledges for sea birds such as guillemots, razorbills and kittiwakes. There are sheer cliffs of nearly 400 feet on Handa, and in the little screes of earth among these, now covered with fescue and scurvy grass, there are large colonies of puffins and fulmar petrels. The white-tailed sea eagle nested on Handa until the second half of the 19th century. Handa is one of the few places on the Torridonian sandstone which provide true sea-bird cliffs. No other place on the formation can compare with it for numbers of auks, except perhaps Clo Mor, about four miles east of Cape Wrath, where there is a cliff of over 800 feet.

The splendour of the Torridonian is in the peaks it makes inland. Some are fantastic and others superb. There is only one Suilven and it is undoubtedly the most fantastic hill in Scotland (Pl. 3b, p. 44). It rises to 2,309 feet out of a rough sea of low gneiss. Seen from north and south it has a distinctive shape of a very steep frontal cliff and rounded top called Casteal Liath (the grey castle), then a dip and a lesser knob before a more gentle slope down to the east. But when seen from west or east the extreme thinness of the hill is apparent. Probably the Dolomites would be the nearest place where such an extraordinary shape of a hill could be seen. Suilven means the pillar which is a good name for the hill seen from the west. It is often likened to a sugar loaf, also. There are greyish-white quartzite boulders sprinkled on the top, yet there is a little alp of grass up there and an occasional bed of *Rhacomitrium* moss. The great terraces of Caisteal Liath itself are but thinly marked by such grasses and sedges as *Festuca ovina* forma *vivipara* and *Luzula spicata* as can send their roots far into the cracks.

One of the striking things about the Torridonian peaks of the far north-west is their isolation, caused by the vast denudation which has taken place, leaving these few hard cores of sedimentary rock overlying the wilderness of gneiss hillocks and innumerable lochans. The term hard core is here being used metaphorically and not geologically. North of Suilven and Loch Assynt is the massif of Quinag, five conical peaks capped with quartzite, with a fine rampart of cliff and scree on the west side, which is nearly three miles long.

The massif is no higher than 2,653 feet, but how much more impressive is it than half a hundred three-thousand-footers in the Central Highlands! South of Suilven there is Cul Mor, 2,786 feet, surrounded on three sides by great precipices; and Stac Polly, 2,009 feet (Pl. 4b, p. 45, Pl. 10, p. 85), the narrow ridge of which is like one of those fairy castles of childhood tales perched on the top of steep slopes. Ben More Coigach rises to over 2,000 feet in under a mile from the sea as the crow flies. The air of this countryside with its lower rainfall is generally much clearer than farther south in the Highlands and adds to that sub-arctic quality which characterizes the area.

Before leaving this far northern corner, the ranges of Foinaven, 2,980 feet, and of Ben More Assynt, 3,273 feet, must be mentioned. The group culminating in Foinaven is without doubt the barest range in Scotland, and composed of that unyielding white rock, the Cambrian quartzite. The northern part is like a giant E, the crossbars being ridges peppered heavily with boulders which form screes again below the shoulders: the hollows of the E are fine corries on the slopes of which the snow bunting has bred. The southern part is a horseshoe-shaped ridge of which Ben Arkle, 2,580 feet, is the western rampart. This hill of Cambrian quartzite with its banding of white scree may be viewed to perfection from the highroad on the shores of Loch Stack; but for the greatest glory of this range a six-mile trek must be made to reach the vast horseshoe corrie and Loch an Easain Uaine, the loch of the green falls. It is well to rest here awhile and realize that the pine marten is probably commoner in this neighbourhood than anywhere else in Britain, to remember the snow bunting up in the tumble of boulders and possibly see him feeding on the buds of *Saxifraga oppositifolia*. The alpine species of plant creep far down these bare hillsides and one wonders what there is here to recompense the deer for the energy used in attempting to graze these slopes. The boreal affinity of this range was further emphasized by the occurrence of alpine butterwort (*Pinguicula alpina*), which was found nowhere else in Britain but on the high tops of Sutherland and Ross; unfortunately this species may now be quite extinct, as it has not been found since 1900, according to Druce's *Comital Flora*. The same authority puts 1794 as the last date on which this plant was found in Skye.

Ben More Assynt itself is a solid quartzite cap with igneous intrusions set upon a mass of Lewisian gneiss. There has been a series of geological overthrusts in the region, in which tumults areas of limestone

PLATE III

Robert M. Adam

THE CUILLIN PEAKS, across Loch Eishort, Skye

Robert M. Adam

AN TEALLACH from the east. Dundonnell Forest, Wester Ross

PLATE IV

F. Fraser Darling

SCRUB BIRCH on Lewisian gneiss, Gruinard Forest, Wester Ross. April 1934

have come to the surface. This limestone has affected the natural history of the whole region, causing a wealth of crustacean and other aquatic life on the waters affected by the limestone, differences in the temperature of the water of some streams which suddenly rise from the rock, allowing the formation of water-worn caves in which have gathered soil and bones of animals of earlier times. Such organic remains are rare in the Northern Highlands.

The comparatively low ground of all this northern region of the gneiss, so difficult of access and so plentifully strewn with lochs, is also a place where sub-arctic birch scrub (Pl. IV, p. 33) is common and there is a certain amount of hazel. There are large stretches of birch in Inverpolly Forest (Pl. 4b, p. 45) in the vicinity of Loch Sionnascaig, which is one of the most beautiful lochs in the whole Highlands. There are pristine birch-wooded islands in the loch where the grey lag goose bred not so long ago and where the pintail duck has bred recently. There is more birch round Lochinver and below the north face of Quinag, and many a stretch may be found on the hill far from the roads, in places which are almost unknown to the naturalist. Some day we may find the redwing building in these woods, for this bird has been heard singing here from time to time in April, and the redwing is essentially a native of the sub-arctic birch wood.

The eastern side of the extreme Northern Highlands is given up to extensive sheep-farming. The hills are of no great height and are of easy slope. The herbage is sweet and good. The largest sheep farms in Great Britain are here, some having upwards of 10,000 ewes. The breed kept is the Cheviot of the distinctive lustrous-woolled Sutherland type. The lambs are sold annually at the great sales at Lairg. No man was more responsible for the development of Cheviot sheep-farming in the North than Sir John Sinclair of Ulbster, in the 1790's. The influence of sheep-farming on the natural history has been profound and will be given special attention in a later chapter.

This far northern area has been treated at some length, because it is the most remote part of the Highlands and one of which detailed studies in natural history have been rare. It may be recommended as an exhilarating and fruitful field for exploration.

South of Loch Broom, the Torridonian hills are more thickly grouped and reach their highest peaks. Their spiry form and the high corries facing to the east are distinctive. The quality of herbage is generally poor and the terraces formed in the lower reaches of the

Torridonian hold up the heavy rainfall so that it is often quite impossible to get about dryshod. How different is the nature of the ground from those smooth dry slopes of glacial sand and gravel which are such a marked feature of the Central Highlands! The differences brought about in the vegetational complex have not been sufficiently stressed by plant ecologists in the past. The ground has not been well walked through and explored as yet.

There are two high hills of the Torridonian which have north-eastern corries quite the most magnificent of their kind and few who have seen them both can decide which is the better. This in itself should show how similar are such groups of hills and the forces which moulded them. I allude to An Teallach of Dundonnell (Pl. IIIb, p. 32, Pl. 4a, p. 45), 3,485 feet, and Beinn Eighe, 3,456 feet, between Kinlochewe and Loch Torridon. Each of these hills has three corries facing NNW. to NE. Coire Mhic Fearchair is the most westerly of the corries of Beinn Eighe, and the Toll Lochan corrie of An Teallach is the easterly one of the range. Some of the buttresses in Coire Mhic Fearchair are exceptionally fine and the corrie makes an almost perfect horseshoe, but for myself I think I prefer the Toll Lochan corrie, for the cliff face at the head of the lochan is of greater depth and of superb architecture, nearly 1,800 feet of it.

Between An Teallach and another corried Torridonian peak, Beinn Dearg Mor, 2,934 feet, is the broad amphitheatre known as Strath na Sheallag, at the head of Loch na Sheallag, from which the Gruinard River runs. This strath is beloved of the deer, and though so remote it draws cattle, sheep and ponies to it from far away. Just as An Teallach has Beinn Dearg Mor as an outlier, so has Beinn Eighe her Beinn Dearg, 2,995 feet, almost a replica of its cousin of Strath na Sheallag. Liathach, 3,456 feet, Beinn Alligin, 3,232 feet, and Slioch, 3,217 feet, these are just three more of these splendid Torridonian peaks—clear of peat from 1,750 feet upwards and often topped with a white cap of quartzite boulders. The sudden change from wet peat-laden terraces to the upper slopes of bare rock, or thin covering of brash and alpine vegetation, results in a sharp snow line in winter which gives these hills a special seasonal beauty. This sudden cessation of the peat immediately allows a different flora, one of plants which can withstand droughts and sudden changes of humidity, and which prefer sweeter conditions than are possible on peat. Here and there among the alpine poa grass and viviparous sheep's fescue are straggling plants of dwarf juniper, clinging close to the rock. Sea pink and thyme are also to be found on the gravel. Eagle, peregrine falcon and wild cat abound in this country, and as it is all deer forest and not grouse moors of any consequence, the eagle is allowed more sanctuary than it has been given farther south and east.

The glens of the Torridonian area of the North are often well wooded. They have been owned by people with a fair (or perhaps unfair !) measure of worldly riches, who have been able to spend a good deal of money on planting for amenity. Take Dundonnell for example, at the head of Little Loch Broom : the loch side is bare of trees and is given up to crofting townships, but soon after the head of the loch is reached one is into a fine wooded glen. There are a few hundred acres of Scots pine of greatly varying density stretching up the southern side to an altitude of 1,000 feet. There are alders, oaks, rowans, and hazels along the river bank, and some hundreds of acres of birch at the head of the glen reaching up to 1,500 feet. But all round the cultivated strath and the house which was built in 1769 there are signs of planting for beauty : limes, many fine beeches, sycamores, ashes, elms, oaks, chestnuts and big old geans ; and until a few years ago there were many acres of fine larches on the north side. The wild life of such a glen is obviously profuse and varied. We have these men of a past age to thank for planting that which we now enjoy, just as we may blame those of a century earlier who were denuding the Highlands of timber.

Loch Maree is another place where there are some very fine woods, but here the sub-arctic quality of the northern zone is being lost and replaced by the complex of sub-alpine vegetation. Near where the Ewe River from Loch Maree goes into the sea in Loch Ewe there is a famous garden which grows a great variety of rhododendrons and azaleas and many sub-tropical plants and plants from Oceania. This is just another facet of the Highland paradox, the garden at Inverewe lying between the stark precipices of Ben Airidh Charr and the bare windswept slabs of Greenstone Point where the sea is never still. And if I may add one more touch of paradox, I saw a kingfisher on the rocks at Greenstone Point at the edge of the tide, one September day.

CHAPTER 3

RELIEF AND SCENERY
(continued)

The Western Highlands or Atlantic Zone

SOUTH of Skye the coasts of the West Highlands fan out much more than to the north of that island. Indeed, there are several considerable islands reaching out into the Atlantic. The Outer Hebrides are not masking the influence of the Atlantic on this area as they do on the north coast of Skye. The influence of the Atlantic Ocean on this zone is both direct and inhibitory, and indirect and encouraging to a wealth of plant growth. The island of Islay, for example, changes character completely between its western and eastern halves. On the Atlantic side there is the lack of trees and shrubs and the presence of short sweet herbage salted by the spray from innumerable south-westerly gales, whereas there are beautiful gardens, palm trees and some forestry on the south and east sides. The Rhinns of Islay on the Atlantic coast are not heavily covered with peat as is a good deal of the eastern half. Islay is an island of many good arable farms, and it has several square miles of limestone country.

The waters of the North Atlantic Drift cast up on these Atlantic shores pieces of wood and beans of West Indian origin, and plants such as the pale butterwort (*Pinguicula lusitanica*), pygmy rush (*Juncus pygmaeus*) and the moss *Myurium Hebridorum* which occur again on British coasts only in the south-west, here turn up in fair numbers. The pale butterwort occurs in the bogs of Portugal and western Spain, and on the west coast of France; Myurium moss is found in the Azores, the Canaries and St. Helena as well as in our Outer Isles. Dwarf cicendia (*Cicendia pusilla*) has also turned up in this zone, though previously found in the British Isles only in the Channel Islands. More recently, Campbell and Wilmott (1946) have found another Lusitanian plant in Stornoway Castle park, namely *Sibthorpia europaea*. The work of Professor Heslop Harrison and his group from the University of Durham should be consulted. It is his opinion that these western cliff edges escaped the last glaciation and thus their Pleistocene flora was not exterminated. Others hold that the flora must have been introduced since then.

PLATE I

John Markham

GLACIAL DRIFT COUNTRY, with burn. Cairngorm foothills, Inverness-shire
September 1944

PLATE 2

John Markham

Loch Morlich, Valley of the Spey, Inverness-shire. June 1945

Jura is not so well served with the rich quality of vegetation we may find in Islay or even in small Colonsay and in Mull. It is composed of quartzite, which is poor stuff. Jura is also heavily covered with peat and suffers in consequence. A thick blanket of peat has a very great depressing effect on the variety of vegetation and in limiting the growth of deciduous trees. Jura is an island of high hills. The Paps rise to 2,571 feet and are quite rough going. It was on these hills that Dr. Walker of Edinburgh in 1812 conducted his classic experiment on the differential boiling-point of water at sea level and at the top of the Paps. Jura has a very small population of human beings on its nearly 90,000 acres. The island is so poor that its long history of being a deer forest will probably continue. In mythological literature Jura appears as being uninhabited and a place where heroes went a-hunting. It was on Jura during the latter part of the 19th century that Henry Evans conducted careful studies on the red deer. His were the first researches of a scientific character on Scottish red deer, yet he never set out to be more than a scientific amateur.

The island of Scarba, of about 4,500 acres, high and rocky, lies north of Jura. The Gulf of Corrievreckan is in the narrow sound between the two islands. This celebrated whirlpool and overfalls is caused by the strong tide from the Atlantic being funnelled through a strait, the floor of which is extremely uneven. The sound is quiet at the slack of the tide but is dangerous to small craft when the tide is running. The largest whirlpool is on the Scarba side of the sound, but there is a spectacular backwash on to the Jura coast which used to be reckoned very dangerous in the days of sailing boats. The maximum current is probably about 8½ knots which is very fast for a large bulk of water. No herring drifter or ordinary motor fishing-boat could hope to make headway against such a current, for their maximum speed in calm water is not more than 10 knots.

This West Highland zone has what the North Minch lacks, a number of sizable islands which are not big enough to lose their oceanic quality, and not so small that they are utterly windswept. The islands of Colonsay and Oronsay, west of Jura, are an excellent example of islands which have the best of almost all worlds. Naturalists may be glad that Colonsay is in the possession of one who recognizes its value and beauty in the natural history of the West. Most of the island is of Torridonian sandstone of a different complex from that farther north, but there are overlays here and there of limestone and its derivative soil, and the 100-foot beaches are another place of good soil. There are sand dunes, cliffs and rocky beaches where several rare maritime plants are to be found. There are fresh-water lochs with water lilies and the royal fern in profusion. Natural woods of birch, oak, aspen, rowan, hazel, willow and holly also occur, and beech has been planted. The sight of these, so near the Atlantic and its gales, may be imagined from this short passage from Loder's exhaustive book :

"The woods are being rejuvenated by young plantations of Birch and Aspen, which are springing up naturally and contending for supremacy with an annual luxuriant growth of bracken. The Woodbine twines over the trees, and festoons along the edges of the numerous rocky gullies that cut up these slopes. Ivy has climbed up and formed pretty evergreens of the more stunted of the forest trees. The Prickly-Toothed Buckler Fern grows in profusion, and the little Filmy Fern is also to be seen under mossy banks."

There has been considerable planting of coniferous and deciduous trees for amenity in this Atlantic island so that it now presents a luxuriant and well-wooded aspect in the neighbourhood of the house. But in gazing on these woods now and noting Colonsay's wealth of small birds, we should remember the effort entailed in *beginning* to establish these conditions. Loder says :

"When planting in the island first began, the trees made so little headway that it was considered amply satisfactory if they formed good cover. For the first ten years or so they made little progress, and many places had to be planted over and over again. Protection from animals and weather was provided in the first instance by dry-stone dykes, 5 feet high. Alder and Sea Buckthorn were planted along the most exposed edges. Alders and various species of Poplar were used in wet situations but the poplars did not last well, and were liable to be blown over. It was only as the trees made shelter for each other that they began to show any vigorous growth. Indigenous species such as Birch, Oak and Rowan, have sprung up on hilly ground where the planted trees failed to establish themselves."

The trunks of trees in these Atlantic places tend to become covered with lichens such as *Parmelia perlata* and *Usnea barbata*, and mosses such as *Eurhynchium myosucoides* (on birch), *Ulota phyllantha*, *Hypnum cupressiforme* and *Brachythecium rutabulum*. These trees seem to be much more affected by the humid climate than such exotics as *Escallonia*, *Ceanothus*,

Verbena and Mimosa (*Acacia*) which grow luxuriantly. This is one aspect of Colonsay, but there are also its sedgy and heathery moors like those of many another island of the West, and at the southern tip, where the Atlantic has full play over the Torridonian and mudstone slabs gently rising from the sea to make platforms and pools near the tide level, the Atlantic grey seal breeds in fair numbers. Elsewhere, on the cliffs, kittiwakes, razorbills and guillemots breed ; and there are three species of tern, arctic, common and little, breeding on the island.

Colonsay and Oronsay together might well be looked upon as an epitome of the West Highland world in its full range and consequences of Atlantic exposure and sheltered mildness.

Farther to the north-west are Coll and Tiree, two more islands which receive practically the full force of the Atlantic, but which show decided differences in natural history. Tiree is very low indeed. The rocky portion of the island, of Lewisian gneiss, reaches its highest point in Ben Hynish, 460 feet, but by far the greater part of Tiree (Pl. 25, p. 212) is but a few feet above sea level and composed of blown shell sand resting on a platform of gneiss. The island is one of good-sized arable crofts and is so far different from most West Highland districts that it has a Clydesdale horse-breeding society of its own. The sandy pastures of Tiree are deficient in cobalt but recent researches in mineral nutrition of animals have allowed the farmers of Tiree to dress the land with as little as 2 lbs. an acre of a cobalt salt and prevent the onset of pine in sheep. The island has particular interest for the bird-watcher : first, it is on a migration route and gets both summer and winter visitors which would not be seen anywhere in the North Minch, and its rich arable land also attracts a large number and variety of birds. Loch Vasapol of Tiree is a famous place for various duck. Tufted duck breed there and the gadwall is found there in winter though so uncommon elsewhere in the West. The vast beaches encourage certain waders, including the bar-tailed godwit, sanderling and greenshank. In the past the snipe-shooting was reckoned the best in Europe. Happily, there is less of it now.

Glacial action in Tiree is shown by the Ringing Stone, a huge rounded boulder of augite which probably came to rest there after a journey in the ice from Rum. The stone is marked by many ringed hollows on its surface.

The island of Coll, once one is within it, reminds one of the low gneiss country of Sutherland. Here the innumerable little hills are still smaller than in Sutherland and not so steep, none rising above 339 feet. The island presents a uniform rocky appearance when seen from a distance on the east side. On the west side of Coll are miles of shell-sand dunes, a feature which tends to be characteristic of many of the islands which meet the full force of the Atlantic and are low enough to have allowed the sand preliminary lodgment. The interior of Coll is just peat where it is not bare gneiss, yet with its western pastures it has always had the reputation of being a good place for cheese and sound dairy cattle. This island is important for the student of distribution of plants in relation to the last glaciation and associated changed ocean levels.

The low, sandy islet of Gunna lies between Coll and Tiree. It is a great place for Sandwich, common and arctic terns and I believe the little tern nests there too. Such burrowers as the sheld-duck are plentiful, of course. Barnacle and grey lag geese are common in winter.

The small group of tertiary basalt islands known as the Treshnish Isles lie between Coll and Mull. The most southerly one has a rounded cone of an old volcano, 284 feet high, which gives the island the name of Dutchman's Cap (Pl. Va, p. 52). The middle island of the group, Lunga, also has a volcanic mound rising to 337 feet, but the other small islands are all flat-topped with sheer sides of amorphous basalt resting on a platform of lava. This platform is of great importance in the natural history of the Inner Hebrides because it makes a breeding ground for the Atlantic grey seal. The Treshnish group, especially the Harp Rock of Lunga (Pl. XIXa, p. 156), is a nesting place of kittiwakes and auks and fulmars. Storm petrels nest in the Treshnish also, and the Manx shearwater on Lunga at least. The quality of grass on these islands is excellent and attracts a vast flock of barnacle geese in winter. The green rich grass of the islands is reflected again in the presence of large mixed flocks of starlings and peewits. In winter-time hundreds of blackbirds and a good many thrushes live on the Treshnish group. Lunga, being infested with thousands of rabbits, has a stock of seven buzzards.

The Cruachan of Lunga will be a good place to rest for a few moments and look at the topography of Mull, that very interesting member of the Inner Hebrides, Mull of the Mountains as the Gael calls it. The eye is first struck by the shapely peak of Ben More, 3,169 feet. This is the highest point reached by the tertiary basalt in Scotland. The cone itself is the result of great weathering, and the various beds of this amorphous lava are evident now in the truncated edges of the lower slopes of the hill. For sheer hard going, the descent from the summit to Loch Scridain takes a lot of beating, for the traveller is constantly having to make his way round these faces of rock which are not readily obvious to him as he comes down the hill. The terraced quality of Mull is obvious in a large part of Loch Scridain, the terraces being exactly the same height on either side. The peninsula between Loch Scridain and Loch na Keal reaches on the north side a stretch of some miles of very fine cliffs with sweeping talus slopes at their foot. The cliffs of Balmeanach are to my mind one of the striking features of Mull. The 1,600-foot basalt cliffs have trapped the cretaceous sandstone layer beneath them. The cretaceous sandstone—the local representative of the chalk—may be found in a narrow stratum just above sea level. These cliffs are difficult to explore and remain largely unexplored. Down below, the small island of Inchkenneth, the burial place of old Scottish kings and chieftains, is also composed of low strata of this cretaceous sandstone. If there is anywhere where chimneys must have cowls it is on Inchkenneth, for the down draughts from the great cliffs in a south wind are tremendous. Slates have to be specially cemented on the roofs. Corn and hay stacks suffer badly in this abnormal situation.

The whole of the north end of Mull consists of green even terraces with occasional gullies. The islands of Ulva and Gometra are similarly terraced flat cones with occasional gullies. The ground is porous and does not form basins for freshwater lochs ; peat is absent. Bracken grows rampant here ; indeed, Ulva is almost a museum piece for showing what luxuriant growth bracken can make in the Highlands. On the terraces, only the tips of the horns of Highland cattle can be seen above the fronds, but in the gullies the bracken tries to reach the same height as the plants on the terraces and may grow to a height of 12–15 feet. Trees of many kinds grow well in the sheltered parts of Mull on this soil from the volcanic rock. Just as trees were impossible on the tertiary basalt cliffs of Balmeanach and on Inchkenneth, they reach extraordinary luxuriance and beauty where the calcareous cretaceous sandstone appears again round the edge of Carsaig Bay on the south coast of Mull. This pocket will well repay a visit from the botanist and, I should imagine, from the entomologist. The cliffs to the west of Carsaig are by no means as impressive as at Gribun, but in their face there is to be seen a fine fossil tree fern first brought to the notice of geologists and naturalists by Dr. Macculloch in the early 19th century (Macculloch, 1824). Delicately coloured crystals are also to be found in these cliffs of the south coast.

The south-east end of Mull is dominated by bosses of gabbro called Sgurr Bhuidhe and Creach Bheinn (2,352 and 2,344 feet). From them we may look down on the north side to the long, bare, impressive valley of Glen More and on the south to the tree-lined waters of Loch Uisge and Loch Spelve. The southern peninsula of Laggan, formed by Loch Buie and Loch Spelve and almost made an island by Loch Uisge, reaches nowhere to more than 1,250 feet, but it is extremely rough and rocky, with plenty of scrub birch. Few people have walked through that ground which for many years now has been kept as a small and very private deer forest of 5,000 acres.

The islands of Muck and Canna are both of tertiary basalt on an erosion platform at tide level of lava that looks like clinker. Their soil is so good and their position in the Atlantic so favoured that these islands can grow what are probably the earliest potatoes in Scotland, i.e., May 31. The sheep of these islands do extremely well and come to the mainland in such good order that mainland buyers are hesitant to buy the lambs because they know they have nothing so good to offer them to keep them growing. The wealth of species of insects, molluscs and other invertebrates on these tertiary basalt islands is much greater than would be found on those of the Torridonian or gneiss formations, even though the basalt does not tend to allow lochans to form. The Glasgow University Expedition to Canna in 1936 published a full report of their extensive finds. Muck and Canna both offer the right kind of cliffs for sea birds, and Canna is also a breeding station for the Manx shearwater.

The island of Eigg (Pl. 5, p. 48) is a big shearwater station, the birds nesting well up towards the Sgurr, 1,280 feet. The Sgurr is the most obvious physical feature of Eigg and by far the island's most interesting natural phenomenon. It is a geological curiosity which has shed light on the geology of other areas far distant. The late Sir Archibald Geikie solved the riddle which Hugh Miller answered unknowingly at an earlier date. The Sgurr itself is of pitchstone, resting on a thin river bed of conglomerate which contains fossil pieces of driftwood from some far distant time. Beneath this is the tertiary basalt again. The pitchstone shows columnar jointing in places, a character which is still more strongly marked on Oidhsgeir, 18 miles away to WNW. This low islet of pitchstone is considered to be part of the same sheet as the Sgurr of Eigg. There is one other feature of Eigg deriving from its geology which should be mentioned here—the musical sands of Camus Sgiotag, a small bay on the north side of the island. These sands are of partially rounded quartz grains of similar size. If the sand is dry a shrill sound is heard as one walks over it.

To return for a moment to the few acres of Oidhsgeir, an islet which does not reach higher than 38 feet above sea level. Here on the top of the pitchstone columns which are 8 inches or so across the top are found the nests of kittiwakes in the season. There are also great numbers of common and arctic terns and eider ducks. Harvie-Brown, visiting the islet several times in the '80's and early '90's of last century found teal breeding and was convinced that the pintail duck had nested there also. This phenomenon of a small islet in the open sea gathering to it an immense number of living things for the purpose of their reproduction is one to which we shall return in a later chapter on the oceanic island. The deep-cut channels among the pitchstone columns are also a playground for the Atlantic seal. One channel on the south side runs up into a pool where a boat may lie in perfect safety. Many are the occasions when lobster fishers and venturers in small boats have been glad of the quiet pool of Oidhsgeir. What a strange feeling it is to be lying snug in such a place with the mighty ocean pounding but a few yards away and the spray flying over !

The island of Rum, with its three rock types of gabbro, Torridonian and granite, is for the most part a closed book to naturalists. We may hope this unfortunate period of its history is drawing to a close and that it may yet have a future as a priceless wild-life reserve. There are red deer and wild cats on Rum, there are otters round the shores and on the burns, and such species as badgers and roe deer could be introduced if introductions were thought desirable. Some of the finest kittiwake cliffs in the kingdom are to be seen on Rum, and the Manx shearwater nests in holes high up the 2,600-foot hills. The golden eagle is there still, though the sea eagle disappeared during the second half of the 19th century. Given the chance, we may expect the chough to return to Rum.

Skye may be looked upon as the northern outpost of the Lusitanian zone. It has suffered human depopulation like many another Highland area, but Skye is still one of the most heavily crofted areas of the West. Preservation of game has practically ceased and almost all the hill ground is now crofters' grazing. Topographically, Skye is magnificent, with its Cuillins and its Quirang, but from the point of view of wild life it is somewhat disappointing. The whole area facing the Minch is faunistically poor, as was pointed out by Harvie-Brown fifty years ago.

The island of Raasay, however, between Skye and the mainland, has a surprisingly rich variety of small birds, doubtless as a result of the woods and the large amount of park-like ground which is of Liassic origin. Personally, I should say that the Lepidoptera of Skye and Raasay would repay close scrutiny, not only from the point of view of numbers of species, but from the areas of distribution. Heslop-Harrison and his group have already made fruitful researches in this direction. Raasay, like Mull, has its own sub-species of bank vole (*Clethrionomys = Evotymys*).

The islands of the Atlantic zone are by far the most interesting part. The mainland coasts are often hidden and tend to lose character. But the country bordering the long sea lochs is of exceptional beauty and contains some habitats—such as the indigenous oak woods—which are almost unique in Scottish natural history. To walk the length of Loch Sunart, ten miles out of the twenty through these oak woods, in the fine weather of June is an aesthetic experience, if only for the sight of the redstarts which are here in great numbers. The scenery of the distance is as beautiful as the redstart among the oaks and hazels near at hand. Perhaps the better way is to travel eastwards from Kilchoan and Ardnamurchan Point where the quality of ocean is apparent as on the islands. Sanna Bay on the northward tip of Ardnamurchan is one of the most beautiful shell-sand bays of the West, but it is rarely visited because of its remoteness. East of Glenborrodale the sense of sea is lost and we are in the woods with the loch below us. The peak of Ben Resipol, 2,777 feet, dominates the landscape and is most shapely when seen from this airt. The traveller can hardly miss seeing Ben Iadain, 1,873 feet, and on the other side of the loch in Morvern. It is a little cap of tertiary basalt perched on the Moine schist, but between the two is a very narrow band of chalk. The sight of this little hill cannot fail to impress one with the immense amount of denudation which must have taken place to remove this molten layer of amorphous volcanic rock from so much of this countryside.

Though the oceanic birds such as kittiwakes and auks are lost as one moves up these long sea lochs, it is surprising how many sea birds are to be found breeding in the season. Arctic terns, eider ducks,

James Fisher

SHEEP COUNTRY, Lyne, Sutherland, with shepherd's cottage
The almost plant-less slopes of Breabag in the background. May 1945

James Fisher

SUILVEN: its western face, the Caisteal Liath,
from Loch Culag, Lochinver, Sutherland. May 1945

PLATE 4

James Fisher

ISLE TANERA, Summer Isles, with An Teallach beyond, from Dorney, Wester Ross. May 1944

James Fisher

STAC POLLY: its southern face, with scrub birch woods. Wester Ross May 1944

herring gulls and mergansers—all are here in numbers. And where there are shallow shores and estuaries there are parties of curlews, oystercatchers and ringed plovers. The hillsides above these long sea lochs are almost devoid of heather. The vegetational complex is one of various species of sedge, a few grasses such as flying bent and mat grass, and bog myrtle and deer's hair sedge. Heather will appear at the edge of a gulley perhaps where the drainage is good. From a distance the most obvious plant may be bracken—great sheets of it, darker green in summer than the herbage and red in winter.

The ecology of the long sea lochs and their intertidal zones is a subject of great interest for those who have the techniques to follow such studies. The gradual increase in salinity from head to foot of the loch, the diurnal variation caused by the tide, the spasmodic variations caused by spates and droughts, the currents formed, and their effects on the life of the waters, still remain to be worked out in detail. Space will not allow of individual description of all the narrow and long sea lochs from Loch Fyne to Loch Alsh : each one has its similarities and distinctions, and certainly each should be visited by the naturalist who is also keen on good country. Most of these narrow lochs have high hills rising from their shores, which means that their south side loses the sun for four months in late autumn and winter. Loch Hourn is particularly sombre in winter because the hills of Knoydart, which reach to 3,343 feet, seem to tower above the loch. Loch Nevis, on the other hand, is sheltered from the north by these same hills, and the North Morar hills to the south of this wider loch do not rise above 1,480 feet. Inverie, therefore, in its sheltered bay on the north side of Loch Nevis, is one of the kindest places in the West Highlands, despite the high rainfall. Indeed, the West Coast is full of these pockets of kindly shelter allowing luxuriant growth. Many of the policies of the large houses have magnificent specimen trees which have grown within a hundred years or so to a size which would have been impossible in a large part of England.

When these sea lochs narrow at their mouth there is a diurnal tide race of considerable force. That at the Corran Narrows of Loch Linnhe runs at 8 knots at ebb and flow, but that at Connel Ferry on Loch Etive is very much more than this and is quite impassable at half tide. When the tide begins to flow here there is the extraordinary sight of a waterfall in reverse, made by the inrush of sea water.

This section may be concluded with mention of the fine piece of country round the shores of Loch Etive (Pl. Vb, p. 52) and up to Glen Coe (Pl. 6, p. 49). Ben Cruachan, 3,680 feet, is one of the landmarks of the Highlands. Cruachan and Ben Starav, 3,541 feet, are of granite and lie either side of Glen Kinglass which runs from the east bank of Loch Etive. There is happily no road through this glen and it is therefore almost untouched. The sides are lightly wooded ; the river is of that clarity which is common in waters coming off granite, and as one climbs past the trees and by numerous falls the Forest of Blackmount is reached. This great high place has lost all western character which was expressed at the foot of Glen Kinglass. Blackmount has always been deer forest. Its swan song is that charming book by the late Marchioness of Breadalbane, *The High Tops of Blackmount.* You may object to all that this great lady stood for, but if you have a fine taste for country and appreciate writing which conveys the atmosphere of particular country you should read her book.

If one makes a cross-country trek from the heart of Blackmount to the head of Glen Etive, a country of high, spiry peaks is reached. What is more, it belongs to the nation. The Royal Forest of Dalness, Buachaille Etive, Bidean nam Bian, and some of the best climbing ground in Scotland is included, and it is probable that adjacent areas will also come under state ownership before long. The botanical and geological interest of the area is considerable, but the student of animal life will find it rather bare. Once more, at the head of Glen Coe we are on the border of our zone. As we look eastwards across the dreich Moor of Rannoch (Pl. VIa, p. 53) it is into Central Highland country.

The Outer Hebrides or Oceanic Zone

This is the most westerly portion of Scotland, the seventh degree of West Longitude passing down through the middle of this long range of islands which effectually shields the northern half of the West Highland coast. If we study a population map we see that the greater part of the people on the Long Island, as the whole group is called, are fairly densely packed on to the western fringe. Some more dense places are also found on the extreme east of Lewis, as on the Eye Peninsula or Point as it is always called in Lewis. By merely looking at a map one might ask why the people are so densely grouped on the west side where harbours are fewer and where the force of the Atlantic Ocean is unbroken. The very fact of human density of population is surprising to anybody accustomed to the alarming rate of depopulation on the mainland shore of the West Highlands. The Hebridean has a love of home which is unconquerable. There he has remained through thick and thin, sticking to his fringe which is between the mighty ocean and the deadening peat bog of the interior.

The half-million and more acres of the Outer Isles mean nothing in relation to the human population which lives there because to a large extent the interior is just as uninhabitable as the ocean. The people being confined to the coastal fringe live what might be called an open urban existence without town planning.

The overpowering reason for the human species being confined to this fringe is that here the awful blanket of peat ends and the ocean has thrown up an immense weight of shell sand. As the dunes have stabilized through the millennia and the stiff marram grass has given way to kinder herbage, a light lime-rich soil has formed. There are miles and miles of the white sand on the Atlantic shore, and above it the undulating *machair* (Pl. XIXb, p. 156) of sweet grass on which are reared great numbers of Highland and cross cattle. Flocks of barnacle geese come to the *machair* in winter and add to the humus content of the sandy soil. The prevailing south-westerlies continue to blow winter and summer, year after year, century after century. The tangle from the shallows of the ocean, the various Laminarias of the marine botanist, is torn from its bed and washed up on the beaches. Man comes down with his ponies and carts and creels and takes up some of it to spread on ploughed portions of the *machair*. All these things are helping to make soil, and the sand itself in these gales, especially if the winds are dry, is being blown up towards the blanket of peat which overlies the archaean gneiss of the Hebrides. The sand sweetens the peat, causes its barren organic matter to be unlocked and become fruitful of herbage for man's beasts. Their dung still further ameliorates the peat. Such is the constant process, in which the storm is a necessary and beneficent factor in allowing and maintaining fertility. But once the coastal strip is crossed the peat reigns supreme. Its blanket must have increased about ten feet since early man came to the Outer Isles, for only the tops of the fine Megalithic stones at Callernish, Lewis, were showing when Sir James Mathieson of the Lews undertook their excavation. The landscape in the bog is shortly described—a low undulating plateau of peat, bare grey rock of gnarled shape, and thousands of small and large lochans of brown acid water. If we wander through these areas of peat we shall come upon drier knolls where the rock comes to the surface or is not far beneath, and here we shall find turf and greenness for a space. The shielings of Lewis have been and still are here. They are the summer dwellings of a pastoral people taking advantage, for their cattle and sheep, of the short spell when the peat grows its thin crop of sedge and drawmoss. The people lived on the little knolls as on islands, bringing their cattle up to them twice a day for the milking; throwing out their household waste—little that it was—and adding their own quota of dung and urine. The shieling life is mostly gone but the green knollies in the sea of rock and peat remain.

We may digress at this point to consider the nature of peat, this substance which covers a million and a half acres of the Highlands and Islands and the existence of which is a most important factor in the natural history of the area and of the scenery. A study of the peat is interesting not only for what it grows and harbours now, but for the history to be deduced from a deep profile of it. Peat forms under the influence of certain definite conditions and their consequences: the first requirements are high precipitation and a general coldness of atmosphere in the growing season sufficient to inhibit bacterial activity in the waterlogged soil, but not cold enough to prevent growth of certain plants. A vegetational complex of sour bog plants, such as sphagnum moss (Pl. 22b, p. 145), sedges of various kinds and cross-leaved heather, soon occupies the ground to the exclusion of all those plants which need a well aerated soil and a supply of basic compounds. The rain impoverishes the original soil by washing out plant foods and then, by creating waterlogged and therefore anaerobic conditions, prevents the action of normal soil bacteria in breaking down the dead vegetation into humus. Such necessary decomposition does not keep pace with vegetative production by the plants, so that a gradually thickening layer of peat forms. The peat, thus composed of organic matter without lime, is highly acid in character, which is a still further check to bacterial action. Even the run-off water from the poor rocks such as gneiss and Torridonian is charged with unneutralized carbonic acid. With compaction and age, the peat becomes colloidal in texture, a fact of much influence in the behaviour of peat in holding water or being dried. The normal water content of peat as it lies in the bog is as high as 93·5 per cent.

Peat varies in consistency from being highly fibrous to the state

F. Fraser Darling

LOCH MOIDART, with Eigg in the far distance. Inverness-shire
August 1945

PLATE 6

B. A. Crouch

THE STUDY, GLENCOE, Argyll. September 1941

of a black amorphous substance, depending on age and the type of vegetation. The Highland crofter is well aware of these details and his methods of winning peat for fuel vary from place to place. Cotton-sedge peat is tough and fibrous and can be "footed" (i.e. set up on end to dry in pyramids of four bricks) and handled later with very little loss. Lower, older, amorphous peat is very brittle and cannot be set up.

The ages of the peat deposits have been tentatively fixed as beginning about 7000 B.C. at the close of the Boreal period. The warmish dry climate which grew forests of pine, birch and hazel now became warmish and wet, bringing about destruction of the scrub hazel vegetation by moss. The Atlantic period closed between 5000 and 4000 B.C. and a cooler and somewhat drier sub-Boreal period set in with a rapid development of peat. This continued until near our era which may be termed cold and wet and sub-Atlantic. The peat to-day is still making in some places as on the main bog of Lewis, and receding in others, as in parts east of the Cairngorms where the stumps of forest trees are coming forth as the peat crumbles away. Continual burning on western hills is probably having more influence than we know in checking or denuding the peat which is the only cover the rocks have, but in Lewis there is very little burning, the slopes are gentle and the succession of blanket bog is not being much disturbed, except by cutting for fuel.

The colours of the Atlantic coast are vivid blues and greens and the bright cream of sands. Inland, sombre colours are paramount and the lochans do not reflect the colour of the sky from their dark depths as does the sea above its floor of white sand. But the Hebrides are not all a dark plateau. The southern end of Lewis (Pl. VII, p. 60) and most of Harris are hilly. The Forest of Harris gives us rough going as anywhere in the Highlands and the Clisham rises to a fine peak of 2,622 feet. The red deer which live in these fastnesses are small, but have very well-shaped heads. The pine marten was also to be found there until recently. Its very wildness is the best protection this piece of country has. The lower deer forests of Park and Morsgail are fairly heavily poached of their deer, in an island of such heavy human population.

The Hebridean burns a lot of peat. His peat stacks are far larger than those of the mainland. By cutting peats he is doing two jobs—providing the wherewithal for comfort at the fire, and removing some of the great pervading blanket. He does not come upon bed rock at the foot of the peat banks but on to a layer of boulder clay which, when mixed with the top thin layer of sedge and peat, will shortly turn into fairly good soil providing much better grazing than anything from the top of the peat. The boulder clay came there by glacial action before the peat was laid down. Our Lewisman makes new ground this way and there is no doubt that if the modern mechanical tools such as the scraper and bulldozer were brought into operation on what is commonly called the skinned land, the agricultural scientist could make much good land in Lewis without attempting to conquer the upper layer of the peat.

As might be expected, the bird life of the interior of the Outer Hebrides is poor in variety and scanty, the nesting grey lag geese and red-necked phalarope (Pl. XXXIIa, p. 237) being probably the most interesting members. The geese feed on the crofting ground and on the *machair* but return into the maze of the interior to nest. The coasts are rich in sea birds, ducks and waders.

The Outer Hebrides are often described as being treeless, but the term is relative. The people who write about them are usually those who have a considerable experience of trees and tend to take them for granted. The Outer Hebrides are neither treeless, nor need they continue to be so desperately short of trees as they are. The grounds of Stornoway Castle on the east side of Lewis are famous. There are hundreds of acres of trees here, mostly conifers, but with a fair sprinkling of hardwoods and deciduous trees. These are Lady Mathieson's legacy to the Hebrides. Indeed, it needed courage to start tree-planting from scratch. She planted another piece with larch and other conifers half-way across Lewis, near Achmore, and these made good trees, but were blown down by a terrific gale on March 16, 1921. There are 90-year-old Corsican pines of hers at the head of Little Loch Roag, growing quite straight to 35 feet high. There is another plantation of deciduous and coniferous trees at Grimersta on the Atlantic coast of Lewis. Another plantation of conifers sheltering a house, Scalisgro, on the east side of Little Loch Roag, is less than twenty-five years old, and twelve years ago several acres of conifers were planted in Glen Valtos in the Uig district of Lewis. Sycamores are the great standby of a tree lover on an ocean coast. Several good ones are to be seen at Tarbert, Harris. And at Borve on the west side of Harris there are several acres of stunted mountain pines. More trees are to be found about Ben More Lodge in South Uist, and there are a few more in the north glen of Barra. Heslop Harrison has recently drawn attention to the birch wood, complete with bluebells and wood sorrel, on the slopes of the Allt Vollagair, South Uist. As has been mentioned already, many of the islands in the Lewis lochs are covered with dwarf rowans. That the Outer Hebrides were once a wooded area may be deduced on archaeological grounds as well as on the living relics. Baden-Powell and Elton (1936–37) excavated an Iron-Age midden at Galson on the north-west coast of Lewis. They found bones of wild cat and blackbird among the refuse, both creatures of woodland and savannah. The age of the midden was reckoned at 1,500 years or thereabouts.

What is most heartening in the woodland situation in the Outer Isles is that the crofters themselves are taking an interest in trees for shelter, and in many a garden you will see a host of willow cuttings bravely shooting forth in summer and making some certain headway against the gales and spray from the Atlantic. Rhododendrons are growing quite well in many places and are at least providing the first cover for something else to grow within their shelter.

The sands and the *machairs* of the Hebrides are often referred to in this book : in the Sound of Harris there are several islands which seem little else but shell sand, such as Ensay and Berneray ; and there is Vallay of North Uist. But I would not wish to neglect the cliffs which are also important in the natural history of the Outer Isles. The great ocean pounds against them and must be gradually wearing them away, but the rock is the old gneiss and holds remarkably well. Sir Archibald Geikie in his *Scenery of Scotland* calls to mind the measurement of the pounding effect of waves which was made at the Atlantic rock of Skerry-vore before the lighthouse was begun in 1845. The summer average weight of pounding was 611 lbs. per square foot ; in the winter months it was 2,086 lbs. per square foot, and in the very heavy south-westerly gale of March 29, 1845, a pressure of 6,083 lbs. per square foot was registered. Even when it is water alone that strikes the rock, the wear-ing effect is far from negligible, but when other loose rock is moved by the water and pounded against the cliff, even our short lifetimes may be able to notice the denuding effect of wave action. I remember an incident on North Rona which certainly opened my eyes to what a big sea could do. It was in December, 1938, in a period of south-westerly gales which would veer to west and north-west and begin again from south-west before the wind had fallen. They were worst in the nights and I would go out in the mornings to see the magnificence of sea against the low cliffs of the northern peninsula. These cliffs were perhaps forty feet high, but sheer, and going into deep water. The top was irregular with occasional ten-foot gullies a few yards wide in which were some very big boulders eight to ten feet thick, and a lot more of a size just too heavy for a man to lift. When there one morning, a sudden shower caused me to take shelter under one of the big pieces of rock. Peppered scars were visible all over the big boulder above and on the smaller ones lying on the smooth floor of the gully. It was evident that the sea had come green into here and rolled the smaller boulders up and down. But observation was not critical enough to question how these smaller boulders could pepper the big one several feet above. When sheltering there again after another tremendous night, it was obvious that the big boulder was not in the same place as it was the day before. Those pepperings had been caused by its own rollings to and fro in the gully under the impulse of the sea which had filled the gully thirty to forty feet above its normal level. That boulder, probably, had done much to wear the gully itself in the course of thousands of years.

Some of the cliffs of the Hebridean coasts are impressive and become the crowded haunts of ledge-breeding sea birds. The precipice of Aonaig in Mingulay is 793 feet. The stacks of Arnamull and Lianamull in Mingulay are also very fine. Harvie-Brown thought Lianamull the closest-packed guillemot station he had ever seen. Barra Head or Bernera, the most southerly island of the Hebrides, has some fine cliffs and in front of the lighthouse on the southern face is a gully which takes a terrific updraught of spray in southerly gales and makes the dwelling of the lighthouse suffer a heavy rain of salt water, a rain of sudden torrential showers of a moment's duration.

The influence of the sea in times of storm has already been mentioned as a land-making one on the western side of the Hebrides where it throws up sand for biological agencies to work upon. The islands in the Sound of Harris probably change shape through the years, sand being laid down in one place and taken away in another. Pabbay, for example, was the granary of Harris but the sand has encroached over the south-east end and has gone at the west. West again of Vallay, a sandy island of North Uist, the remains of a forest of trees may be discerned at low spring tides. This submerged forest is probably the result of Holocene sinkings, but nevertheless the shell-sand beaches

PLATE V

F. Fraser Darling

DUTCHMAN'S CAP, Treshnish Isles, Inner Hebrides: tertiary basalt
October 1937

Robert M. Adam

LOCH ETIVE, Argyll: typical of the estuarine conditions at the head of long West Highland sea lochs

PLATE VI

Robert M. Adam

RANNOCH MOOR, and Blackmount Forest

F. Fraser Darling

BOG COTTON, Priest Island, Wester Ross
June 1936

have certainly advanced within historical times. The minister in Harris who was responsible for the account of that parish in the Old Statistical Account of 1794 remarks that certain lands had been lost to the plough within living memory, and that when a sand hill became breached by some agency and was eventually worn away, good loam was sometimes found beneath and even the ruins of houses and churches. Whatever we may have lost in the Holocene sinkings, it may be remarked that the last three thousand years have seen more rising than sinking along Highland coasts.

The tides in the Sound of Harris have an interesting rhythm of their own, accurately noted by the minister in the Old Statistical Account. The following quotation is from the Admiralty Chart of the Sound of Harris : " It may be generally stated that in Summer, in neap tides, the stream comes from the Atlantic during the whole of the day, and from the Minch during the whole of the night. In Winter this precept is nearly reversed. In Spring tides both of summer and winter the stream sets in from the Atlantic during the greater part of the time the water is rising, but never for more than $5\frac{1}{4}$ hours, and it flows back into the Atlantic during most of the fall of the tide. Where the water is confined by rocks and islands . . . the velocity is nearly 5 knots . . . during springs, and not much less during neaps, whilst in other places it does not exceed a rate of 2 to $2\frac{1}{2}$ knots."

The east side of the Outer Isles is entirely different from the populous and spacious west side. Admittedly, north of Stornoway there are the sandy lands of Gress, Coll, Back and Tolsta, and the Eye Peninsula, supporting many crofts, but south of there the land is peat-laden and comes to abrupt cliffs at the sea's edge. The bird life is nothing like so interesting as on the western side and on such cliffs as exist there. Long arms of the sea, such as Loch Seaforth and Loch Erisort, Loch Maddy and Loch Eport, run far into the interior ; indeed, the last two named almost reach the west coast in Uist. To me this east coast of the Hebrides is uninviting and curiously dead. It is my experience that many of the islands off the West Coast of Scotland are much more interesting on their western sides than on their eastern shores. Raasay is an exception.

The east side of Harris from East Loch Tarbert to Rodel is well worth a visit to see what man can do in the shape of difficult cultivation. Take for example the township of Manish where the ground rises at a steep slope from the sea. It is in reality a rough face of rock devoid of soil but holding the peat here and there. The lobster fishers of Manish have actually built the soil of their crofts by creating lazy-beds or *feannagan* with seaweed and peat. By building up these little patches varying from the size of a small dining-table to an irregular strip of several yards long, the inhabitants have overcome the difficulty of drainage. The women carry seaweed up to the lazy-beds each year, all in creels, for the ground could not be reached by ponies. And all cultivation is of necessity done with the spade. Two crops only are grown, potatoes and oats, and the oats are *Avena strigosa*, which more than one naturalist has thought to be extinct as a cropping oat and only occurring here and there as a weed. The industry of the people of East Harris and their steadfast persistence with a thousand-year-old style of husbandry are remarkable. The potato is the only new thing, being brought to the Outer Isles in 1752. There are many more primitive townships in the Outer Hebrides working lazy-beds, but none in more disadvantageous position than Manish and its neighbours.

The Outer Isles also have their Atlantic outliers, each little group having its own strong individuality. There is St. Kilda (Pl. VIIIa, p. 61) on the west of the Uists, seventy-four miles out from Lochmaddy via the Sound of Harris ; this group of magnificent gabbro architecture has already been mentioned, with the fact that it is the largest gannetry in the British Isles and in the world. It is also the place from which the still growing fulmar population of the British Isles may originally have spread. The islands and their peculiar sub-specific fauna will be described in a later chapter. The Monach Isles are only eight miles west of North Uist, and are likely to follow so many small island groups in becoming uninhabited by man. They are islands of sand caught and built up on reefs of Lewisian gneiss. Another reef to the south of them, Haskeir, has not collected the sand. It is much smaller and uninhabitable but has long been a haunt of the Atlantic seal and was one of the last strongholds before the revival of the species in the present century. The Flannan Isles are twenty-two miles west of Loch Roag, Lewis. They are of gneiss and bounded everywhere by cliffs. The seals feed near them, but of necessity do not breed there because they cannot haul out. The relatively flat tops of the islands are covered with very fine grass which feeds a few sheep. The difficulties of gathering and getting the sheep to and from the boats are likely to be the cause of even this usage being discontinued. The lighthouse is the only inhabited place in the Flannans and to get ashore there can be a ticklish job.

Then to the north and north-east of the Butt of Lewis are Sula Sgeir (Pl. XXIII, p. 192) and North Rona (Pl. XXIV, p. 193), forty and forty-five miles away respectively. There are no beaches on these islands. Their natural history will be described in greater detail in Chapter 10. Suffice it to say here that Sula Sgeir is a gannetry, and like North Rona, St. Kilda and the Flannans, is a station for Leach's fork-tailed petrel. It is doubtful whether we should be justified in calling Leach's petrel one of the rarest British birds, but its breeding places are so few and so remote that it is unknown to all but half a dozen naturalists.

We have come to the end of our arm-chair tour of Highland country, from the frontier zone of Perthshire and Angus to that other frontier, the oceanic zone of the Atlantic. I have given but a glimpse of what is without doubt one of the finest scenic and faunistic areas in the world. Whether it survives as such depends very much on the good will and active, participant care of British people. Any area of natural history which is adjacent to a highly populous industrial region is in peril from that very proximity, but there is always the point of view that men's minds become awakened to natural beauty and the right of wild life to existence for its own sake, and then the proximity may be to the advantage of wild life and the wild places, in the same way that no country sparrows or moorhens are as tame and safe as those of St. James's Park.

THE HUMAN FACTOR AND REMARKABLE CHANGES IN POPULATIONS OF ANIMALS

IT IS of the very nature of humanity to alter the complex of living things wherever man is found. Man must be considered as part of the natural history of the earth's surface, however unnatural he may be. Of course, all animals alter the rest of the complex of living things in some way or other, but none does it with reflective intention as man does, and, I might add, none does it with much less regard for consequences. The animal, lacking the power of reflection, is as much at the mercy of its environment as the environment has to endure that particular animal; but man has power quite beyond his own physical strength; he can make the desert bloom, or ultimately fill an oceanic island with the beauty of bird song, and equally he makes deserts as spectacularly as any horde of locusts.

What has man done to the Highlands and Islands and what is he doing? Something of that story will be discussed in this chapter, but not so much as might be desired. Professor James Ritchie, now Regius Professor of Natural History at Edinburgh, has written a large volume entitled *The Influence of Man on Animal Life in Scotland.* It is an interesting and often depressing story, but Professor Ritchie would probably be the last to suggest that he has told the complete tale. There is much of the story we do not know or are only just learning how to infer and deduce. And our methods of recording are never complete enough to mark down, for future minds to work upon, the doings of the present generation of men.

Scotland, and the Highlands particularly, have nothing like such a long human history as England has. The last glacial epoch prevented that, for Scotland was under the ice thousands of years after man had inhabited the south of England. The tradition apparently established at that time has persisted with remarkable tenacity, because many people still seem to think that the north of Scotland endures arctic conditions in winter—which is a pity, considering the picnics this writer has enjoyed on a New Year's Day, and the times he has taken his siesta in comfort in the sun on a Highland hill in December and January !

It is generally accepted then that the Highlands as a whole have a human history of but a few thousand years as against tens of thousands in southern England, and it is possible that such areas as West Sutherland and the north-west corner of Ross-shire did not know man until two or three thousand years ago. When man first came to the Highlands the sea was 50 feet higher than it is at present. His kitchen-middens appear near the 50-foot raised beaches in various places such as Colonsay, Mull, Islay and Oban. He was a hunter and fisher and knew no arts of husbandry. One wonders what large effects early man can have had, because a small population of hunters taking life only for its own subsistence, and not for any export, would hardly bring to extinction many of the animals we know were present at that time. It is probable that natural causes were much more important in changing the natural history of the Highlands in those days. A few degrees' change of temperature for a period of years, for example, whether up or down, would work very great changes in the tree line and the specific constitution of the forests. The mountain tops would appear from the ice or disappear under it again for considerable spells, and everywhere the vital factor of moss growth would be affected. The growth-rate of sphagnum moss under optimum conditions has, in the deduced history of the Highlands, felled forests as surely as the fires and the axes of mankind.

The biggest effect man has exerted on the history of the Highlands has been in the destruction of the ancient forest—the great Wood of Caledon. This has happened within historic time, partly between A.D. 800 and 1100 and then from the 15th and 16th centuries till the end of the 18th. Even our own day cannot be exempt from this vast tale of almost wanton destruction, for the calls of the two German wars have been ruthless (Pl. 7a, p. 64). Much of this priceless remnant in Strath Spey and Rothiemurchus has been felled for ammunition boxes and the old pines of Locheil Old Forest went up in smoke during Commando training. These facts should never be forgotten as one of the *consequences* of war, and if nature reserves ever become a reality in the Scottish Highlands (as something distinct from National Parks, which are lungs for the people and playgrounds), the authorities should go to a great deal of trouble to bring about regeneration of the true Scots pine which is a tree different in many ways from the sombre article commonly grown in plantations as Scots. The true Scots pine (Pl. 17, p. 128) of the old forest is a very beautiful tree: its bottle-green is distinctive, and so is the redness of its boughs; the needles are very short and the shape of the mature tree is often much more like that of an unhindered hardwood than the commonly accepted notion of a pine. A long clean stem is not necessarily typical. The true Scots pine is not easy to grow now, and when it is suggested that the authorities should be prepared to go to a lot of trouble to bring about its regeneration, it is because care and patience will be needed in addition to willingness. Regeneration, however, is a subject for a later chapter; we are now woefully concerned with destruction and its effects.

The old forest consisted of oak at the lower levels, with alders along the rivers and in soft places, and pines and birches elsewhere. Pines clothed the drier portions and birch the higher and the damper faces of the western hills. The true Scots pine is a relic in the ecological sense, and where fire or the hand of man swept away an expanse of the old pine it was birch which within a year or two provided the new growth. An excellent example of this opportunism of the birch is to be seen at Rhidorroch, above Ullapool, Ross-shire, where the early felling line is clearly marked, pines above and birch below, the opposite arrangement to what would be found in nature. The oak forest has nearly all gone, Argyll and southern Inverness-shire being the main parts where it is to be seen to-day in any quantity. Scarcely anywhere is it being taken care of, or regeneration active.

Nairn (1890) says that the great Caledonian Forest extended "from Glen Lyon and Rannoch to Strathspey and Strathglass and from Glencoe eastwards to the Braes of Mar." The imagination of a naturalist can conjure up a picture of what the great forest was like: the present writer is inclined to look upon it as his idea of heaven and to feel a little rueful that he was born too late to "go native" in its recesses. But probably it was not so idyllic; the brown bears would have been little trouble, nor would the wild boar, and perhaps the wolf would not have given too many sleepless nights, but there would almost certainly have been more mosquitoes than at present, and malaria would have been a constant menace to our enjoyment of this primitive sylvan environment and its rich wild life.

The main trouble between A.D. 800 and 1100 was the Vikings, whether Danes or Norwegians. They were a destructive and parasitical folk, however colourful and well organized the civilization of the North may have been. Sometimes they set light to the forest to burn out the miserable natives who had taken refuge within it, and sometimes these same poor folk set light to strips of forest to act as a protection and screen from the Vikings. It would all depend on the airt of the wind, but the forest suffered anyway. The tradition of the burning by " Danes " or " Norwegians " still exists in legends which may be heard in the North-West Highlands to-day. I know of several places said to be concerned with the burning in the forest of a Viking princess and the site of her grave has been pointed out to me in two places fifty miles apart. The West Highlands were also a source of boat-building timber for the Norsemen in Orkney and Iceland (Brögger, 1929).

The wanton burning of the western portions of the forest would doubtless be eased after Somerled's Lordship of the Isles became established in the 11th century. This period was the most cultured and well ordered the West Highlands were to know for hundreds of years. Even as late as 1549, Dean Monro speaks of the wooded character of Isle Ewe and Gruinard Island in Ross-shire, affording good hiding for thieves and desperate men.

The woods of the Central Highlands were destroyed from the south-east. Gentlemen like the Wolf of Badenoch (*floruit* 1380) who was a brother of King Robert of Scotland, wandered through the country with large armed bands bent on plunder. Once more it was found that setting light to the forest was an easy way of smoking out or finishing off anyone who resisted. Local clan feuds must also have been a constant cause of forest fires of greater or lesser extent. The forests about Inveraray were destroyed by Bruce in an expedition against Cummin.

All these causes of destruction considered, we are still brought back to what I believe is a fundamental factor in the relation of man to the wild life around him, whether animal or vegetable. Man does not seem to extirpate a feature of his environment as long as that natural resource is concerned only with man's everyday life : but as soon as he looks upon it as having some value for export—that he can live by selling it to some distant populations—there is real danger. The forests of the Highlands were *discovered* (this word was used at the period) by the Lowland Scots and the English at the beginning of the 16th century. Queen Elizabeth of England prohibited iron smelting in Sussex in 1556, and in the Furness district of Lancashire in 1563, because of the devastation caused to English woodlands. The smelters had to move farther north. The Scottish Parliament saw to what this would lead and passed an Act prohibiting anyone " to tak upoun hand to woork and mak ony issue with wod or tymmer under payne of confiscatioun of the haill yrne." We can see exactly how this Act would work from the operations of black markets in Britain during the second German war. The game was so profitable that an occasional heavy fine was accepted as a normal tax on trade.

At this time also the woods were being destroyed actively for another reason—or perhaps two reasons. Thieves and rebels hid in the woods and wolves bred therein. It seems that infestation of the forests with these two forms of predatory fauna was so bad that it could be endured no longer. Menteith in *The Forester's Guide* quotes an order by General Monk, dated 1654, to cut down woods round Aberfoyle as they were " great shelters to the rebels and mossers." Ritchie, in giving an account of the extinction of the wolf in Scotland, mentions local tradition and definite record of woods being destroyed in the districts of Rannoch, Atholl, Lochaber and Loch Awe for this very purpose.

The suppression of the first Jacobite rebellion of 1715 gave an impetus to destruction. English business enterprises such as the York Buildings Company purchased forfeited estates and quite unashamedly set out to exploit them. Whatever was worth taking was taken, and the timber was one of the first things to go. But for the obstructive tactics of the Highlanders themselves it is probable that every vestige of pine forest would have gone at this time. The York Buildings Company went bankrupt, but not soon enough from the naturalist's point of view. Even after this period between the rebellions, the higher standard of living which was more or less imposed on Highland proprietors by their taking up the English way of life, caused them to sell large areas of forest for smelting purposes. The prices paid for the trees were often ridiculously small. Ritchie says :

" The destruction wrought by these later and larger furnaces was irreplaceable. In 1728, 60,000 trees were purchased for £7,000 from the Strathspey forest of Sir James Grant . . . About 1786 the Duke of Gordon sold his Glenmore Forest to an English company for £10,000; and the Rothiemurchus Forest for many years yielded large returns to its proprietor, the profit being sometimes about £20,000 in one year."

The last of the felling and smelting with charcoal seems to have

Robert M. Adam

BLACK HOUSE, Isle of Scarp, Harris, Outer Hebrides
Traditional domestic architecture

Robert M. Adam

SUAINAVAL, a Hebridean gneiss summit, sands of Uig, and black houses, Lewis

James Fisher

VILLAGE BAY, Hirta, St. Kilda, showing uninhabited settlement
June 1939

Robert M. Adam

MINGULAY, Outer Hebrides, a crofting township now uninhabited
An example of living on the fringe

been as late as 1813. The brothers Stuart, 1848, mention twelve miles of pine, oak and birch being burned in Strathfarrar to improve the sheep pasture.

The effects of the normal spread of arable cultivation with a rising population may be taken for granted, but this does not by any means round off the story of the changed face of the Highlands through the destruction of the pine and oak forests. The passing of the forests heralded another biological phenomenon of great significance for the natural history of the Highlands, and which was also brought about by man's agency. This was the coming of the sheep. The old husbandry of the Highlands and Islands was a cattle husbandry, a well-ordered sequence of rearing in the islands and of feeding in the mainland glens and on the hillsides before the strong store beasts were driven away south to the great fairs such as Falkirk Tryst. The Highlands were a country unto themselves into which Lowlanders ventured with some wariness. The collapse of the second Jacobite rising in 1746 allowed flockmasters from the Southern Uplands to think about the exploitation of the new expanses of grazing in the North. "The Coming of the Sheep," as this colonization of the Highlands was called, is one of the epic events of Scottish history, though it is one not commonly referred to in history books.

The end of the rising of 1745 meant an end of internecine warfare among the clans, which in turn favoured the survival of more men. The human population of the Highlands rose considerably during the second half of the 18th century, a fact we know as a result of Dr. Alexander Webster's industrious work in effecting a census in 1755. Yet the extension of sheep-farming on the ranching system of the Southern Uplands meant a way of life in which fewer men were needed ; also, the new sheep farms needed the crofting ground of the glens for winter pasture. The Highland gentry at this time varied greatly in achievement of the aristocratic ideal. Some had little thought at all for the clansfolk in the glens now that they had no further military significance, and others, finding themselves drawn into English metropolitan life, needed ready money—and a lot of it. Whether they were sorry or not to see their forests go in the space of a few years, it is unlikely that they considered with anything but satisfaction the new and profitable use to which it was now possible to put their land. The flockmasters offered high rents which the new clean ground amply repaid.

The old sheep of the West Highlands and Islands were akin to the present Shetland breed, but apparently they were never very numerous. The sheep now coming north with the Border men were Blackfaces which had been bred there since the 16th–17th centuries. The Scottish Blackface (Pl. 8, p. 65), now so common on Highland hills and through the Islands, should not be thought of as indigenous. Its origin is in the Southern Uplands; before that the north of England; before that the Pyrenees (where a prototype may be seen to-day) and possibly before that somewhere in Central Asia. The sheep were crossing the Highland Line into Dumbartonshire before 1760; by 1790 the occupation was complete in most of Argyll and in Perthshire and the sheep were plentiful in Mull and Inverness-shire. The first sheep farm in Ross-shire was settled in 1782 where it is said the occupant was a lonely man for some years. He was joined by many others at the turn of the century. Cheviot sheep-farming in Sutherland (Pl. 3a, p. 44) and Caithness was begun largely through the energy of Sir John Sinclair of Ulbster in the early years of the 19th century. Extensions continued until 1850. Profits were large for both landlord and farmer, but the poor folk found themselves in a bad way. Their husbandry was relatively intensive, the ground being made into lazy-beds (*feannagan*) wherever slope and exposure made cultivation possible. These well-drained ridges, all turned by hand, grew good crops of barley and oats, and later of potatoes, which crop in itself allowed a greater density of population by its great increase of food supply. Fencing was relatively unimportant for there were so few sheep and the cattle were tended and kept out of the arable ground by the old men and children. The arrival of a heavy stocking of sheep on the hill made the position of these people untenable. They were cleared by the landlords and many thousands chose to emigrate. The folk who remained were pushed to the coasts where their crofting townships are to-day.

Sometimes these coastal townships were places of such extreme exposure and poverty of soil that after a hundred years of hand-to-mouth existence the crofts have gone empty. The sight of such a derelict and decrepit township (Pl. VIIIb, p. 61) is a most saddening and disturbing thing. It does not present the ruin of a civilization by sack or natural catastrophe, but the quiet failure of simple folk to obtain subsistence from their environment. In other places, the shift to the coast has proved almost a salvation, for the people have found a mild, sheltered and early climate, and natural resources in fish and seaweed which have enabled them to live much better than they could have in the inland glens. These coastal crofting communities vary greatly in habits and thus in their influence on local natural history. Some have a shore from which they can fish, others have a rocky shore or no aptitude for fishing and they turn their energies inland to breeding sheep. It is an unfortunate characteristic of many of the crofting townships, whether fishing or pastoral, that the small quantity of arable land is being neglected, and the vegetational complex of rushes and sedge is creeping in to both unoccupied and occupied crofts.

The coming of the sheep finished the process of changing the face of the old Highlands of the time of the forests. Large areas of birch scrub were burned. Where the birch trees were larger they were cut that their bark might be exported for tanning material for sails and rope. I know of one sheep farm in the North-West Highlands (now back to a famous deer forest) where the shepherds were paid in part with the value of birch bark which they themselves had to cut and peel while they were in the hill. The flockmaster's firestick was a destroyer of ground cover over hundreds of thousands of acres, for even where the pine trees had been cut a new growth of birch was taking place which might yet have made a less bare Highlands than we know to-day. Every spring some patch of heather or purple moor grass (sometimes known as flying bent grass or *Molinia coerulea*) would be burnt and seedling trees would suffer. Much birch was cleared in the 19th century by the bobbin-makers working for the cotton mills of the Lowlands and Lancashire. The pirn mill at Salen, Loch Sunart, was the principal reason for the establishment of that settlement.

The sheep themselves, as we shall see in the next chapter, are the destroyers of a habitat in which scrub trees such as birch, willow and rowan are a part (Pl. 23a, p. 132). Regeneration in places where they reach beyond a very low density is impossible, and even the many flowers of the countryside disappear beneath their ever-questing and selective muzzles.

Even the sheep have not been quite the last straw in man's despoliation of the Highland forests, because his railways have happened to run through some of the last expanses. The old Highland Line (now L.M.S.) running through the Grampians and Strath Spey has been the cause of burning a good many acres of the ancient pine woods.

This incidental destruction is hard to bear in a time when we have come to treasure the few remnants of primitive sylvan beauty. But I would say this : we still do not take enough care. Every year or two there are fires in Strath Spey which take away more and more of these beautiful trees. The present Laird of Rothiemurchus, discussing the question of national parks with me, said that 3,000 acres of wood had been burnt in his lifetime. If some of the last remnants of the forests are to become the property of the nation, each one of us must be conscious of his personal responsibility in preserving them.

The destruction of the forests meant the end of a habitat for much other wild life which thereupon became extinct, was compelled to change its habits or was reduced to a very low population which would be in danger of extinction from other and often obscure causes. It has come to be generally understood nowadays, that the animal population of a region is not static. There is constant fluctuation in progress. But the purpose of this chapter is not to dwell on this natural rising and falling of numbers, so much as to mention the more startling events such as actual extinctions, retrogressions, resurgences, and introductions of new species within the area of the Highlands. The list of such events and movements is a considerable one.

The causes of extinction may be various but in the main, as has been said, the active disturbing factor is man, and as one looks through the list, the losses of the last 200 years are large in proportion to those of the previous 10,000 years.

Changing climate is an immensely important mover of species and when climate changes in a relatively small island such as Britain, extermination is often the fate of land mammals which cannot readily adapt themselves. Again, if man is present and the animal of fair size, he may speed the influence of climate.

The lemming and the northern rat-vole may be taken as examples of changing climate being the dominant factor in exterminations in the Highlands and in the country as a whole. They must have disappeared with the advent of the warmer Atlantic climate and the extension of forest growth. Vestigial arctic climates such as that of the 4,000-foot plateaux of the Cairngorms have been insufficient to maintain the lemming, which occurs in similar country in Norway.

The giant Irish elk (*Megaceros hibernicus*) disappeared in prehistoric days also, probably before the advent of man. Climate was an active factor, but the organism itself was heading for disaster. The

F. Fraser Darling

DEFORESTATION in the Second German War. Sutherland
September 1943

F. Fraser Darling

ARABLE LAND: a small patch among scrub birch of gneiss country. Sutherland
September 1943

PLATE 8

F. Fraser Darling

MOUNTAIN BLACKFACE EWES gathered for shearing. Loch Sunart, Argyll. July 1945

biological principle of heterogonic growth was at work in extravagant fashion. The evolution of antler form and weight had no particular relation to function, but was a concomitant of increasing body size and followed a different growth rate. The great annual drain on the constitution of the Irish elk, of growing 80–90 pounds of bone tissue, was too much in an age which was changing from that of the rich pasturage of the Pleistocene. Whereas the red deer grew smaller in every way, and thus adapted itself, the giant deer apparently died in all its glory. It is thought that the northern lynx persisted in the Northern Highlands until man came, but soon afterwards it became extinct. The species was probably in decline with the rise of the warm Atlantic climate, but was given the final push into extinction by Neolithic man. Bones of the northern lynx were found near the hearths in the limestone cave of Allt na Uamh near Inchnadamph, Sutherland. Ritchie says this is the one appearance of the species in Scottish history.

The brown bear was probably never a numerous species in the Highlands. The assumption of its disappearance in the 9th–10th centuries means that man must have been responsible, for climatic change had long ceased in its more violent forms and the destruction of the forests had scarcely begun.

The reindeer inhabited the Northern Highlands well into the historic period. The rise of the Atlantic climate may have reduced its original numbers, but had it not been for man's influence it would probably have survived as the woodland type of the species. The destruction of the forests must have greatly restricted its range and finally its extermination must have been due to direct hunting. The Orkneyinga Saga mentions the hunting of the reindeer by Rognvald and Harald of Orkney, and the date assigned to the event is about the middle of the 12th century, but the species was extant later than this.

The elk (or moose) persisted in the north until rather later than the period of the brochs, defensive stone towers which were built about the 10th century, and given up when the Norse raids developed into conquest, i.e. about A.D. 1000–1100. Man, by direct hunting and the indirect means of destruction of forest which had then begun, was the cause of its disappearance by about A.D. 1300. Legends of a large dark species of deer are common in the Highlands.

The beaver was found in the Highlands until the 15th–16th centuries, Hector Boece mentioning its existence about Loch Ness, and its being hunted for its skin.

We may consider next a group of three diverse creatures which are extinct as wild animals of the type they were in the 13th, 14th and 15th centuries, at which time they disappeared; but which still lived on in domesticated forms or crosses with other domesticated stocks. The wild boar would be found wherever there were oak woods and would impoverish the flora therein by its constant delving. Its domesticated descendants persisted in the West Highlands and Islands until the middle of the 19th century, at which time swine ceased to be kept as a general practice. The conversion of the people to an extreme type of Presbyterianism engendered a Judaic attitude to the pig, and numbers fell away rapidly after the 19th-century conversions. Any fresh pigs to come in were of the improved type from England, where the quick-fattening Chinese pig was altering the form of the old "razorbacks." The great wild ox or Urus, surely the most magnificent member of the northern fauna, also disappeared through hunting and the clearing of the forest, but its blood may be presumed still to run in the veins of the West Highland breed of cattle (Pl. 9, p. 84). The Highlands also had their wild ponies which were truly wild and not feral. Cossar Ewart has pointed out that these ponies lacked callosities on the hind legs. Hector Boece mentions the ponies in the same passage as that in which he records the beavers of Loch Ness. The Scottish wild horse received crosses of Norse blood, and later of Arab, so that the Highland pony of to-day (Pl. IX, p. 80) has at least some claims to represent the indigenous stock.

The white cattle with black hooves, muzzles, eyes and ears remain to us to-day in a few herds in large parks. They are rather poor creatures, having been greatly inbred through lack of numbers. None of them is in the Highlands. Cattle of this colouring arise from time to time, and I believe that it would not be difficult to build up a herd of strong-coated white cattle with black points from the existing cattle stocks of the Highlands and Islands. Similarly with the ponies, we could find a few Celtic ponies (*Equus caballus celticus*) cropping up as segregates from the Hebridean herds, and build up a stud of them. These two species would be an asset to a future wild-life reserve in the Highlands.

The story of the wolf in the Highlands is important because this animal was responsible for a good deal of the later history of the destruction of the forests. Clearance of the forest by burning was doubtless the easiest way of restricting the wolf's range. The last wolf of Scotland was killed by one Macqueen on the lands of Mackintosh of Mackintosh, Inverness-shire, in 1743. Passage through the Northern and Central Highlands in the 16th century was hazardous enough for hospices or " spittals " to be set up where the benighted traveller could rest in safety. Wolves were plentiful and hungry enough to cause people in the Highland areas to bury their dead on islands offshore or in lochs. Examples of such islands for which this tradition exists are Handa, Sutherland ; Tanera, N.W. Ross ; and Inishail, Loch Awe, Argyll. A detailed account of the wolf in Scotland may be found in Harting's *British Animals Extinct within Historic Times* (1880).

Only one mammal has become extinct in the Highlands in the 20th century, though several have come near extinction in our day and have then rallied. The polecat has gone from Scotland though it still exists in moderate numbers in mid-Wales. The intensity of game preservation and the skill of Scottish gamekeepers in trapping are doubtless responsible. Even as I write, Highland fox-hunting organizations have expressed " satisfaction " at kills not only of foxes but badgers, otters, weasels and stoats. These same men will soon be yapping their dissatisfaction at plagues of voles and rabbits and calling on that universal Aunt Sally of Scotland, the Department of Agriculture, " to do something."

From the animals and dates mentioned so far in this chapter, we gather that several mammals disappeared between the years A.D. 1000 and A.D. 1743. Birds were more fortunate, but their turn was to come with the improvement and lightening of the fowling-piece, the rise of game preservation and the spread of land reclamation. Almost as the last wolf howled in the Highlands, extermination of certain birds began. The first were the crane and the bittern which went in the 18th century, partly by direct hunting for feathers and food, but mainly through draining the marshes for land reclamation. It may be said, incidentally, that this characteristic 18th-century movement for draining was also responsible for the extirpation of malaria from Scotland.

The absolute extinction of the great auk is a story so well known that there is no need to recount more of it than the gradual diminution on St. Kilda as a breeding species during the 17th and 18th centuries. By 1840, when the last great auk was caught and killed on St. Kilda, the captors were unaware of its identity, and the bird was actually killed because of their fear of it. Where there is no written word current, tradition is unsure in its action.

All the other extinctions are of the raptorial tribe. The decline and disappearance of the osprey in the 19th and 20th centuries is recorded elsewhere in this book. The least-known extinction is of the goshawk, which was still present as a breeding species in the 19th century, having its eyries in great pine trees of the remnant of the Caledonian Forest. The kite was finished but a few years afterwards. The Harvie-Brown *Vertebrate Fauna* Series are good sources of information on the last haunts of all these raptors. The white-tailed or sea eagle has been the last to go. Shetland has the last breeding record in the present century. The West Highland and Hebridean coasts, being nearer to extensive sheep-farming interests, lost their sea eagles rather earlier. By 1879 they had gone from Mull, Jura and Eigg. The species finally ceased to breed in Skye, the Shiant Isles and the north-west mainland about 1890. It is all a dismal story ; and it is a matter for doubt whether, should these species try again to colonize this country, they would be allowed to breed in security. The vested interests of game preservation (by no means dead in a Socialist Britain), of a decrepit hill sheep-farming industry in the West Highlands and Islands, the pressure of egg collectors and irresponsible gunners, are heavy odds.

A local extinction is worth noting, namely, the ptarmigan in the Outer Isles. Their last haunt was on Clisham, Harris, the highest hill in the Hebrides. Seton Gordon in his recent book *A Highland Year* (1944) says that rabbits became very numerous on the drier slopes of the hill, and that ferrets were turned down to cope with them. He says the ferrets also preyed upon the ptarmigan and are in his opinion responsible for their extermination. This animal achieved what the related pine marten failed to do in its day in the Forest of Harris.

There is one invertebrate extinction to be recorded, the oyster. The northern oyster was common in many sheltered shallow bays up and down the West Highlands, but it has now gone, probably due to gross overfishing, with possibly a run of low-temperature summers which would hinder breeding. Experiments have been made in re-introduction, but the southern oyster from French waters has been used, and as might have been expected, has not been successful. The temperature of the water does not reach and remain at 60° F. for a long enough time.

The status of our two British seals, the Atlantic grey seal (*Halichoerus gryphus*) and the common or brown seal (*Phoca vitulina*), is interesting as an example of the influence of man on the species. The common seal is truly common though local : it occurs in large numbers in the Tay estuary where it is regularly hunted, but without complete success owing to the sanctuary given by the sand banks ; it is common in Orkney, and the seas of Shetland hold very large numbers. The common seal is of much less frequent occurrence on the West Highland coast, though there are pockets of twenties and thirties in some of the sea lochs and among the groups of islands. The Atlantic seal is much commoner on this coast though it favours the more outlying places.

The common seal is immensely more damaging to nets than the Atlantic seal, but its habits are such that any attempts by man to lessen its numbers severely have little success. When the young are born they go to sea with the mothers immediately and the adults spend no more than a few hours at a time lying out on rocks and sand banks. The species does not flock to some traditional breeding place as does the Atlantic seal. We shall study the life history of this latter species in a later chapter ; our concern with it here is in the habit of retreating to more or less remote islands to breed, and in spending some weeks out of the water. The Atlantic grey seal is at the mercy of man at such a time, for he finds gathered at these places the population of a great length of coastline, with the animals at a severe disadvantage.

The grey seals (Pl. 28, p. 221, Pl. XXX, p. 229) were regularly hunted in the Hebrides during the autumn breeding season, without reference to age, sex or condition of the animals; for the visits to the nursery islands were governed by the state of the sea. The result was a diminution in numbers which did not become dangerous until the 19th century when the species was faced with the fact which I have mentioned and repeated elsewhere in this survey of Highland natural history—danger for the species comes when the toll taken is for export and not for the limited and constant needs of a resident human population. The skins of the Atlantic seals were being bought and resold by the Danish Consul in Stornoway. The fishery was wasteful in the extreme and quite unorganized. Then came a remarkable relief for the seals in cheap rubber boots for the fishermen, and synchronously, almost, the arrival of cheap and clean paraffin for lamps. Rubber boots were much less trouble in every way than those of seal skin, and only those who have tried the smoky flame of seal oil can fully appreciate the boon of paraffin. The seals got some respite except for the fact that the hunting had become a traditional social occasion which had to be gradually broken down. Happily, the Government made an Order prohibiting the slaughter of Atlantic grey seals during the whole of their breeding season. The species has increased and is now numerous again to an extent it cannot have known for centuries. It is spreading to islands and mainland coasts from which it had long disappeared, and is now a feature of the natural history of the West which anyone can hope to enjoy, and have the opportunity to see and watch in the course of a short holiday. This story of an animal's survival is an example of the importance of human ecology in relation to that of the animal. No British mammal could be more easily exterminated, because of the nature of its breeding habits. Its future is entirely in man's hands.

St. Adamnan records that in Columban times the religious community treated the Atlantic seals on Soay, near Iona, as a natural resource. They conserved the stock but took a certain toll of it. This is one of the earliest records of conservation in the modern sense.

The history of the squirrel (*Sciurus vulgaris*) in Scotland is one of remarkable interest and has been studied in detail by Harvie-Brown (1880). Remembering Dr. Johnson's facetious remarks about the value in Scotland of such a piece of timber as a walking-stick, it may well be understood that the extreme course of deforestation in the greater part of Scotland must have restricted the range of the squirrel until it was nearing extermination. It had long gone from the Lowlands by the time Dr. Johnson was making epigrams, and was in a much reduced state in the Highlands where some pine and oak forest still existed. Birch wood, of course, is of little attraction to a squirrel. Harvie-Brown says that some severe winters killed off most of the Highland stock. Some were left in Rothiemurchus and apparently a few persisted in South-East Sutherland until 1795.

From this date onwards the species began to increase in the Highlands, both from the resurgence of the Rothiemurchus stock and from introductions. The Southern Highlands were colonized in the first half of the 19th century from the stock liberated by the Duchess of Buccleuch at Dalkeith, Midlothian, in 1772. The Eastern Highlands were colonized from the Duke of Atholl's importation from Scandinavia in 1790, turned down at Dunkeld, where much tree-planting of conifers was taking place. There was another introduction at Minard on Loch Fyne in 1847 which allowed a spread over the South-West Highland area and northwards to Dalmally and Glen Dochart. Finally, and of great importance, there was the introduction by Lady Lovat in 1844 to Beaufort Castle, Beauly, Inverness-shire. The squirrel, we see, has reason to be thankful to the Scottish aristocracy. The Beaufort Castle stock spread in all directions, recolonizing Sutherland, crossing from the Oykell to Loch Broom and Little Loch Broom, down the Great Glen and into North Argyll. Personally, I cannot help but wonder why the squirrel did not persist in the considerable areas of oak wood interspersed with pine along Loch Sunart and up to the woods round Achnacarry and Loch Arkaig, though Harvie-Brown in the *Vertebrate Fauna of Argyll and Inner Hebrides* (1892) says that the squirrels had not yet reached Strontian. Ritchie says they reached there in 1896. I have seen them in the woods round my house on this very day, and I know that now the squirrel is well down into Ardnamurchan, the most westerly peninsula of the mainland.

The squirrel has become a forestry pest of importance. Squirrel-shooting clubs have shot thousands and thousands, but the species remains plentiful and will doubtless hold its own in this era of intention towards reafforestation. What the effect of the squirrel has been on the small woodland bird population of the Highlands can never be known, but on such species as the Scottish crossbill, it must have been considerable and depressing. The squirrel does not occur on any of the islands and it is unlikely that it will reach them now.

The American grey squirrel (*Sciurus carolinensis*) is an introduction to Scotland which has not got far into the Highlands and will probably not do so. A single pair was released at Finnart, Loch Long, in 1890 (Ritchie, 1920) and their offspring has spread over to the west bank of Loch Lomond and thus comes within our area.

The pine marten (*Martes martes*) has persisted in the Highlands only by an extraordinary adaptation to a different way of life. It was primarily and by preference a woodland animal, a beast of the old pine forest, living on squirrels, such other rodents as it could catch, and on birds and their eggs. Steady persecution and the destruction of the forests reduced its numbers to very few, but it retreated to the cairns of the treeless hills in North-West Sutherland, and was there fortunate enough in this 20th century to be protected by a group of landowners and sportsmen, foremost among whom Commander Edmund Murray Fergusson should be mentioned. There is now a definite increase noticeable in the number of martens, individuals appearing as far from the

Sutherland sanctuary as Berriedale, Caithness; Loch Broom and Invermoriston. A pair of martens was turned down in Ardverikie Forest, Loch Laggan, south of the Great Glen, in 1930, and Commander Fergusson (1945) is of the opinion that a marten seen at Loch Voil, Perthshire, in 1944, would be of the progeny of this pair. The animals are great travellers. It is to be hoped that if Britain is ever to have a system of nature reserves—as distinct from national parks—that the sanctuary given by the Sutherland group will be implemented and made sure for all time by Government authority. The marten's escape from extinction has been a narrow one.

There are no pine martens in the Outer Isles, though there were until the '70's of last century in the Forest of Harris. It should be realized, of course, that forest here means a wild expanse; there are no trees at all in the stony hills of Harris. The late Osgood Mackenzie of Inverewe (1924) who saw much of the old wild Highlands in their last days before the rabbit and the sheep destroyed what was left by the woodcutter's axe, told a story of finding a pine marten and a big wether lying dead together in the Forest of Harris. The marten had evidently got its canines into the throat of the wether and that animal, dashing downhill in fright and pain, had struck a rock and killed the marten; then the sheep had dropped and bled to death. Such ferocity and such big quarry must be rare in the martens left in the Highlands to-day. Rabbits, squirrels where there are woods, and birds are probably the mainstay of the marten's diet.

The red deer (*Cervus elaphus*) (Pl. XIV, p. 101, Pl. 14, p. 117) have had to undergo a considerable change of habits in order to survive. From being a creature of the open forested ground they have had to become animals of the bare hillside. Doubtless in the old days they would go high in summer to the treeless corries and upper slopes, but now the large majority of the 150,000 deer in Scotland have to live the year through without much shelter. They have achieved this survival by a diminution in their size and in the elaborateness of antler growth. The Highlands of to-day would not carry a stag of the size and magnificence of antlers seen in the Highlands of 500 years ago.

Even the roe deer (*Capreolus capreolus thotti*), though it has not had to change its habits, seems to have undergone some lessening of antler growth. Though it is still plentiful and inhabits relatively better ground than the red deer, its range has undoubtedly been curtailed, and this factor must influence the animal's food selection to some extent, because the roe is a beast that does not stick closely to a territory day after day, but makes quite considerable moves.

The variable, blue or alpine hare (*Lepus timidus*) is an indigenous member of the mainland Highland fauna, but it has also been the subject of introduction to island areas of the Highlands—to Islay, Arran, Mull, Skye and Raasay, and Harris and Lewis. The colonization of the Southern Uplands by this species, following its introductions in 1834 and 1838, has been phenomenal, and the blue hare is there a pest which has to be kept down by organized shoots. There are not sufficient raptors and carnivores to keep numbers in check, and the drier hill faces suit them admirably. The West Highland introductions have not fared so well. Since about 1913 there has been a great reduction in numbers of the blue hare in the western parts of its range. They are not common in the Islands now and are scarce all the way up the West Coast hills. When I was working the Dundonnell, Gruinard and Letterewe Forests in 1934–36, I saw a blue hare on two occasions only, each time on a peat-free gravelly plateau at an altitude of 2,250 feet. The blue hare is still plentiful in Perthshire and the Eastern Highlands. Unfortunately, the blue hare being one of the food staples of the golden eagle, its decline in northern and western forests has caused the eagle to depend more on grouse and lambs, with results which can be imagined. Harvie-Brown in the Moray Basin volume of the *Vertebrate Fauna* (1895) remarks on a diminution in that area north of the Great Glen. He calls attention to the fact of fluctuation in numbers in this species, an example of a principle which has since been well worked out for small rodents and their predators by Elton.

The rabbit (*Oryctolagus cuniculus*) (Pl. 13, p. 116), was introduced to Scotland and probably the first mention of it in the Highlands is in Monro's manuscript (1549) that they were present in great numbers on Mull and Inchkenneth. Lighthouse keepers have the name of being great rabbit introducers to islands and promontories, and lobster fishers have also taken them to islands, e.g. to Lunga of the Treshnish Isles. Many mainland stations in the North-West were established as late as the 19th century, *vide* Osgood Mackenzie's account of the care taken to acclimatize them to Gairloch about 1850, in his *A Hundred Years in the Highlands*. Their effect on the Highland landscape was supplementary to that of the sheep, of checking regeneration of tree growth. To-day they are a terrible pest throughout the Highlands wherever the ground is suitable for them. The tertiary basalt soils of Mull, Morvern and Skye are perfect for the rabbit, and the sandy *machairs* are as paradise. Even the second German war has not proved the setback to the rabbit in the Highlands that it did in England, for the War Agricultural Executive Committees have not been strict in ordering destruction. Many thousands of couples are exported every year, but they merely represent a crop and are not an inroad on the awful capital liability.

One thing the rabbit has done: it has acted as a buffer species, providing food in plenty for forms we might otherwise have lost by now—the wild cat, pine marten and buzzard. This last has increased greatly in the past half-century and is now accepted as a useful species in the Highlands. Nevertheless, Argyll alone of Highland counties will not put the buzzard on the protected list, and the Government vermin trappers can boast of over fifty killed in the year in this county.

The brown rat (*Rattus norvegicus*) is an introduction to the Highlands as it is to the rest of the country. Rats are found in remote glens wherever there is a human habitation, their passage along the water-courses being relatively simple. Their worst disturbances in the natural history of the Highlands are when they invade small islands offshore, either to colonize permanently or to occupy seasonally. Their food staple is shell fish and littoral detritus, but in early summer they play havoc in tern colonies, devouring both eggs and young. I know of several small islands being cleared of terns because the birds were quite unable to breed. Herring gulls' eggs on such places are not touched by the rats. The difference in size is apparently sufficient to save them.

The rat was responsible for clearing the island of North Rona of its human population of thirty, soon after 1685. The species, in this case, was probably the ship rat, *Rattus rattus*, since *R. norvegicus* was scarcely known in Western Europe, and quite unknown in Britain, at this date. The rats came ashore from a wrecked ship, established themselves in the semi-underground houses which were of dry-stone surrounded by dry earth. They ate up the barley meal stored in sheep skins and the people eventually starved to death, the steward of St. Kilda finding the last woman lying dead on the rocks with her child on her breast. The rats also starved thereafter, because the immense swell on Rona prevents any hunting of the rock surfaces of the intertidal zone. The Shiant Isles and Ailsa Craig are both heavily infested with brown rats which live in the talus slopes at the foot of the cliffs and live well during the summer season on injured or young sea birds which fall from the ledges above.

Turning to happier mammalian introductions in the Highlands, there are fallow deer (*Cervus dama*) and Japanese sika deer (*Cervus sika*). Fallow deer are found in Mull and Islay; in Central Argyll; at Arisaig in western Inverness-shire, and in the Dornoch Woods, Sutherland. The fallow deer keeps to the scrub-covered areas and does not take to the open hill freely as do the red deer and even the roe. The sika deer were introduced to Loch Rosque between 1880 and 1890, and have thriven. The Achnasheen area is still their headquarters, but they range a good way from there. I once saw a stag of this species at Dundonnell, in November 1934. A further introduction of sika deer was to Carradale, Cantyre, in 1893. They are still there.

The goat of domestic origin (*Capra hircus hircus*), itself derived from the Persian wild goat (*Capra hircus aegagrus*), was introduced into Scotland in the dim past. This animal shows a ready tendency to go feral, and there are now "wild" goats in many parts of the Highlands, North-West Ross and Cromarty being an area where there are several herds. They also occur on several of the islands—Rum, Eigg, Jura, Harris, and Arran and Holy Island in the Firth of Clyde. Those on the slopes of Ben Lomond are reputed to have a history going back at least to King Robert the Bruce, that monarch having a special kindly word for this herd. Distribution has been summarized by Boyd Watt (1937). The herds do not seem to increase. The feral goats of the Highlands have become similar to the wild type. They inhabit the hills above the peat line where conditions are drier for them and but rarely descend to the low ground. Their young are born in January and February, so the criterion of selection these animals undergo in the Highlands is a severe one and is doubtless responsible for the steady population in the wilder parts. The habits of feral goats in the Highlands have been described by Darling in a supplement to Boyd Watt's paper.

There have been introductions and remarkable changes in the status of several birds in the Highlands. First, the capercaillie (*Tetrao urogallus*) (Pl. XIc, p. 96) which should also be regarded as an extinction. Once more it was the destruction of the pine woods which restricted the bird's range and its end was hastened by direct hunting. The last capercaillie of the old stock disappeared in about 1771 from the Glenmoriston area. The gap which followed was one of 67 years, though the Earl of Fife attempted an introduction at Mar Lodge, Aberdeenshire, in 1827–29. It was unsuccessful. Lord Breadalbane did better at Taymouth Castle in 1837. He got 13 cocks and 19 hens (Ritchie 1920) and turned them loose in the woods. There were over 1,000 birds present on the estate 25 years later. Harvie-Brown traced the spread of the capercaillie over Scotland from this point up to 1879, in his *Capercaillie in Scotland*, 1880. A successful introduction of caper to Strathnairn just east of Inverness in 1894 is doubtless responsible for the spread into Easter Ross.

The general spread from Taymouth was north-eastwards and south-westwards along the river valleys where there were successions of coniferous plantations. The capercaillie is now well distributed through Tay, Dee, Spey and Moray and into South Argyll. The new era of forestry which is about to come to the Highlands should ensure the continuance of the species, though its winter food of pine shoots is likely to make it an enemy of the single-minded forester.

When the capercaillie is extending its range the hen birds move first and the cocks follow in a year or two. It has been found that under these circumstances the hen caper will mate with blackcock and produce a hybrid generation. A hybrid with a pheasant has also been recorded.

The pheasant (*Phasianus colchicus*) has been constantly imported into the Highlands, but those days are probably over. The West Highlands at least are not pheasant country, and unless replenished, stocks are not persistent. I remember that of a stock reared at Gruinard, Wester Ross, in the '20's, practically the only survivor in the '30's was a cock bird at Dundonnell, 14 miles away. He was tame but wary and seemed well enough in the mixed wood there. His journey from Gruinard was over at least 12 miles of treeless country.

Two more birds still present in Scotland have had their ranges severely restricted by the destruction of the forests. These are the crested tit (*Parus cristatus scoticus*) and the Scottish crossbill (*Loxia curvirostra scotica*). The crested tit (Pl. XV, p. 108) is now only certainly found as a breeder in the Moray Basin, principally in the Spey Valley and the Findhorn Valley. It is possible that it was from the Easter Ross birds that the pair came which I saw at Dundonnell in 90-year-old Scots pines in June 1934. The crested tit also occurs in Glen Garry, Inverness-shire, and again it may have been a vagrant from this group which I saw at Fort Augustus, 7 miles away, in the summer of 1943. The crested tit tends to keep to the native pines of the old forests, where the trees are not too close, but we may yet see some adaptation in habit which would enable the species to spread ; and if it can wander in the way that my Dundonnell and Fort Augustus records seem to show, there seems to be no reason why it should not establish itself, *if protected*, in Deeside and other parts of Aberdeenshire, and in the Rannock-Tay-Tummel districts of Perthshire, where there is plenty of suitable habitat for it. It has been suggested that all that is necessary to bring the crested tit into Deeside is a line of pine-trees over the Lairig Ghru, between Rothiemurchus and Glen Dee !

The range of the Scottish crossbill is very much that of the Scottish crested tit, but a little wider. It reaches South-East Sutherland, Wester Ross, and southwards to Dunkeld. Its nest is placed high (30–60 feet) in pine or larch trees, and usually well out towards the end of the branch. It is thus harder to reach than the nest of the crested tit. Both species are in danger from collectors, but especially the tit. A recent statement in *British Birds* (July 1946) by P. A. Clancey reads that he "had cause to prepare for research purposes several dozens of specimens of crested tit (*P. c. mitratus* and *P. c. scoticus*)."

The December 1946 issue of *British Birds* contains a letter from P. A. Clancey saying "it is now evident that my imperfect phrasing of the note has led to the erroneous impression on the part of many interested persons that numbers of the highly localized *Parus cristatus scoticus* were taken. The correct interpretation is that my statement of 'some dozens' refers solely to the Central European race, *Parus cristatus mitratus* . . ." Mr. Clancey must excuse the common reader accustomed to plain English for mistaking the meaning of what appeared to be an unambiguous statement, and it may be suggested that a person unable to make himself clear in such simple words would be advised to leave research alone. Good research is orderly thinking plainly said.

The goldfinch (*Carduelis c. britannica*) was once common in the Central Highlands and Moray Basin. Its extinction in the third quarter of the 19th century was caused by excessive birdcatching for the dealers, who sold the goldfinch to the nostalgic industrialized workers of the Clyde Basin who wanted a song bird.

The great spotted woodpecker (*Dryobates major anglicus*) is a species which became extinct as a breeding species in Scotland about 1850 (Harvie-Brown, 1892). The destruction of the forest was responsible for the decline, but there are some who firmly maintain that the rise of the squirrel was in part the cause in the last years. This would hardly apply north and west of the Great Glen, for the squirrels were not introduced there until 1844 and took a fair time to spread. However, after the turn of the century the birds came back to the Highlands and have spread consistently up to the present day. They are now far beyond the bounds given in the *Handbook of British Birds*, Volume 2, p. 287. They are in Coigach in the north-west, in the Sunart section of Ardnamurchan, in Glen Garry and in Glen Moriston, and as far north as Dunrobin in East Sutherland. It has been a truly remarkable return of a lost species.

The wood-wren (*Phylloscopus sibilatrix*) has extended its range markedly in the last 60 years in the Highlands. In Harvie-Brown's *Vertebrate Fauna* series he frequently mentions the enlarging range of the species, but in 1904 he was careful to say that it had not yet reached Wester Ross. It is a regular summer resident there now, extending to within a mile or two of the Sutherland border. The wood-wren did not appear in Dalgleish's list of the birds of Ardnamurchan in 1877, but Harvie-Brown saw several at Glen Borrodale in 1881. It is now a common bird in the peninsula. He puts 1895 as a year of great expansion. Sixty years before that, very few wood-wrens had been seen in Scotland. Macgillivray in *A History of British Birds* (1839) gives the first public dated mention.

The spread of the fulmar (*Fulmarus glacialis glacialis*) will be described in the chapter on the sub-oceanic islands.

The chough (*Pyrrhocorax pyrrhocorax pyrrhocorax*) is possibly on a different stage of the same journey as the woodpecker. The woodpecker went as its habitat was cut from under it and has come back to a more tree-clothed Scotland again. The chough faced the blast of 19th-century game preservation and went under. Whether it was truly inimical to game is highly questionable, but it was one of the crow tribe and therefore must be bad. (Similarly the shag still suffers for the sins of the cormorant. Lovers of cheap shooting, and coastal fish and game preservers have never taken the trouble to ascertain the harmless food habits of the shag.) By the middle of the 19th century choughs had gone from inland districts of Scotland and were to be found only on the wilder coasts. Then they had to be cleared from these fastnesses. Graham mentions three pairs breeding on Iona in 1852, where they were left alone, but there are none there to-day. Skye lost its last chough by 1900 and no one knows how few were left on the cliffs of Islay when at last their rarity made them birds to be protected (and equally birds to have their eggs stolen). However, there has been a distinct increase in recent years on South-West Highland coasts. The bird is breeding regularly in Jura and has been seen on the forbidding cliffs of Ardmeanach in Mull. It was in Eigg till 1886 and this island is a likely station for a new colonization if the egg-collectors allow the bird to increase. The Northern Irish island of Rathlin must have been a reservoir which helped to stock Islay and make possible the spread from practical extinction, but for some years now Rathlin has been systematically sacked by British collectors. Nevertheless, if we can achieve some effective protection for our wild life in the future, the chough is in the way of coming back. The bird has one serious avian enemy in the peregrine falcon, particularly serious at the stage of low numbers of the chough. But peregrines have had a thinning time in the second German war as far as numbers are concerned, for they have had to be shot because of their depredations on carrier pigeons, on the safety of which birds the safety of aircraft crews might depend. There is probably no time more propitious than the present for the chough to increase—if man will but allow it.

Finally, among birds, the spread of the starling (*Sturnus vulgaris*) in the Highlands must be recorded as a remarkable change in status. This spread of a bird unknown for many years over most of the area does not apply to the Outer Hebrides where there has been for a long time a population of the sub-species *Sturnus vulgaris zetlandicus*. Even on North Rona there is a flock of a hundred or more of this form and there is another very old-established flock on St. Kilda. But on the mainland the country-wide colonization began about 1840 and was complete by 1890. Harvie-Brown (1895) gives a detailed account of the spread suggesting that the West Highlands were colonized by two thrusts, one coming down from the north, and the other pushing north by the Callander-Argyll route. Harvie-Brown could not know then what Bullough discovered only in 1942, that the British and continental starlings behave differently, have different thresholds of gonadic development and are for this reason physiologically isolated. The enormous incoming flocks to the East Coast in September are of no consequence in the spread of the starling as a breeding species in Scotland. From contemporary accounts, it would seem that the flocks of native young birds coming north and west in June were of greater significance in colonization. Harvie-Brown's fears of what might happen as a result of the vast increase and spread of the native starling have proved unfounded.

At the present time, it should be mentioned that human habitation and cultivation are not a necessity for the starling's spread, though the general distribution would indicate that such factors are helpful. For example, the tertiary basalt, uninhabited islands of Treshnish are heavily populated, flocks joining with the peewits in winter. The reason is that this geological formation produces plenty of good green ground. The starling needs grassland. Farther north, as on the Torridonian, real grassland occurs only where man has won the soil, or on the few places where there is sand beneath. The starling does not frequent poor bog or solid heather.

Man's behaviour, aimed directly at a species, or in interfering with a habitat, is one of the primary factors affecting the welfare of wild life, as much in the remote Highlands as in the fields of England. These hills and glens and rivers and lochs are not wild, even if unpeopled. The ground is covered by observant men, burnt by shortsighted men ; the water is fished and sieved. So far we have dealt only with warm-blooded creatures in this chapter, but the story could be continued with fish and invertebrates.

The herring fishery (Pl. 10, p. 85, Pl. X, p. 81) of the West Highland coast is an integral phenomenon. The young herring (*Clupea harengus*) feed well outside the herring-fishing area, in the Atlantic and Arctic Oceans, but as they become adult and approach their first spawning period, immense shoals come close inshore, beginning off Southern Ireland and making a clockwise migration round the West Highland and North coasts of Scotland until they eventually reach the Southern North Sea.

The migration as a whole has remarkable regularity but the detailed routes undergo some modification in the course of years. These changes of detail can be of great significance to the human populations on the way. For example, throughout the 18th century the herrings came up the length of several of the sea lochs of the west, but before 1850 the fish had changed their route slightly and passed the lochs. During the 1700's and for centuries before, the herring had been so regular as to pass up one shore of Loch Broom and down the other, with the result that fishing took on an almost clockwork precision. Fishing stations such as that on Isle Tanera were built at great expense, and

PLATE IX

Robert M. Adam

BARRA PONY at the peats, Outer Hebrides; larger than the Shetland, but smaller than other types of Highland ponies

PLATE X

Robert Atkinson

PACKING HERRING. Stornoway, Lewis
July 1938

Hugh Lelacheur

MUIRNEAG, the last surviving sailing drifter (now broken up), and steam drifters
Stornoway, Lewis. August 1939

paid handsomely for fifty years or more as the herring passed so near and so regularly. The fish were cured and exported to the West Indies and to southern Ireland. All the local people filled their barrels for the winter. There seemed no reason to believe this seasonal manna would ever cease. Unfortunately it did, for the herring ceased to visit the lochs in quantity or with any regularity. It seems certain that the fishing was too heavy. The fishery stations fell into decay so that people like myself were ultimately able to buy such properties for a few pounds. The herring busses rotted and the fishing passed almost entirely to the East Coast boats, Zulus and Fifies, and later the steam drifters, except for the fleet of smallish boats at Stornoway (Pl. Xb, p. 81) and the Loch Fyne smacks. The landing of herring was concentrated on certain places such as Oban, Mallaig, Castlebay (Barra) and Stornoway until the migration carried the fishing round to Wick.

Where there is a tradition of fishing on the West Highland coast, there is seasonal activity which may affect the inshore natural history. Lobsters, for example, are heavily fished (Pl. 11b, p. 92)—on the mainland coasts in winter and off the Outer Hebridean coast in summer. Mainland crofters often conduct this fishing from small row-boats, a method which limits the size of creel being used, which in turn limits the size of lobster caught. It is possible—and even probable—that the West Coast lobster is being overfished and an undue selection being made of the one pound to one-and-three-quarter pound sizes. The larger traps used by foreign boats such as the Brittany smacks which used to fish illegally about the outlying rocks, caught the large lobsters which the native tackle does not touch. A law now prohibits the sale of lobsters under one pound weight and of "berried hens," as the females are called when carrying the eggs. Nevertheless, far too many berried hens are not put back into the sea. We may be glad as naturalists that a fairly recent law prohibited the use of flesh of warm-blooded animals being used as bait in lobster creels. Until this law was passed (presumably for the good health of consumers of lobsters) many cormorants, shags and other sea fowl were killed to be used as bait. Nowadays, the lobster fisherman has to do some fishing for haddocks, codling and rock fish before he can shoot his creels.

The salmon-fishing industry is an important one in Scotland. Its influence on this fish in inshore waters and in the rivers is considerable, but had not the salmon (*Salmo salar*) been a game fish—a human classification in itself—the influence of the sea fishery of the salmon would probably have been much more to the detriment of the species than it has been up to now. You cannot fish salmon in the sea as you can haddock or mackerel. The rights of salmon fishing are owned and jealously guarded. The right to net salmon offshore is let to fishermen by the proprietor on the condition that the nets (Pl. 11a, p. 96) are made unfishable from 6 p.m. on Saturday until 5 a.m. on Monday. These 35 hours out of the 168 in the week mean that, for over 20 per cent of the time the salmon are in the shallow water seeking the rivers, they are free from danger as far as human beings are concerned. This measure enforced by proprietors for so long is no doubt the result of selfish interest, but the fact remains that it is a measure of conservation of the species. The numbers of nets are also closely limited so that there should remain an ample number of salmon having the chance to run up the rivers. Now once the salmon—and the sea trout as well—are beyond tidal water, they are not fished by methods which would give the maximum catch. If they had been so fished they would doubtless have disappeared altogether by now. Salmon in fresh water are angled by rod and line and lure, a method which allows the vast majority of fish that get into the river to run up it. Even then, no salmon are fished on Sunday, so for one-seventh of each week and for the hours of darkness the salmon is free from human danger. Salmon poaching is unfortunately common and one's feeling of repulsion at the practice need not be bound up with class distinction and notions of what are private rights, but with the necessity for an easily-caught species to be given its free time. The men who will poach salmon with a splash-net at night at the mouth of a river when the water is low, are breaking a rule for their own ends which society as a whole has decided to keep for the benefit of the salmon.

Here and there in the Highlands, as in the Don and the Esk and one reach of the Spey, spawning of salmon is interfered with by pollution of the rivers by industrial or sewage wastes. Soon, the hydro-electric schemes will cause further interference, but it should be well understood that the North of Scotland Hydro-Electric Board is spending a lot of time and money on facilitating the passage of fish, and wherever possible increasing the fishing potentialities of the water.

Ritchie (1920) mentions the Loch Insh char, the only migratory race of this fish in the Highlands ; they used to move up the Spey to spawn in such numbers that great quantities were netted and snared. Now the Loch Insh char are few.

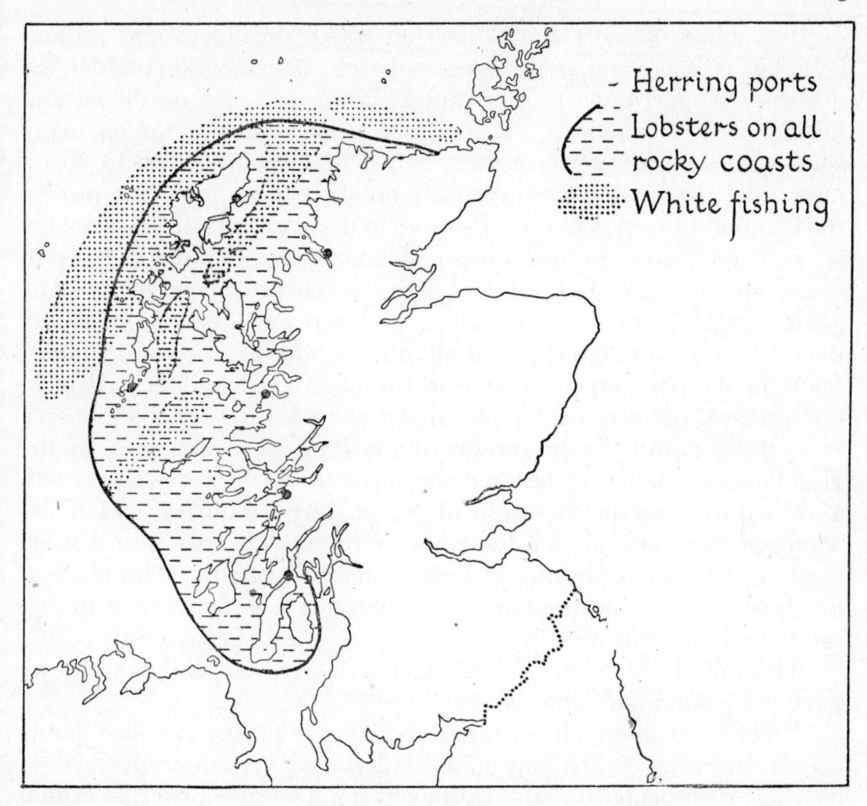

FIG. 5.—Fishing ports in the Highlands and Island

The freshwater mussel (*Unio margaritifer*) is in like state in West Highland rivers, the floor being combed by the tinkers who open thousands of mussels to find but very few pearls.

Whelks (*Purpura lapillus*) are still picked on West Highland coasts but nothing like so carefully as elsewhere, so the human factor on their population and ecology can be ignored. Mussels (*Mytilus edulis*), which were earlier much picked for bait, are now being left alone, partly through the decline in fishing and partly because the techniques of fishing are changing. Baiting lines was very hard on the womenfolk. In those places where mussels grew large, we may expect to see some change in the ecology of the foreshore as a result of a changed human predation.

The ethics of sport is a subject on which we may argue without end, but it is not our main concern here. We have to consider the influence of sport as part of the human factor operating on the natural history of the Highlands. It has been a depressing factor on many species such as most birds of prey, herons and saw-billed ducks, foxes, otters and the smaller carnivorous animals, but we must not neglect the fact that the red deer owes its survival to sport, the salmon probably as well, and with the assignment of large areas of wild country to sport, certain animals have had a better chance of survival. The golden eagle is an example: it is accepted and even protected in the deer forests, though it is shot out on sheep farms and grouse moors. Sport in the past has not taken on the nature of exploitation which, for instance, has seriously depleted the white-fish stocks of the North Sea. One cannot be so certain of the future because sport in the Highlands is tending to become syndicated and commercialized, with a consequent loss in the sense of personal responsibility. Man has arranged close seasons for his game birds, but the red deer has no legal close season, only that of well-mannered consent. This leaves a loophole for the unscrupulous, one which has been freely used during the second German war.

The following excerpt from Mackenzie (*op. cit.*) shows what we have left behind and what we have lost:

"There was so much vermin in those days that the so-called game-keepers were in reality only game killers and vermin trappers were only just then being started. In the old times all the lairds had in that line was a *sealgair* (hunter) who provided their big houses with venison and other game; for, until my father and uncles started stalking, not a Gairloch laird had ever troubled to kill deer either for sport or for the larder. The vermin consisted of all kinds of beasts and birds, a good many of which are extinct. The fork-tailed kite swarmed, and I have heard that the first massacre of them that took place was when my father poisoned with strychnine the dead body of a young horse. . . . The last kite had disappeared before my time. There were plenty of pine martens and polecats and some badgers even in my young days. My mother used to have an average of forty or fifty skins of martens brought to her by the keepers every year, of which she made the most lovely sable capes and coats for her sisters and lady friends."

Will the commercialized hotel sport which is creeping into the

PLATE 9

F. Fraser Darling

HIGHLAND CATTLE. Morvern, Argyll
July 1945

PLATE 10

F. Fraser Darling

HERRING DRIFTERS in Tanera anchorage. Stac Polly in background. Wester Ross. June 1942

Highlands under the noses of a slow-witted legislature do any better by our wild life?

The effect of reafforestation, by the method of close stands of conifers with occasional rides kept clear of undergrowth, has yet to be seen. A million acres of reafforestation are projected as a national programme—let us hope with revised methods. I believe that with a little give and take, planting of fringes with berry-bearing bushes and keeping the unplantable ground free of sheep, our forestry policy could have a buffering and even stimulating effect on much of our wild life, as distinct from the certain depressive effect of sheep farming. Unfortunately, forestry policy in Great Britain in the past does not appear to have been influenced by the ecological outlook, and by some skilled observers is thought to have been a hundred years behind that of France and Germany.

The research of good natural history puts us in possession of knowledge which enables us to control the country's wild life, preventing extinctions and undue increases in numbers, and conserving wild-life resources. It will soon be for the British public to decide whether the knowledge gained shall be applied and further knowledge gained, or whether some other poor natural historian a century hence will be able to write another chapter more generally dismal than this one.

THE DEER FOREST GROUSE MOOR AND SHEEP FARM

THE FACT of two and a half million acres of deer forest in the Highlands has been a matter for congratulation or for execration, dependent on whether the comments come from a sportsman, a naturalist, a sheep farmer or crofter or a member of a political party opposed to the existence of what is considered an anomaly in modern times. Deer forests and deer have been the subject of an extraordinary amount of misunderstanding and bad thinking. Our approach need not be political or coloured by sectional bias ; it is that of the biologist who wants to know truth and how far the deer forest fits into the natural history of the Highlands and Islands. It is unfortunate that the rise of the deer forests in the middle years of last century has been debited with the Clearances which to a very much greater extent were conducted half a century earlier when the sheep farmers came. It is quite wrong historically to saddle the deer forests with the depopulation of the Highlands. It is equally unscientific to work up a personal animus against a very beautiful and useful animal because its hunting has been jealously confined to a certain class of society.

It may be said that 90 per cent of the 2,500,000 acres of deer forest is among the poorest and roughest grazing in Scotland. For the remaining 10 per cent there is little excuse for its remaining as deer forest and nothing else. But in fact, and especially since the outbreak of the second German war, much of the total ground styled deer forest has also helped to graze some sheep and cattle. The remainder is of such a nature that either it will not carry domestic stock or will not carry them economically. Much of the ground is over 2,000 feet high, with a lot of bare rock and scree, difficult to travel through and without much wintering. On such ground there is no animal, wild or domesticated, better adapted than the red deer to use it and to render a crop to humanity—if such a return is considered the only reason for being allowed to exist. No other beast will spend five or six months on the high ground and interfere so little with other animals grazing the glens and lower slopes, even in winter. The red deer can be a curse to the gardener and the enterprising farmer or crofter attempting to grow winter crops, but so are the sheep. The worst cases of damage by deer are either in the frontier zone where they should not be at all, or else on places where their normal winter ground has been denied them, e.g. an area being fenced off for afforestation.

The red deer is a thriving, colonizing species and needs to be kept in check or it would soon be all over Scotland again, making the pursuit of arable farming almost impossible; but having said that, let us value our Highland red deer. There has been a rise of shepherds' wages to over £200 a year. Nobody should be less thankful than the shepherds themselves for this change of financial status. But it should be remembered that even before the second German war when shepherds were getting the poor wage of £70–80 a year cash, with certain perquisites, some of the rougher ground was going out of sheep and reverting to deer. There are three reasons why ground may go out of hill sheep farming: *a*, it may be too high and therefore short of winter grazing; *b*, it may be so rough and broken that shepherding is altogether too difficult for one man to manage a full hirsel, i.e. about 600 ewes; *c*, the ground may be so poor that it will carry no more than a sheep to 10 acres, when shepherding a full hirsel again becomes almost impossible for one man. The Hill Sheep Committee's Report, 1944, confirms general opinion among Highland sheep farmers that unless one man can manage 500–600 ewes with a little extra help at lambing time, shearing and dipping, hill sheep farming is uneconomic. It is almost certain that the rise in shepherds' wages will put the poorest, highest and roughest of Highland ground out of sheep farming. The only other animal, it is repeated, which can utilize that ground efficiently is the red deer, and the beast should not be begrudged his share of the winter grazing. The foregoing is a bit of human ecology which should ultimately link up with the range of red deer in Scotland.

A glance at the Distribution Map 8 (p. 281) will show that by far the largest stretches of deer forest are north and west of the Great Glen, where it is possible to walk over a length of a hundred miles of continuous deer forest without a fence. It is part of the tradition of deer-stalking that boundaries between forests should not be fenced; even without this tradition fencing would be almost an impossibility. It would also be foolish, because the fence would disappear under snow in some places in winter and spring so that the deer would go over the top. Finally, the life of the fence would be short.

The north-western stretch of deer forest has for the most part a different vegetational complex from the Central Highland region where the deer forests are on ground so high and snow-bound that it is of little use to sheep in winter. As has been pointed out in an earlier chapter, the deer forest country of the north-west is grassy and sedgy rather than heathery. It is on peat overlying rock, not on glacial drift. Large expanses of heather (*Calluna vulgaris*) are not common ; bell heather (*Erica cinerea*) grows in tufts on the drier spots and among cairns and rocks ; but most of the low ground is covered with purple moor grass or flying bent (*Molinia coerulea*), sweet vernal (*Anthoxanthum odoratum*), wavy hair grass (*Deschampsia flexuosa*), fiorin (*Agrostis stolonifera*), bent grasses (*Agrostis* spp.), a variety of sedges and rushes (*Carex* and *Juncus* spp.), and cross-leaved heather (*Erica tetralix*). The sedge and *Molinia* content increases the farther west. Throughout the lower ground there are patches of birch and willow scrub (*Betula* and *Salix* spp.), and many plantations of coniferous trees in various states of careful foresting or complete neglect, as well as single rowans (*Sorbus aucuparia*).

The flowers of this lower zone are predominantly milkwort (*Polygala vulgaris*), tormentil (*Potentilla erecta*), bedstraw (*Galium saxatile*), wood-rush (*Luzula* spp.), with yarrow (*Achillea millefolium*) and bird's-foot trefoil (*Lotus corniculatus*) on dry places and old crofting lands. Wild white clover (*Trifolium repens*) also occurs freely in favoured places and on roadsides. All these serve in greater or lesser degree as food plants. Plants occasionally eaten by the deer and generally present are common rush (*Juncus communis*), furze (*Ulex europaeus*) on the drier places, bramble (*Rubus* spp.) on edges of woods, nettle (*Urtica dioica*) where human habitations have been, and eaten when dead, ragwort (*Senecio jacobaea*) on river flats, coltsfoot (*Tussilago farfara*) on gravels near rivers, dog and marsh violets (*Viola* spp.) and wood sorrel (*Oxalis acetosella*).

The plants obviously present but not normally eaten include primrose (*Primula vulgaris*) in sheltered situations and woods, devil's-bit scabious (*Succisa pratensis*) on the open bog, silver weed (*Potentilla anserina*) on river flats and shieling sites, spotted, butterfly and fragrant orchis (i.e. *Orchis ericetorum*, *Platanthera bifolia* and *Gymnadenia conopsea*) generally in the herbage, marsh thistle (*Cirsium palustre*) in woods, bracken (*Pteridium aquilinum*) generally spreading over drier places, bog myrtle (*Myrica gale*) and bog asphodel (*Narthecium ossifragum*) in the wetter bog. The dry, poor places support eyebright (*Euphrasia officinalis*). Ferns of various species occur in birch woods and spleenwort (*Asplenium* spp.) grows on rocks and tree trunks along with many mosses and lichens. It will be obvious that these plants mentioned sort themselves out into loose associations and into separate habitats which I have but barely sketched.

From 250 to 1,750 feet is the herbage floor which provides the main food of the deer. Many plants noted already as occurring on the low ground extend upwards as long as the conditions for them remain. But there is a big increase in the sedges such as *Carex rostrata* (=*C. ampullacea*), *C. flacca*, *C. limosa*, *C. flava*, *C. pallescens*, *C. filiformis*, *C. caryophyllea*, *C. goodenovii*, *C. pauciflora*, *C. dioica*; deer's-hair grass (*Scirpus caespitosus*) and cotton sedge or bog cotton (*Eriophorum vaginatum* and *E. angustifolium*). The cotton sedge (Pl. VIb, p. 53) is thinly distributed through much of the bog, but it occurs as the main constituent of certain flats of deep peat which are wet but not too wet. This plant is of very great importance in the natural grazing of sheep farm and deer forest. *Eriophorum* comes earlier than anything else in spring so that it is usual to see both sheep and deer on the drawmoss in February. The other sedges also provide good grazing in a country where good grass is not to be had.

These flats also hold *Carex flava*, club mosses (*Lycopodium* spp.) and such lichens as *Cladonia*. The *Lycopodium* is a favourite with the deer and the *Cladonia* is eaten also.

This main mass of the hill also grows a quantity of wavy hair grass, early hair grass (*Aira praecox*) and silvery hair grass (*A. caryophyllea*). Milkwort and tormentil continue to be common and wild thyme (*Thymus serpyllum*) is found in abundance where there is sufficient sand in the peaty covering of the hill to provide dry enough conditions. Blaeberry (*Vaccinium myrtillus*) (see also Pl. 18, p. 129) is fairly generally distributed, but the conditions are too wet for this plant and its presence may go unsuspected if not sought, except in those dry places as on top of a big rock, where it will flourish but not spread. Crowberry (*Empetrum nigrum*) occurs towards the upper end of the zone where conditions are drier. The deer graze both these plants wherever they find them.

The high ground above 1,750 feet varies in its vegetational composition depending on the geological formation and the land form. As has been mentioned when describing the gneiss areas, the characteristics of the lower slopes may be carried well up to 2,000 feet and more. But where the peat ceases at about 1,750 feet, the herbage becomes sweeter and more alpine in character. It is richer in proteins and minerals and is grazed whenever there is sufficient growth and when the weather allows. The grasses are sheep's fescue (*Festuca ovina* forma *vivipara*), alpine meadow grass (*Poa alpina* forma *vivipara*), alpine tufted hair grass (*Aira alpina*), a short form of mat grass (*Nardus stricta*) and very occasionally the alpine foxtail (*Alopecurus alpinus*). *Luzula spicata* also occurs along with *Carex curta*. Wild thyme goes to well over 3,000 feet. The alpine chickweed (*Cherleria sedoides*) is to be found among the herbage and is well eaten down by the deer. The cushion moss *Grimmia* is common on the boulders, being eagerly nibbled off by the deer if they happen to be on the high ground on a winter's day. But for many days of the winter this ground is under snow. It is after a sudden melting, which can be quite spectacular in this area so much nearer the sea than the central region, that the deer go high to graze the newly-washed herbage. It looks very short and bare to the human observer, but there is no doubt that deer are able to nibble it successfully. This habit of the deer to go high in winter whenever weather allows—and to get down again in plenty of time before it changes—all without human shepherding, is but one example of this animal's efficiency in its total environment. Sheep could never manage the two journeys in the short time in which the deer can do them.

It will be realized that with so much of the area being covered with freshwater lochans, bare rock and scree, there is a lot of dead ground in a deer forest. One of the differences—perhaps the only big difference between a deer forest and a Highland sheep farm—is that the forest has the higher proportion of dead ground, and that is its main reason for being deer forest. In order to get a sharp impression of such difference, the naturalist may compare the hills of Morvern which are green to the summits and are sheep farms with deer on the ground in moderate and tolerated density, with hills like Ben Arkle or Suilven in Sutherland, or the upper reaches of the Cairngorms.

The deer forest of the Grampian or Central Highland zone is much more heathery in character because of lower rainfall and better drainage. The main reason for their unsuitability as sheep farms is their lack of winter grazing. Nevertheless, many of these forests do carry a summer sheep stock. I know of one very high forest in the

Grampians which has its own stock of about 400 ewes on 12,000 acres, but the forest carries another 800–1,000 sheep all summer; these belong to an adjacent sheep farm which fills a glen ten miles long running down to the lower ground where wintering is possible. It is difficult for the shepherd on that sheep farm to prevent his sheep summering on the deer forest, and its value as a deer forest would be greatly lessened by constant dogging of the sheep in trying to keep them on their own ground. In fact, then, the proprietor of the deer forest accepts the decision of the sheep and puts up with summering that stock for nothing. It is doubtful whether the rabid anti-deer-forest section of society realizes how little Highland ground is devoted absolutely and exclusively to deer or how little of it could be better used than it is.

The grouse population of the north-western deer forest country is not large, for this bird (Pl. XId, p. 79) needs *Calluna* as a herbage floor and does better on a dry, well-drained peat than on the wet slopes, terraces and flats of the deer forests. It is even scarcer on the Argyll and north-western sheep farms, for these areas take up the green sedgy ground that carries least heather. Grouse are, however, nearly always present in low density, with ptarmigan on the high tops. The sport of deer-stalking makes no effort to preserve grouse, because the sudden uprush of one or more of these birds in the course of a stalk can move the deer well beyond reach; as a result, the eagle is tolerated and deliberately preserved in the forest, the peregrine falcon is troubled but little and the wild cat also breeds in fair security. The fox is as much hunted in the deer forest as on the sheep farm because deer calves are preyed upon as much as are lambs. The vixen is hunted in June by terriers put into the cairn where the cubs are, and at other times of the year foxes are trapped and killed by any means possible. Despite this constant attention, the rise and fall of the fox population seems to follow a cycle beyond the control of man. Mange seems to be the great decimator of the foxes of the Highlands, and after a period of low numbers the increase is quite extraordinary. From my inquiries among stalkers and shepherds, the cycle, if there is one, is fairly long—of about twenty years.

The deer forest, then, tends to be a greater repository of wild life than the sheep farm and grouse moor, not only through the tolerations mentioned in the last paragraph, but because it can allow and even encourage a greater variety of habitats. Birch woods remain, and the ground is not burnt anything like so frequently as it is on sheep farm and grouse moor. Some fairly long heather is considered an asset in a forest because it does not become covered with snow like young growth. Deer come into such long heather when the snow is new and deep. They shake the stalks so that the snow falls off and the green top is then browsed. The deer also shelter in the long heather in snow. It is no uncommon thing to see a head and two long ears silhouetted against the snow in a winter's dusk. A hind is lying there protected from the wind and very snug.

The practice of burning heather is one of those which can be a blessing or a curse. There is no rule of thumb to be followed in relation to burning or " making muir burn " as it is called in Scotland. Unfortunately this is not generally understood, with the result that burning the hill is responsible for much damage ; worse in some years than in others. Heather is one thing in the Southern Uplands and on the eastern moors of Scotland, but it is a very different plant through a large part of the West Highlands. It grows so well, and is such a close carpet on the drier moors, that regular burning is necessary on a ten- or even seven-year rotation if a good crop of young heather is to be kept going for sheep and grouse. Great care is practised in burning properly and all leases contain clauses to ensure that sufficient men are engaged to control the burning ; notice must also be given to the laird. The heather crop is so important that no one, whether sheep farmer or sporting tenant, wishes to burn out of season or badly or in such manner that the fire will get out of control. But in West Highland hills where sedge and flying bent are much denser on the ground, a hill ought not to be burnt oftener than once in fifteen years. It is unfortunate, therefore, that burning in the West and North-West Highlands is such an haphazard affair. Men are scarce and burning usually means setting light to a patch of flying bent here and there, which fire may spread over ground heavily burned the previous year. Some crofters' hill grazings have been ruined for many years to come by this constant burning. The theory is that where burning has taken place there comes an early bite of *Molinia*. Those early stems may appear in extremely low density, and after the ground has been punished by the sheep it lies derelict for a long time, giving neither food nor shelter for bird or beast. By far the biggest trouble arising from this indiscriminate over-burning in the West is the subsequent spread of bracken. This plant grows strongest where it is free from

F. Fraser Darling

Salmon Bag Net, drying. Ardnamurchan, Argyll
July 1945

F. Fraser Darling

A Tiree Lugger ; lobster creels in foreground. Tiree, Inner Hebrides
July 1945

F. Fraser Darling

WOODED ISLANDS in freshwater loch, showing effects of protection from grazing and burning. Sutherland. September 1943

Ronald Duckering

GREENSHANK COUNTRY, Glen Derry, Aberdeenshire June 1943

competition. Its deep rhizomes are unaffected by the burning and send up the first shoots thereafter. Tormentil is the second plant to appear, or first if bracken is not present. The marks of such bracken colonization can be seen in many places to have followed the line of the burning with absolute sharpness.

The careful burning of good heather moors needs a knowledge of what is going to happen. If heather gets too old before it is burnt there is no regeneration. If the ground is too dry (which does not happen often) the heat may be so fierce as to kill the seeds and again there is no regeneration. Heather on a sheep farm has to be burnt in sufficiently large pieces, otherwise the animals congregate on the newly burnt ground densely enough to injure and retard new growth. Further, such heavy densities of sheep bring about undue worm infestation in the flock and there is serious trouble. Much of a shepherd's time is taken up with keeping his animals well dispersed, and it is one of the fortunate natural tendencies of the Blackface breed to disperse in grazing instead of working the ground as a flock. Sometimes, when a whole sheep farm *cum* grouse moor has been neglected and the heather over all is rank, the only remedy is a complete burn of the whole lot, because the animals cannot be got back on to the old heather at all. The result then is death of the new heather and semi-starvation of the sheep. Burning not only prevents regeneration, but aids the establishment of the ultimate climax of deer's-hair grass and sphagnum. Fraser (1933) says it is the form of vegetation to which all others give place in the north-west, and that burning and grazing hasten the process. Blanket bog is the final result.

It will be realized that heather burning is a major interference with natural succession. Done as it should be it preserves a *status quo* which would otherwise be a temporary phase in the succession. Persistence of a dense growth of *Calluna* is assured and colonization by, or regeneration of, trees is prevented. Ground-nesting birds are deprived of cover, but such as do nest on burnt ground are not seriously put out, because moor burning finishes on April 10, or on special occasions with written consent it may be continued until April 25. Here again burning in the west falls short of good traditions, for fires may be seen well after the closing date and into May. Burning then becomes plain vandalism.

Sheep and grouse make a very good combination on a moor. The sheep not only crop the heather and keep growing the little green shoots of which the grouse are so fond, but they make narrow tracks through the heather which are bare of all herbage. Grouse use these, especially when their young ones are leaving the nest. They are able to keep the young birds dry when they move off for food and water.

The life history of the red grouse (*Lagopus s. scoticus*) (Pl. XId, p. 96) is that of a bird excelling in hardiness. Surely the ptarmigan (*Lagopus mutus*) (Pl. XVIIb, p. 148) is the only other bird which can exist in more unsheltered and inclement conditions. When the snow falls heavily and without wind the grouse come down from the higher moors, but if there is sufficient wind to keep patches of heather and grit clear of snow, the grouse will stay high and endure the weather. The birds move upwards immediately the snow begins to melt and may sometimes be seen following sheep or deer which happen to be scratching through to the heather.

Breeding time on a grouse moor is full of chances of failure. The birds and their eggs have certainly evolved characteristics which minimize loss. For example, a snowstorm is a common thing during April and there is even the " cuckoo " snow of May with some very cold nights ; the hen birds are laying at this time and they do not sit until the clutch of 7–10 eggs is complete. This means that the eggs may be quite severely frosted, yet experience seems to show that they rarely fail to hatch from this cause. Reliable gamekeepers have given instances of incubation having actually started and for some reason or another the hen bird having been caught off her nest while the snow was drifting. The eggs would be covered within a minute but perhaps not deep enough to escape frosting. Yet hen birds have come back as long as three days afterwards and have successfully completed incubation. Some keepers say that the eggs of grouse and ptarmigan will not split with frost as soon as those of other game birds. If an April storm puts grouse off their high breeding grounds they do not seem to start breeding again when they go back, and the year is generally a barren one.

The hen grouse at all times sits close and may herself be buried for a day or two under snow, but in winter grouse as a species do not get snowed up as sheep do under a peat hag. The birds tread with their feet all the time and rise with the snow. An observer can prove this to his satisfaction by digging a profile through the snow at the place where a grouse has spent the night during a storm. Droppings will be found all the way through the compacted snow. Hoodie crows are the greatest menace to sitting grouse in spring. These sharp-eyed birds quarter the moor ready to suck the eggs of any unprotected nest. Usually, the cock and hen grouse between them are pugnacious enough to repulse the crows during incubation, but when the chicks are hatched it is much harder for the hen to keep the brood close together. Many observers say that the hen grouse has the power to prevent her scent carrying while she is sitting. Certainly dogs do not point grouse nearly so actively at this time, but it is an idea I cannot accept myself until I have some experimental proof. As far as we know, birds have no sense of smell, so we can hardly expect the bird to exercise control over an emanation from herself bearing on a sense of which she has no experience.

The red grouse of the Outer Hebrides are assigned to the Irish subspecies *Lagopus scoticus hibernicus*. The plumage differences are extremely slight, and then only in winter, but Campbell (quoted in *Handbook*) notes several differences of behaviour. They are more silent than the typical form, they are very unobtrusive and do not flush and swing away for a long distance in the characteristic fashion of *L. s. scoticus*. The grouse of the Outer Hebrides are to be found much more on areas of wet, boggy *Scirpus* ; the mainland birds prefer dry moors, and, in fact, wetness of a moor may be a limiting factor to the maintenance of a steady population.

The food of grouse is varied, but the shoots of young heather are the mainstay of its diet. As sheep favour the same food, the management of moors becomes the highest type of husbandry of uncultivated ground.

The Report of the Committee of Inquiry on Grouse Disease, 1912, gives much detailed information on the food of the red grouse. It shows how the *Calluna* plant is grazed at different times of year—in winter, the green shoots growing in the shelter of the canopy ; after May, the new green shoots of the canopy ; in August and September, the flowers in bud, in bloom and in new seed head ; and throughout the autumn the seeds are picked from the plant. After January, when the seeds have fallen, they appear to have no significance for the birds. The shoots of blaeberry (*Vaccinium myrtillus*) are also eaten, and the berries which appear in season on the herbage floor, such as crowberry in June, blaeberry a little later, then the bearberry (*Arctostaphylos uva-ursi*), and in September the cloudberry of the high tops (*Rubus chamaemorus*). The young flowers of cotton sedge and the seeds of woodrush are also taken. Thus we see that the grouse must be grouped with the sheep and the deer as grazing animals, though their direct influence is much less positive than that of the mammals.

We should not pass this point without mentioning the black grouse (*Lyurus tetrix britannicus*) for it is also a grazer as well as being a browser. It is not so much a bird of the open moor as of thin scrub. It eats the buds of birch and the young catkins, and the buds of conifers and such other trees as it may find in its habitat. Its influence on limiting the growth of birch scrub may be negligible, but the Forestry Commission finds the bird sufficiently damaging in young plantations of conifers to make every effort to exterminate it. The rest of its food is similar to that of the red grouse. Both species, especially when young, consume many insects and are certainly beneficial to the sheep farmer. The crop of the black grouse may be packed at certain seasons with *Bibio lepidus*, a dipterous fly, the maggots of which live in the roots of herbage and are destructive to it. The heather beetle (*Lochmaea suturalis*) is also consumed in quantity when present. This latter insect is of great importance in the heather districts of Scotland because it destroys large patches of *Calluna*, giving it that frosted appearance which was not fully understood until the 20th century. Cameron (1943) has conducted a study of the life history of the beetle and shows the importance to the species of damp mossy patches in moors, in which places one stage of the beetle's life is spent.

The black grouse is decreasing in numbers throughout the Highlands : in many places it has completely disappeared. Coccidiosis has been blamed in the past ; my own feeling is that the disease may have decimated the species at some time, but two other factors have been the direct cause. These are the social factor and the wrong idea of the sportsman in shooting cock birds. The black grouse is a species in which the males gather at traditional places in spring and join in a ceremonial posturing. This dancing ground is called the "lek," coming from the Gaelic *leac*—a flat place or slab. It is after these meetings and stimulating evolutions of the male birds in concert that mating takes place with the hens, which are not far away. The formalized postures of attack indulged in between the males at the lek are nevertheless distinct from the actual sexual display which precedes coition. Meetings at the lek occur in March before mating is to be expected, as well as later. Morley (1943) has recently drawn attention to the phenomenon of autumnal display in many species of British birds, in which the blackcock is a prominent participant. On

PLATE XI

John Markham

SISKIN, the *Carduelis* finch of the old pine forest
Rothiemurchus, Inverness-shire. June 1946

Eric Hosking

TWITE, the *Carduelis* finch of the upland moor
Yorkshire. June 1944

Eric Hosking

CAPERCAILLIE (hen), the game-bird of the pine forest
Inverness-shire. May 1939

Eric Hosking

GROUSE (hen), the game-bird of the moor
Inverness-shire. May 1939

BIRDS OF PINE FOREST AND MOOR

John Markham

Common Sandpiper. Glenmore, Inverness-shire
A wader of all Highland freshwater systems. June 1945

Eric Hosking

Greenshank, removing eggshell from nest
A wader of marshy moors. Inverness-shire. May 1940

the theory of social stimulation to breeding condition outlined by Darling in *Bird Flocks and the Breeding Cycle*, 1938, it seems to me probable that the blackcock is incapable of mating successfully unless he is able to join with sufficient of his fellows at the lek in spring. If this theory is correct in relation to the blackcock, the sportsman's practice of shooting cocks only is just hurrying the species down the road to extinction.

Shooting old cocks tends to become a fetish with owners of grouse moors. The idea is that the cocks interfere with each other and cause barren hens. The theory has been questioned among sportsmen themselves and it would be a good thing perhaps if this point could be given critical attention. The much-mentioned fighting which cocks are supposed to do in October and November should be considered and more closely watched as being possibly an example of that autumnal display which Morley (*op. cit.*) describes.

These remarks on our British grouse lead me to digress for a moment : here is a highly organized social system in being alongside our own but one which has developed quite independently of us. Thousands and thousands of years have passed with the black and red grouse fulfilling their formalized social meetings, certain manifestations of which are taking place in the half light following the dawn, with man observing in part, but not comprehending. Within the last century or two man has concerned himself directly with the life history of these two birds and with a half knowledge has imperilled the continued existence of one and has brought about a remarkable artificial increase in the other in certain places. The beauty and complexity of this social life should cause us to be humble in our lack of comprehension and lead us to the resolution to know, rather than to repeat half truths and to act positively on insufficient observation.

The avian fauna of the deer forest, hill sheep farm and grouse moor is distinctive, if small in numbers of species. Commonest bird of all is the meadow-pipit (*Anthus pratensis*) whose small, thin song and parachuting display flight are linked inevitably in one's mind with this country in April and May. Its range of habitat is wide, even including newly burnt heather as long as there are occasional tufts to provide nesting sites. During the course of census work on Isle Tanera, A. Morley found that the occurrences of meadow-pipits were practically the same on heather burnt within two years (i.e. still bare) as on heather 6–8 inches high. She found that wheatears (*Oenanthe oenanthe*) would inhabit burnt ground and country where the herbage was not above 6 inches in height. Conversely, stonechats (*Saxicola torquata hibernans*) were found only where the heather was long and above 6 inches. The twite (*Carduelis flavirostrus pipilans*) (Pl. XIb, p. 96) is also an inhabitant of the long heather but is not averse to coming into the settlements and lonely gardens of stalkers, keepers and farmers, where it is much to be preferred to the absent sparrow (*Passer domesticus*). Twite and sparrow may meet and mix, however, on the border of their habitats, e.g. in the streets of Ullapool, Loch Broom.

The wren is a surprisingly common bird in a particular type of deer forest country ; that which is steep and rocky, with long heather and occasional birches and rowans. In such ground the wren may be found to 1,250 feet above sea level. At moor-edges and roadsides, nesting often in gorse or long heather, the whinchat (*Saxicola rubetra*) is locally common, with " pockets of abundance." A little bird sitting on a telegraph pole or wire in a Highland glen is more likely to be a whinchat than any other species.

The meadow-pipit is the basic food of the merlin (*Falco columbarius*) (Pl. XIIIb, p. 100) while that falcon is present for the summer. All the same the merlin is not a common bird, and certainly not as numerous in the Highlands as the buzzard (*Buteo buteo*). It would be interesting to know what the predatory value of the buzzard was on a wild rabbit population. Such a study remains to be done, but Chitty (1938) has done a laboratory study on another bird, the short-eared owl (*Asio flammeus*) which inhabits the terrain under review. The main food of this owl is small rodents, which for all general purposes means the field vole. Chitty reckoned from careful recording of meals taken and pellets disgorged over a period of four months that a short-eared owl would certainly eat more than 47 lbs. of voles or mice, and probably more than 95 lbs. but less than 142 lbs. This represents a consumption of 2,000 ($\pm$50 per cent) voles. He correlated this figure with the known number of short-eared owls on an area of State Forest of 2,000 acres, and reckoned that the total predation by this bird would be between 0·02 and 0·05 per cent of the vole population. This was considered too small to have any appreciable effect on checking the voles. But, of course, the naturalist would wish to know the same valuable potentials for other predators and to make a sum of the whole.

The waders are not well represented in the deer forest and moorland country. There is water in plenty but not of the right sort. Many of the lochans have a low hydrogen-ion concentration of pH 4·2 to 5·6, which means that food for the waders as a class is not plentiful. Nor are the shores of the lochans right. The commonest wader by far is the common sandpiper (*Actitis hypoleucos*) (Pl. XIIa, p. 97) which, being so closely linked with the vicinity of water, will fall to be considered in the chapter on fresh waters. The snipe (*Capella gallinago*) is fairly common on the river flats and low bogs, but is not a bird of the heather or *Scirpus* flow. If one is at the head of some remote glen where a tumbling burn flattens out to a slow stream winding through the green fringes it has made by the deposition of sand and gravel, there in the quiet of evening it is almost certain the drumming of the snipe will be heard in spring. Perhaps the night is clear and concentration coupled with good eyesight may pick out the swiftly-moving snipe high above : then the fall at an incline for 50–100 feet and the sound of the drumming through the specialized tail feathers. The observer should be camping there so that he will hear the pleasant chick-chack of the snipe when they come to earth from their aerial display.

The chief wader of the deer forest country of the north is the greenshank (*Tringa nebularia*) (Pl. XIIb, p. 97), a bird not found elsewhere in Britain in the breeding season and uncommon on grouse moor and sheep farm. Its habitat (Pl. 12b, p. 93) is the remote flats and soft places among the hills. This rare British bird still has its eggs much sought after by the egg collectors who persist even now in their out-of-date pursuit. It is extraordinary that the beauty of the greenshank, its fast, wild flight and still wilder call, have not charmed them or at least shamed them. The sound of the greenshank echoing among the hills in the summer evenings or very early mornings is one of those nostalgic sounds which bring back to the mind in swift pageant the whole wild complex of the deer country.

The golden plover (*Pluvialis apricaria*) is fairly widely distributed about the moors rather than among the high hills, though the species breeds at heights up to 3,000 feet in the Grampians, where, as pointed out in an earlier chapter, there are wide expanses of ground at that height. This bird is also found in flocks in autumn at 4,000 feet, but it cannot be said with certainty whether these flocks are of the northern or the southern (British-breeding) sub-species. The display flights and behaviour of the golden plover are very fine to watch and the open nature of the country in which the bird breeds renders watching fairly easy.

The ring ouzel or mountain blackbird (*Turdus torquatus*) is nowhere as common in the Highlands as in the Southern Uplands, but is, nevertheless, fairly evenly distributed through this type of country. I used to hear it when I was in the forest with the deer, in the very early mornings of June, at heights of about 2,000 feet on the hill. At that quiet time its eerie treble piping carries a long way and fills a corrie with sound.

The golden eagle (*Aquila chrysaetus*) (Pl. XIIIa, p. 100) has already been mentioned several times in this book in relation to its habitat and food supply. As things are at this moment, the deer forests are the golden eagle's protection. Laws relating to protection count for very little in the Highlands. The survival of a bird like the eagle depends on the good will of the proprietors and their servants and on sheep farmers. There is a good deal of agitation for the general release of strychnine for poisoning foxes and hoodie crows in the Highlands. I have heard a man openly admit to having poisoned six eagles in a winter season with strychnine bait put down for foxes and crows. This is the great trouble with poison ; it is impossible to confine its effects to the animals intended to be killed. Poisoning on a large scale in California some years ago resulted in serious thinning of the desirable wild life. Instead of allowing strychnine to be obtained easily, it would be in the interests of the countryside generally to tighten up the conditions of sale. The golden eagle is an easy bird to shoot, trap or poison, for its eyrie is often accessible to a man with a gun and it eats a lot of carrion as well as taking live food such as grouse and blue hares —and a few lambs in season. A pair of eagles needs 10,000 acres of deer forest to keep going. Repressive measures must be taken if their density much exceeds this.

Lastly the cuckoo (*Cuculus canorus*) : this bird is extremely common in the Highlands, the meadow-pipit once more being the basis of another bird's existence, this time as foster-parent and not as food. It is almost characteristic in the open country of moor, deer forest and sheep farm to see the cuckoos followed closely by the pipits which are so ineffectual in their mobbing of the larger bird. The cuckoos of the Highlands are very tame. They will make the gatepost of the stalker's or shepherd's cottage their continual perching place and the rowan tree so commonly found by the byre may hold three or four cuckoos in the sunny weather when the birds are active in their short flights hither and thither. I have seen as many as seven cuckoos together in moorland country where there are a few birch trees. The

Eric Hosking

GOLDEN EAGLE, the largest raptorial bird of deer forest and moor. Argyll
June 1939

Eric Hosking.

MERLIN, the smallest raptorial bird of Highland moors. Orkney
June 1946

F. Fraser Darling

RED DEER STAGS: antlers hard and still unshed
April 1938

F. Fraser Darling

STAGS IN EARLY VELVET. Dundonnell Forest, Wester Ross
May 1935

cuckoo's partiality for meadow-pipits does not seem to extend to following them on to burnt ground. In spite of its liking for perching posts and occasional trees, there is no doubt the cuckoo uses ground cover a good deal. Man's manipulations of the moorland herbage certainly affect what might be called the cuckoo's micro-distribution.

If there is one bird which I feel we could do without, it is the hoodie crow (*Corvus cornix*) ; but there is little likelihood that the species will become conveniently rare. The hoodie is abundant throughout the Highlands and is most difficult to kill. This bird is extremely destructive to other bird life, being much given to emptying nests of eggs and taking young birds. It will even take young rooks able to fly. The raven (*Corvus corax*) is neither so destructive in its habits nor so numerous. The density of ravens is heavier on the coasts of the West Highlands and Islands than inland, but it is nevertheless a firm inhabitant of the deer forest now that persecution has lessened. It is my opinion that the corbie does more good than harm by his assiduous clearing of carrion. His tremendous beak is the first to puncture the hide of the dead stag in spring and clear the entrails before the blowflies get busy. Some species of these blowflies are the scourge of the sheep farmer throughout the summer. The hoodie crow must also be given its little bit of credit for feeding on maggotty carrion, but the raven is a much better scavenger and costs us less.

The ecology of grazing is a subject in which natural history and pastoral husbandry meet and mingle. We cannot dissociate the two ; indeed modern natural history has ceased to concern itself only with the collection of wild species and the tabulation of habits ; it is now a rounded study of animals in relation to their environments ; and environments have a habit in this country of being created, shaped, modified or destroyed by man and his domesticated animals, so we must include him and his beasts in a broad study of natural history. We have seen the forest disappear and the herbage complex of the hill sheep farm arise. For well over a hundred years we have seen positive attempts to maintain that complex. The sheep farmer knows in his way, as the plant ecologist knows in his, that the vegetational complex of sedge, flying bent, deer's hair, and some heather of the three kinds, is not a climax. If the density of the sheep grows less or the farmer ceases to burn regularly, the grazing floor will disappear in its present state. The seedling trees which even now appear plentifully if we look for them would raise their little heads above the herbage, and, in the case of heather, this plant itself would grow three feet high and be coarse and open, giving exactly the right shelter from weather for young trees. The physical stiffness and impenetrability of old heather would also prevent grazing animals from reaching the young trees. Rowans and birch would be most numerous, some willows would be present, and an occasional Scots pine or an escaped larch or spruce. The hazel would come in the drier places, and the aspen (*Populus tremula*) would grow where the soil was thin. The occurrence of single aspens in the deer forest or on the cliff of a small, off-shore island, has often surprised me, but the surprise has been even greater when I have found on their leaves caterpillars of the puss moth (*Dicranura vinula*) and of the poplar hawk moth (*Laothoe populi*). These insects must be far and sure travellers. Oak would come back much slower, though this tree also I have seen growing as a wind-shattered bush in the cliff of one of the Summer Isles. In various parts of the North-Western Highlands where lochans are so numerous we see tiny islands (Pl. 12a, p. 93) which have been left alone. They are worthy of a much closer study than most of them have been given up to now. They are pristine and untrodden. Without the firestick and the selective muzzles of sheep we should soon be back to scrub over much of the ground below 1,000 feet and later to a new recuperative forest age of the Highlands. There is but little chance of this.

The deer have not been included as destroyers, though they obviously must be to some extent. They are much given to browsing and will easily graze off young trees. Cattle will also kill trees by rubbing, and the deer kill a great many half-grown conifers by rubbing the bark completely away. But deer and cattle between them would not prevent a fair amount of regeneration. The reason rests not on appetite but on numbers of mouths. One cattle beast represents five sheep. Now even if the Highland cow needs the bulk required by five sheep, she does not get it by precisely the same means, and however active she may be she cannot travel over the same amount of ground as five sheep. That is just the point, the bio-mass represented by five sheep in place of one cow means five grazing tracks and five times the destructiveness of a cattle stock. Furthermore, the cattle beast tears several square inches of herbage at a time, and the hill plants being well rooted lose only their tops. The sheep pokes its muzzle farther down and pulls. The crowns of plants are much more affected by sheep grazing. The grazing habits of deer approximate to those of young cattle.

Sheep appear to have a marked depressive effect on many flowering plants. This may be seen better on the West Highland sheep farms than on the sheep farm *cum* grouse moor where *Calluna* is the dominant species. In those little dens and cliffy places which the sheep cannot reach there will be a profusion of flowers in early summer. I once fenced off less than an acre of cliff on Isle Tanera, the dual purpose being to keep the cattle from going over the cliff and to allow of planting some trees and shrubs there. The result of the freedom from grazing of cattle and sheep was striking. For a year or two the heather grew and flowered better than it did outside the fence, but this did not continue. Primroses appeared where they were not seen before. Milkwort grew much longer fronds and was a more conspicuous plant than where there was grazing. Alpine hawkweed (*Hieracium* sp.) now became common and so did St. John's wort (*Hypericum perforatum*) a little later in the year. Grasses grew and seeded and tended to oust such wild white clover as was present. The most remarkable result among the plants was the sudden appearance of many suckers of aspen several yards away from the few stunted trees which grew either in the cliff face or on the edge. These rapidly growing aspens seemed likely to create copse-like conditions in a few years. They would not grow high quickly but would make shrubby growth, because they were naturally pruned each year for the first three years or so of their life by a fungoid disease. The new leader would be covered by mildew in June and would be black and shrivelled in July. The older trees were not affected.

There was a great increase in the number and variety of butterflies on the cliff edge during the second year after fencing. The common blue (*Lycoena icarus*) became really common, the dark green fritillary (*Argynnis aglaia*) was also frequent, and the pearl-bordered fritillary (*A. euphrosyne*) occasional in appearance. The number of meadow browns (*Maniola jurtina*) did not seem greatly affected, nor of the green-veined white (*Pieris napi*). The larvae of these insects live on grasses and dog violet, so through the cessation of grazing many must have escaped being shorn off with the herbage and carried to dissolution in the rumen of the sheep. The thyme pug moth (*Eupithecia distinctaria*) also appeared more commonly with the spread of its food plant, *Thymus serpyllum.*

The ground outside the fence also underwent changes as a result of treatment different from that it had suffered for many years. Sheep were excluded and the grazing of cattle was controlled. There was originally a growth of poor, spray-blasted *Calluna* with sedges and occasional plants of crested dog's-tail grass (*Cynosurus cristatus*). This was burnt and lime and basic slag added. After a year of almost complete barrenness, tormentil being practically the only relief to the blackness, there was colonization of bird's-foot trefoil, of viviparous sheep's fescue and fiorin, as well as marked extension of crested dog's-tail. The bird's-foot trefoil increased for three years, during which time wild white clover was colonizing and forming dense mats. Alpine hawkweed flourished in this herbage and it was particularly noticeable that wild thyme increased to a much greater extent on this open grazed portion than on the part where there were no animals. Antennaria (*A. dioica*) also appeared in three places on dry knolls. When the wild white clover spread farther afield and made a sward, there was some recession of the bird's-foot trefoil. Grasses continued to spread, the sedges held their own, and butterwort (*Pinguicula vulgaris*) seemed to occur about as commonly as on the ungrazed portion and on that which had been grazed but not treated. The *Calluna* was severely depressed, but it went on living as a small and very healthy plant. The experiment has continued for six years and at a glance there has been increasing greenness, but I am inclined to think possible reversion to *Calluna* at a fairly rapid rate has not been ruled out by lime and phosphates and such grazing control as might depress it.

To return to the Highlands as a whole: the decline in cattle grazing in the past 150 years and the intensification in sheep grazing has brought about a fairly general increase in the area under bracken. In fact large areas have degenerated into a pure stand of bracken and are no longer of value for any kind of grazing. An inquiry from the Department of Agriculture for Scotland elicited the fact that there are nearly half a million acres of bracken in Scotland, most of which area is in the Highlands. Cattle and deer tend to depress bracken by mechanical action *when it is not unduly common*, but they cannot limit it when the bracken has got out of control as it now has. The spread of bracken is a direct result of hill sheep farming practice, a spread which is far worse in the West where there was not a close Callunetum but a mixture of sedges and grass and thin heather. A pure stand of bracken is a sub-climax, and as much of the bracken on Highland hills is on slopes inaccessible to machines and uneconomic to cut frequently by hand, it is a matter for concern what is going to happen about the areas of pure bracken. Planting with conifers will possibly be the answer, for spruces at least can benefit from the cover given. This would mean bracken eradication on a 40-year cycle, with expensive fencing of inconvenient places. This measure would probably mean opposition from the sheep farmers who, as a class in the Highlands, have been much against the extension of afforestation as conducted by the Forestry Commission. A Pteridietum has been mentioned in the foregoing as a sub-climax, though while grazing continues it might as well be called a climax. Were grazing to cease it is probable that scrub growth of rowan, birch, alder and hazel would appear from the bracken in due course and bring about healing of a sorely-afflicted soil.

Sheep grazing in the Southern Highlands has resulted in the spread of moor mat grass, as below Ben Lawers. The sheep eat little of this stiff-leaved grass and the result is the formation of a dense mat of decaying vegetation between the true soil base and the young shoots. An acid herbage of comparatively little food value results. Fenton (1937) has shown that the areas where *Nardus* is spreading graze the heaviest densities of sheep in Scotland, i.e. in the Southern Uplands and the South-Central Highlands. The only hope in such places is to reduce the density and stock heavily with cattle, preferably Highland cattle which are great rangers, for the heavy hoof itself helps to puncture the mat as the shearing muzzle helps to reduce its thickness. Smith (*cit.* Fenton 1937) showed that *Nardus* could be depressed and replaced by an *Agrostis-Festuca* association by the cessation of grazing.

There is no doubt that if we are to preserve some of our natural woodlands in the Highlands or even allow regeneration on chosen sites, we must be prepared to fence for a few years until the leaders of the young trees are above grazing or browsing height. It would be a good measure of rehabilitation if private ownership of a deer forest (or public ownership for that matter) was contingent on a certain amount of fencing being done to allow regeneration of natural woodland. And certainly any national park policy should include a scheme of rotational fencing for this purpose.

Earlier in this chapter I have rather given the impression that deer are not greatly responsible for deterioration of grazing and prevention of regeneration. This is so when the deer are kept at the low density which it is their nature to preserve. I have suggested (1937) that a density of more than one deer to 25 acres is overstocking, and that on most of the poorer forests one to 40 acres is probably sufficient.

Unfortunately, some forest owners were not satisfied with this and boosted their numbers by winter feeding of stags and by allowing the hinds on to good low ground. Wars have put a stop to that and it is unlikely that economic conditions will allow such extravagance again for many years to come. This habit was ecologically unsound in that it put too much grazing strain on regenerating scrub.

It is interesting to notice that the blue hare is commonest on those places where sheep and grouse are most dense. The hares are often so numerous as to injure the Callunetum and allow the ingress of mat grass and rushes. As this mammal grazes quite happily to the 3,000-foot contour it is obvious it can do more widespread damage than the rabbit to the herbage floor of a Highland hill. The main reason for its large numbers on the sheep farm *cum* grouse moor is that both these usages presuppose success in keeping down those predatory species usually known as vermin. The golden eagle is vermin on a grouse moor because the advent of this bird clears the ground of grouse for the day. Wild cats are uncommon in the grouse-moor country, and foxes, stoats and buzzards are also discouraged. Obviously the blue hare increases unchecked by these visible predators; and the animal in its present environment presents good material for observation of those unseen checks which operate on populations of rodents and bring about characteristic cycles of increase and decrease such as have been discussed at length by Elton (1942).

There remains to consider the rabbit (*Oryctolagus cuniculus*) (Pl. 13, p. 116) as a factor in the ecology of grazing of a Highland hill. This animal is a newcomer, not known in many parts of the North-West until well into the 19th century. Its effect has been disastrous where it has been allowed to increase unchecked for a long period. Just as we found the sheep more destructive than the cattle because there were more mouths quartering the ground, so can rabbits denude an area completely of regenerating timber because their mouths are legion. Rabbits also destroy heather and encourage moss in pasture. Our good fortune is that the rabbit does not go much above 1,000 feet on Highland hills; and on the wet hills of the West it quite disappears from the peat-covered ground.[1] In the rocky glens and talus slopes

[1] An interesting exception to this statement may be seen on Ben Iadain (1,873 feet) in Morvern. A tertiary-basalt cap sits on top of the schistose to a depth of 350 feet. Rabbits are absent on the ascent over the typical schistose country of poor peaty herbage, but as soon as the green, porous-soiled basaltic cap is reached at 1,500 feet, rabbits appear and are quite common on the summit plateau.

below cliffs the rabbit finds perfect harbourage. The increase of buzzards in the last 25 years has been quite insufficient to keep down numbers. Whereas in England the rabbit has been attacked as a serious menace to the countryside, this attitude has not been generally upheld in the Highlands, for I know of places where the proprietors have refused to do anything about their rabbits.

Finally, as a factor in the ecology of grazing we should consider those tiny feeders on the bases of the stalks of grass, the voles. The field vole (*Microtus agrestis*) is much the most important in the Highlands as elsewhere in Scotland. The several works of Elton and Middleton (1929–1942) have shown that a 3–4-year cycle of increase and decrease is common in many areas, but that local advantageous conditions may alter this rhythm by a year if the voles are approaching a peak year at the time of onset of favourable conditions. Vole plagues have at times devastated large areas of sheep-farming ground in the Southern Uplands of Scotland, but the Highlands seem to have escaped such extreme increases and their results. Nevertheless, the occasional increases of voles have had a destructive effect in some of the young state forests through ring-barking the small trees (Middleton 1930–31). Normally it may be said that a heavy density of sheep has the effect of lessening the perfection of the habitat for the voles : the cover is eaten and the hooves of the sheep may cause traumatic damage. Elton (1942) considers it remarkable that the great Southern Uplands plagues of 1875–6 and 1892–3 should have occurred in the area where sheep farming had gathered such a heavy stock. Personally, I should say that the vegetational complex had much to do with it. *Molinia caerulea* and *Deschampsia caespitosa*, both tussocky in character, are able to create sufficient mat to protect the vole, despite a heavy grazing density. The north-west corner of Ross-shire and the west of Sutherland do not suffer markedly from vole increases and we find in this area that these two grasses rarely get a chance to form a mat. The common *Scirpus* flow country does not give sufficient cover for the voles, nor does it give them the succulent lower stalks on which they feed. Farther south in the Highlands, where the ground cover is altogether more luxuriant, the vole years such as 1929 are fairly common. Summerhayes (1941) has shown that the grazing of voles tends to preserve a varied herbage of *Molinia*, *Deschampsia*, *Holcus* and mosses. Freedom from voles tends to the exclusion of mosses and the dominance of a species such as *D. caespitosa*.

Just as heavy grazing is disadvantageous to voles, the enclosure of ground for afforestation creates perfect conditions for them. It is usual to find great concentrations in these areas, with the result that the number of kestrels to be seen overhead at one time is quite striking. The grasses grow rank and the voles tunnel hither and thither at the level of the crown. Foresters are conscious and apprehensive of vole increases as few other sections of country folk. Elton (1942) has pointed out that the phase of abundant grass growth in enclosed plantations is limited to the first fifteen years or less, after which the trees become dense enough to depress the grass and finally to exclude it altogether. So four vole cycles are possible in any new plantation. Summerhayes has elsewhere noted that a moderate density of voles can be beneficial to newly afforested ground and tussocky hill pasture in providing tunnels which allow aeration and drainage. Finally, a vole plague can have a beneficial effect in the following year on the hill pasture, because the tussocks and the mat have been bitten through ; and after the gales of winter have blown away the detritus, the growth of new grass in spring is extremely good and fresh. The sheep stock consequently does well.

Before closing this chapter on the natural history of the deer forest, grouse moor and sheep farm, it is necessary to discuss at some length an organism which is common to most of the hill land of Scotland, which has significance for all warm-blooded animals and which, in its control, may have marked effects on the constitution of the vegetation. This is the sheep tick (*Ixodes ricinus*), sometimes called the grass tick or castor-bean tick. This animal swarms in the damp herbage of the West Highlands and Islands and apart from the discomfort it causes to other animals, it is the cause of mortality, particularly in sheep, because it is the vector of at least three diseases.

Its life history, as given through Macleod's classic researches (1932), is of interest : the engorged female drops from the host and lies in the grass and sedge for three weeks or so. She then lays 500–2,000 eggs which hatch after four weeks in summer or possibly eight months if winter intervenes. One to three weeks after hatching the larvae climb the herbage stalks and attach themselves to any passing mammal or bird. The six-legged larva clings to the tip of the leaf or stalk with its two hind pairs of legs and uses the front pair for making contact with the host. Macleod says : " Several larvae may be found in this

PLATE XV

Eric Hosking

CRESTED TIT, a species confined to the old pine woods. Inverness-shire June 1939

PLATE XVI

Arthur Brook

BADGER, thinly and discontinuously distributed in the mainland Highlands
(Taken in Breconshire, Wales)

position on the tip of each blade. It was found that immediately an air current was set up, e.g. by breathing on the grass, or if the grass were otherwise disturbed, the larva became excitedly alert and, relaxing its hold with its middle pair of legs, rose on its hind legs, ready to transfer itself to the disturbing object. This reaching out was so pronounced that several actually overreached themselves and became detached from the leaves."

The larvae become engorged in about four days after they have punctured their host. They then relax their hold and fall into the herbage, where they secrete themselves and await ecdysis into the nymphal stage. This may take six weeks or nine months and once again the creature climbs the stalk of fortune and hopes for the best. Five days are needed for engorgement, then another falling off and a three or four months' interval for metamorphosis and ecdysis to the adult stage. There is now the last climb, attachment to the host, seven to eleven days of engorgement for the female and the last fall back into the herbage. The male walks actively about the skin of the host seeking an engorging female. He remains minute because he does not feed; the female swells with blood to the size of a large black-currant or a small gooseberry, dull grey in colour and shiny.

The life cycle as outlined is that of a constantly successful tick. In the field the larvae have extraordinary fasting powers and may go two years before making contact with a host. This ability to wait compensates largely for the tick's inability to walk far. The chances of the passage of a live host in two years are good, considering the way animals have of going over ground the same ways time and time again, and the fact that sheep manage to nibble the ground fairly evenly. The chances are good even if the winter is a close season with ticks!

Now sheep, being fairly low animals and having a long fuzzy coat of wool, are in the way of being likely hosts for ticks, but cattle are also very heavily infested at the spring and autumn invasions. Horses are also attacked but to a lesser extent. The ticks congregate at those places where the skin is thinnest, such as between the fore legs and behind the elbow, between the hind legs and on udder and scrotum. The larval ticks have a habit of aligning themselves along the eyelids where they cause much irritation. Man's animals are not the only ones attacked. The larvae and nymphs will infest and engorge on all wild mammals and birds with which they come in contact. It is therefore impossible to clear a piece of ground from ticks by removing domesticated stock for a long period. Rabbits, blue hares, hedgehogs, field mice and voles—all do quite well for the tick. The adult tick has this one limitation : that she must engorge herself with mammalian blood if she is to ovulate.

As far as can be ascertained, the tick has no natural enemies in this country. Macleod (1933) examined the stomachs of several species of birds found on tick-infested land, but found no traces of ticks at the season when the ticks are most active and most easily found by birds. There seems no chance of control other than lessening their chance of contact. Now deer are heavily infested with ticks in spring and autumn just as sheep are, and it has been suggested that control or extermination of the deer would have a considerable effect in lessening the scourge, together with destocking and burning. The experiment has been tried in one part of a deer forest in the Eastern Highlands. About 13,000 acres of ground were fenced and all the deer within the fence shot. The naturalist would say immediately, " What about all the smaller fauna to which a deer fence meant nothing ? " The theory was that deer by their considerable movement through the seasons (their periods of diurnal movement are actually greatest at the time when the ticks are worst ; Darling, 1937) were a means of spreading engorged ticks, whatever other control methods such as dipping and burning were being undertaken. The experiment has now been running for some years and the general idea which initiated it seems to have been borne out. The naturalist who is writing this book is now anxious to know how long tick-freed land of this nature can be expected to remain free or with ticks at only a very low density. It is realized now that land cleared of sheep can still carry a heavy larval population of ticks and that the species could keep going with but a small number of adults. The water metabolism of insects is an extremely important factor in their survival, and in the case of the tick the damp climate of the West must greatly influence persistence and periods of infestation. Elsewhere, micro-habitats of wet bog must be instrumental in keeping the population going, together with suitable hosts.

The three diseases already identified as being carried by ticks are red-water fever in cattle, caused by a piroplasm ; louping-ill or trembling, caused by a virus ; and tick-borne fever, also caused by a virus. At one time the two last diseases were thought to be more or less one ; Macleod (1932) showed the two to be quite distinct but that the fever was often an aggravating factor towards louping-ill. Cattle reared in the Highlands show a fair degree of immunity to red-water fever or may escape with a sub-acute attack. Highland cattle which are out on the hill all the year round are sometimes attacked by louping-ill, but as yet have not been shown to take the tick-borne fever. A good many young grazing cattle turned out in the deer forests for the summer contract louping-ill in June. Deer may also have louping-ill, but the imperfection of our observation has not allowed us to say anything about the other two diseases in deer. Here once more the deer forest and sheep farm, the wild and the domestic animals are linked and cannot be dissociated in our survey.

It is fortunate that many parasites are specific to their hosts. For example, the warble fly of cattle is *Hypoderma bovis* ; that of deer is *H. diana*. Red deer cannot be blamed as a reservoir of this pest for cattle. Equally, the sheep nostril fly *Cephenomyia ovis* is not the same as that of deer, *C. auribarbis*. The sheep ked (*Melophagus ovinus*) is wingless ; the deer ked (*Lipoptena cervi*) is a winged insect, commonly found in the vicinity of deer wallows in September, until it gets on to a deer, when the brittle wings break off.

Throughout the whole area of deer forest and sheep farm, man and his animals and the wild animals are plagued with Tabanid flies—the big ones such as *Tabanus sudeticus* (rarely), *T. distinguendus*, *T. montanus* and *Chrysops relicta*, and the smaller clegs *Haematopota pluvialis* and *H. crassicornis*. Once more it is the female that does the bloodsucking ; the male is a harmless creature feeding on plant juices. If the female does not get her blood meal she does not ovulate. The Tabanid flies are of interest in relation to the ecology of grazing in the deer forest, for it is these more than anything else which drive the deer to the high grazings—in the daytime only during the middle or third week of June when the flies first appear, but in July when the Tabanids are their most active on the hot, sunny days, the deer stay high altogether.

This book can in no way be a catalogue of species to be found in the Highlands. Certain orders of animals or plants must be left out almost, or mentioned only in relation to the habitat and living complex to which they belong. Insects, for example, are far more numerous in species than any other animal, and few can receive attention here. There are, however, several butterflies and moths characteristic of the deer forest and grouse moor and too obvious to be neglected. The butterflies are rather local in occurrence and the high grounds have only one. The mountain ringlet (*Erebia epiphron*), a glacial relic, is found only in the western half of the Grampians, as far as Ben Nevis and near the head of Loch Fyne where it may reach as low as 1,500 feet. The Scottish form is larger and brighter-coloured than the English (Ford, 1945). Its food is the mat grass frequently mentioned earlier in this chapter, but only the tips are eaten. The Scots argus (*E. aethiops*) is of wider distribution in the Highlands, reaching north to Sutherland, but it does not appear in the Outer Hebrides. Its food is *Molinia*. The meadow brown is as common in the Highlands as elsewhere in Britain; the Highlands and Islands hold the sub-species *splendida*. The small heath (*Coenonympha pamphilus*) is found in the Southern and Eastern Highlands and though absent in the north is yet quite common on the Outer Hebridean moors. The large heath (*C. tullia*) is also local in distribution. It is the sub-species *scotica* which is found, a type almost lacking eye spots on the wings. Ford (1945) mentions this butterfly particularly in that its several types through Britain provide a good example of a *cline*, the term devised by Huxley (1939) to describe a regular geographical gradation in type within the range of a species (see also Chapter 10, p. 199). The fritillaries mentioned earlier in this chapter (p. 103) are of fairly general distribution, the dark green fritillary showing a very dark form in the Islands. The marsh fritillary (*Euphydryas aurinia*) occurs in the Inner Hebrides and to some extent on the western mainland. The small pearl-bordered fritillary (*Argynnis selene*) shows a sub-species *insularum* in the Outer Hebrides. The sub-speciation of butterflies in the Highlands and Islands is of great interest; reference should be made to the papers of Heslop Harrison and to Ford's volume in this series.

The small blue (*Cupido minimus*) occurs here and there south of the Great Glen. The common blue is found throughout the Highlands and Islands except on the high ground. The green hairstreak (*Callophrys rubi*) is also fairly well distributed in the deer forest and moorland country where there are brambles or furze. Rarities occur in the Highlands, e.g. the chequered skipper (*Carterocephalus palaemon*) near Fort William, but this species should more properly come in the chapter on birch wood.

The most conspicuous moths of the moor are the emperor (*Saturnia pavonia*), northern eggar (*Lasiocampa quercus* var. *calluna*), the fox moth (*Macrothylacia rubi*) and the drinker (*Cosmotriche potatoria*). The toll on the larvae and pupae of these moths by Chalcid and ichneumon flies is enormous. Emperors in particular are scarce in many places, my own finds of cocoons showing a Chalcid infestation of about three out of four. The fox moth, and to a lesser extent the eggar, are subject to violent fluctuations from year to year. Heather burning, of course, destroys all these moths which spin their cocoons in the foliage of this plant.

There are many Geometrid moths in the general habitat of deer forest, grouse moor and sheep farm, of such genera as the carpets (*Xanthorhoë* spp. and *Entephria* spp.), and there is the allied argent and sable (*Eulype hastata*) whose larvae feed on birch and bog myrtle. The purple bar (*Mesoleuca ocellata*) is commoner in the Highlands than elsewhere in Britain, bedstraw (*Galium* spp.) being the food plant. The rivulets and the pretty pinion (*Perizoma* spp.) may be mentioned because their larvae all feed on the parasitic herbs, the rattles and eyebright (*Bartsia* and *Euphrasia*). Throughout the West Highlands and Islands, the magpie moth (*Abraxas grossulariata*) is a common insect wherever *Calluna* is found in quantity. The caterpillar in this habitat has taken entirely to a diet of *Calluna*, but if man plants gooseberry or blackcurrant bushes—or particularly worcesterberries—in such surroundings, the moth comes to them and is a serious pest because there is no means of controlling the general population of this prolific moth. Many moorland Lepidoptera of the Inner and Outer Isles are recorded in Heslop Harrison (1937) and in Campbell (1938).

Almost everywhere in the Highlands below 2,000 feet there are vast hordes of midges (Chironomidae) which affect the movements of mammalian life, including man, to a considerable extent. These minute insects help to keep the deer high in summer, especially the stags, which are terribly irritated by midges while their antlers are in velvet. Midges are doubtless preyed on by the several species of dragonflies, by the frogs which are numerous on the wetter moors of the West and by the palmated newts which are found in the small and even temporary pools in the peat. But nothing keeps pace with the ubiquitous midge which has lately been the subject of inquiry by a special committee. The place of the midge in human ecology is such that it is thought a greatly increased tourist industry to the West Highlands could be encouraged if the midge could be lessened in numbers. But the range of the midge is very great. One of the midgiest places in the West Highlands is the narrow line of decaying seaweed left high by the March spring tide and untouched again by the sea until October. This line found on every bay and beach and inlet must be hundreds of miles long between Cape Wrath and the Mull of Kintyre. The Committee's Report, 1946, mentions the several species found, chief of which is *Culicoides impunctatus*. Once more it appears that the midge does not breed everywhere on moors and hill-sides but in particular damp places providing the desired environmental complex. The common lizard (*Lacerta vivipara*), common throughout this type of country, must be one of the few constant predators.

This chapter must close with mention of the spider *Epeira diadeine*, which is known to everyone who walks the deer forest and the moors in summer. Its webs are slung across the narrow sheep and deer tracks which provide them with perfect sites to set their aerial net. Use of the word net reminds me of a day on Tanera when another biologist and I rowed to the quarry face in the cliff where the stone had been taken 150 years ago. The quarry was inaccessible to sheep and was growing long heather and briars. Nests of black ant (*Acantho-myops niger*) seethed beneath almost every stone in the old spoil from the quarry face. (These ants were found nowhere else on the island or in the Summer Isles.) When we came to the sheer face of the quarry we found the mooring strands of the spiders' webs slung diagonally from a height of four feet on the cliff across to the long heather below and four feet away. The webs were placed almost regularly at distances of about two feet and we were irresistibly re-minded of herring fishers setting their nets from shore to mooring buoys at regular intervals, a practice which used to be common in the Anchorage below us.

THE LIFE HISTORY OF THE RED DEER

THE RED DEER (*Cervus elaphus*) is Britain's largest wild land mammal and it is only in the Highlands that it has remained truly wild without a break from earlier times (Pl. XIV, p. 101, Pl. 14, p. 117). The large area of rough country enabled the species to survive the period of the medieval chase and later the age of gunpowder, until, when it was in a much reduced state in the 19th century, a certain William Scrope, Esquire, enjoyed himself thoroughly for ten years in the Forest of Atholl and wrote a book describing his stalking days after the red stag. It was published in 1845. " Literature ?—Heaven help us ! " he exclaimed, " far from it ; I have no such presumption ; I have merely attempted to describe a very interesting pursuit as nearly as possible in the style and spirit in which I have always seen it carried on. . . . The beautiful motions of the deer, his picturesque and noble appearance, his sagacity and the skilful generalship which can alone ensure success in the pursuit of him, keep the mind in a constant state of pleasurable excitement." The book is rather crude ; the illustrations by Edwin and Charles Landseer are in my opinion bad, but William Scrope, Esquire, and his book, had an influence on the Highlands almost as great as the Rising of a hundred years before. *Days of Deerstalking* was widely read at a time when a lot of money was being made out of the heavy industries, distilling, brewing and what not. Here was the very thing : a few of the sporting aristocracy set the pace by acquiring deer forests, the manufacturers and brewers and ship-builders were not far behind, and the impoverished Highland lairds found themselves in clover at last. There was nothing like enough deer or deer forests, and the sheep farmers who had come some time in the previous sixty or eighty years after the eviction of the crofters from the glens now found themselves heaved out from some parts. The ground now cleared of sheep was left quiet for a while to let the few deer increase and thoroughly heft themselves. Large rents were forthcoming and there began a period of lodge-building in some of the most fantastic styles of architecture Britain can ever have seen. Queen

Victoria built Balmoral in the fictitious Scots baronial style more reminiscent of the German *schloss*. It was widely copied, but other original spirits got almost as far as the French *château*, and this in extremely remote places. The industry was amazing and the sums spent were fabulous. A strict code of etiquette grew round the new deerstalking, and it was a good one. Deer were driven no more. Even the use of deerhounds in the way of slipping them cold at a stag in the middle of a forest was given up, and these whimpering creatures (that was ever their fault) were crossed with working collie dogs to produce a truly beautiful and intelligent dog that would track a wounded deer and keep quiet until it was needed. The increasing precision and killing power of the express rifle did away with the need for these dogs and by 1890 hardly any were used. The method was now of the quiet forest, the stalker who knew his ground and who could handle his master's guest, and a straight battle of skill in getting up to the stag. Frock-coats were left at home: Lord Tomnoddy donned the tweeds of the country and was happy to crawl in a burn or through the glaur of peat hags in the acute discomfort which the Highland weather of September and October can impose. He shot his stag clean, at a time of year when it was strongest and on the high ground. He picked his beast and kept to it and did not pot at anything which came along. When he returned to the lodge and had a hot bath in his room (water all carried up and carried down, for interior plumbing was not equal to the façade) Lord Tomnoddy had an individual experience to talk about for the rest of the evening in the smoke-room. It made him feel pretty good.

The influx of such large sums of money created a prosperity of a sort. Many men found jobs as stalkers, ghillies and pony boys. Others did all manner of estate work. Planting and capital works which would otherwise never have been attempted were tackled with gusto by the incomers. County Councils in the Highlands found their incomes rise, as all sporting properties carried a high assessment. Yet at this very time the crofting townships on the coast and in the Hebrides were undergoing a period of great hardship. The Highland deer forest, nevertheless, was a grand place for those who lived there, and the deer themselves entered upon a good century. They were allowed to increase and take back lands from which they had been banished; they were kept quiet; the stalking troubled them very little and for no more than a couple of months in the

John Markham

Young Wild Rabbit, Spey Valley, Inverness-shire. An introduced species inimical to regeneration of tree growth
May 1945

PLATE 14

G. B. Kearey

Photographed through a Stalker's Telescope. Stags in the Cairngorm region, Inverness-shire

year, and in bad winters they were given food on the low ground.

It is rather surprising that in these two generations of deer forest prosperity so little good natural history of the deer was published. There were rows of volumes of anecdote and concern with "heads," but the daily life of the animal was largely left to the stalker to watch, and he, being a fine intelligent sort of man, knew much but he did not put it in writing. J. G. Millais obviously loved his deer and those portions of his books dealing with them are sounder natural history than certain other matters on which he wrote. Cameron (1923) wrote what was probably the first scientific book on them, based on Henry Evans's carefully kept notes of many years on Jura Forest. The animals pose us many fine problems and much remains to be done by an inquiring mind that can give the time to their study.

The most important point in their life history is that red deer are social animals ; their herds are more than mere aggregations. For ten and a half months out of the twelve the sexes remain in separate herds, the hinds in large, close family groups, and the stags in loose companies that do not show the same quality of cohesion as the hind groups. Both sexes in their herds observe territories which cover an area of one, three or four, or even more square miles. They know the topography of their own ground intimately, and by the constant passage of their feet hither and thither there have come into being definite tracks that are sometimes so good and firm as to give the impression of having been made by human labour and by intent. Actually they are just the result of always going the best way over a piece of rough ground. If it is along a steep hillside, some rubble is pushed downhill at every passage until eventually the path itself is level and stable.

The deer make seasonable movements within their territories to the high ground in summer (Pl. 15, p. 124) as soon as the flies trouble them and there is grass on the tops, and down again in the fall for the winter. Although these two movements are broadly true, there is both variation and definite movement at other times. For example, a wild storm in July—which is quite common—will bring the deer down as low as they come in winter ; if there is calm frosty weather after a time of snow and drifting east wind, the deer will go high to the places drifted clear of snow, even if it is January ; and in June when days are hot and nights cold, the deer will make quite long treks to high ground in the day and down to their winter quarters at night.

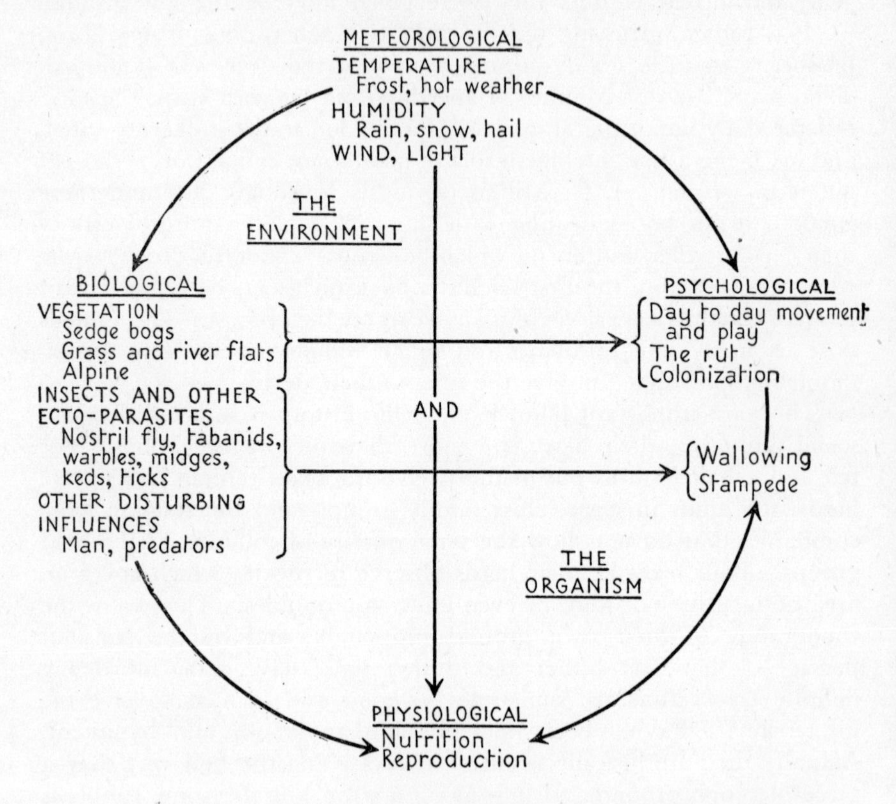

By permission of The Oxford University Press

FIG. 6.—Environmental and physiological factors affecting movements of Red Deer

The nature of the ground influences the distances and frequency of these treks through 3,000 feet of altitude. In the steep hills of the West Coast where the climate is mild, and the tops are often clear of snow, movement is freer, and the distance from 2,000 feet to sea level may entail no more than three miles of a trek. But in the Cairngorm region, Atholl and the glens of Angus, deer may be wintering twenty miles from their summer ground and a long-lying snow will keep them below 1,000 feet for weeks at a time.

The social life of the red deer is founded on a matriarchy and on the fact that the sexes keep apart for so much of the year. Each hind group is led by one particular hind, usually one with a calf at foot. If you are stalking up to a herd of hinds to watch them for a while, you will make a reconnaissance with your glass first to find out from her wary behaviour which is the leader. Thereafter you will give your most careful attention to her. Any small staggies of under three years old which will still be running with the hinds you can almost disregard. They may see you, but they are only little boys with no family responsibilities and they soon forget, or they are not so accustomed to the significance of various shapes as their mothers. Any hind may give the show away, though it is the leader who does most of the sudden raising of the head and looking round. The eyesight of deer cannot be as acute as ours, but it is more practised in that environment and thus makes up for natural shortcomings.

The first sign that you are seen is one loud bark, very sharp and far-carrying, made by whichever hind has seen you. Every beast in the herd stands with its fore feet together, head high and perfectly still. You also lie still and face down. There will be another bark and another and suspicion may be allayed. If so, the young beasts, especially the staggies, will start grazing first and the leader will be the last to drop her head. Perhaps you are still considered a source of danger, but the leader does not know what you are. She may do the bold thing and come to find out while the main bulk of the herd walks slowly with stilted, disconcerted steps in the opposite direction. Or if the ground is right she may climb farther uphill so that she has a better angle of vision on this object in the herbage. Should she get a good view, your shape will be known and she will bark and move off quickly. The rest will follow her, and if she stops to look round they will stop also and not go in front of her. This pattern of behaviour is very common and always pretty to watch.

That hind group will be made up of hinds and their offspring up to coming-three-years-old. Even then it is only the stags which leave to join the stag companies on different ground. The three-year-old hinds stay in the original group. The size of the group will increase to the limit of sustenance in the territory. When that limit is reached there will be budding-off of two or three hinds, often an old one and her daughters, and they will create a new small territory which may grow if the little group grows. There are indications that the boundaries of territories change somewhat as years pass, but on the whole hind ground remains hind ground for a long period of time.

The colonization of new country, such as sheep ground, is usually done by stags, which are much more rangey in nature than the hinds. Their companies are looser and the pattern of a departing company of stags after human intrusion is quite different from that of hinds. It is each stag for himself and the devil take the hindmost.

The calves are born from June 1 onwards till the end of the month. Very few come later. The hind leaves her calf hidden in the heather or bracken for the first few days, feeding it two or three times a day and not allowing the calf to follow. She does not give the calf much mothering in these first days, but as soon as she allows it to follow her, she is extremely attentive and feeding takes place every hour or less. The hind will spend almost an hour sometimes in the slack part of the day, licking her calf's head and ears with her rough tongue. This appears to be sheer joy to the calf. The hind suckles her calf well on into the winter, and as the death rate is heavy among calves anyway—fifty per cent in the first winter—this drop of milk is probably of great benefit to those that survive. The Duke of Bedford wrote to me recently to say that the red deer hinds in Woburn Park did not suckle their calves into the winter and it was his impression that the hinds at Cairnsmore, in the Southern Uplands of Scotland, were also dry before December.

The dappled calves of June lose their spots as the weeks go by and at the end of August are the same colour as their mothers. A dappled calf in October means there has been a late birth and it is unlikely such a youngster will survive the winter.

Rutting begins in the third week in September. During the summer the stags have been grazing by themselves in the high corries, free from the irritation of flies on their growing antlers. Their antlers of last year dropped off in April and May while the stags were on their winter ground, but almost immediately the new ones began to grow (Pl. XIV, p. 101), first as velvety knobs and later bifurcating and further ramifying until the complete " head " was to be seen, still covered by the nutrient skin known as " velvet." The antlers are bone, extending from two cores on the frontal bones of the skull, and not horn and permanent structures as in the antelope. In August, increasing growth of the " coronet " at the base of the antler strangles the blood-vessels to the velvet, with the result that this nutrient skin dies, putrifies, and begins to peel off. The stag feels rather tender at this time and likes to rub his antlers gently against some high-growing tree. All through the growing period he has been careful not to involve his antlers in possible damage. If he has had a little quarrel with one of his fellows, both have been content to settle it by rising on their hind legs like hinds and boxing a few strokes with their fore feet.

The growth of the antlers in the stag, the stoppage of the blood flow to the velvet and the immediate subsequent development of the gonads present a problem which only physiological research can solve. It would be a reasonable hypothesis to postulate that one of the pituitary hormones was being directed towards the stimulation of antler growth from April or May to August—for it is well known that pituitary activity is concerned with calcium metabolism—and that after August, when the velvet peels off from the mature antler, the pituitary secretion is switched over to the development of the gonads. Only then does the secretion of testicular hormone take place and bring about those other physical changes in the stag which accompany the approach of the rut, such as thickening of the neck, development of the larynx and activity of the infra-orbital glands. The diagram below is from *A Herd of Red Deer* (Darling, 1937). At this date (1946), I am not at all sure that light has anything to do with the cycle of antler growth and reproduction.

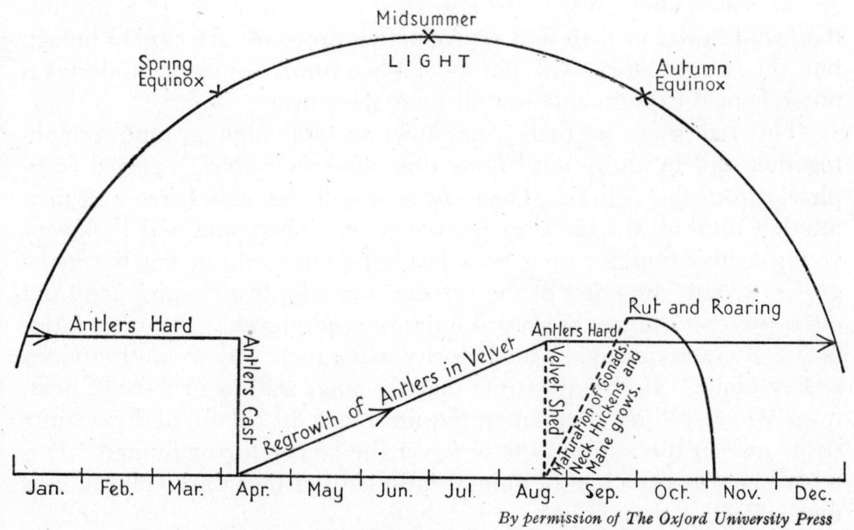

By permission of The Oxford University Press

FIG. 7.—Growth of antlers and maturation of the gonads

Antlers are a sex-limited character in red deer and, considering the annual drain they are on the system of the animal, it is difficult at first sight to see why they should have developed at all. A heavy and numerously pointed pair of antlers is a handicap to the animal rather than a help in fighting and it is doubtful whether such a head is much of an intimidation, for a " switch-horned " stag is a powerful antagonist and a hummel or hornless one is very often a master stag. Huxley (1930) has said that in evolution antlers may have increased in size and branching with increase in size of the deer, and so, given the evolutionary value of an increase in body size, the elaborate antlers would not require to be of an active quality in order to be controlled by natural selection. They may be merely a by-product of size.

It would never be safe to say what antlers are for ; in fact such an approach is bad biology. The reindeer is antlered in both sexes, but the rhythm of growth and shedding is quite different between male and female. The adult bucks shed theirs after the rut in October and spend the winter with defenceless heads when antlers might have been useful against wolves. The females shed their antlers a few days after the birth of the fawn in April or early May, so once more the antlers are no good for helping the deer to defend their young. If a doe fawns out of season, her antlers are also shed out of season. It is obvious then that antler growth and reproductive processes are closely linked, but the whole story will not be known until someone undertakes physiological experimentation on some park deer.

The red stags in their companies on the high ground remain together and in amity until some time after the velvet is peeled completely from the antlers. Then one stag will suddenly leave and then another until all the mature ones are gone. The youngsters look very young at this time for their neck has not developed nor has the mane grown. With the onset of the rut the stag adopts a running gait and often travels distances of several miles to hind ground in another forest or half a county away. The majority make their way to hind grounds nearer home. It is at this time that the stags wallow in dubs of peat, from which rolling they emerge quite black in colour and certainly strike awe in the mind of the observer, be he cervine or human. It is a well-known principle of animal intimidation that dark coloration is more effective than light.

When the stag, newly come into rut, breaks into the hind grounds he proclaims his presence by a loud roaring. This is the only time of year that his voice is used and he seems incapable of emitting the sharp bark so characteristic of the hinds. His roaring is intended as a warning for other stags to keep away from this ground which is his territory for the time being. It now seems to the casual observer in the deer forest that the stag is dominant over the whole herd, but in reality the traditional matriarchy of the hind group is not broken. There is a definite attempt on his part to keep the hinds on ground over which he can run easily, and he is fairly successful in this, for he herds them as a collie dog would. Otherwise the hinds are indifferent to his presence.

Suppose there is a large herd of hinds and followers in a corrie; at the beginning of the rut one stag may have the corrie and the herd to himself, but this state of affairs will not last. As the fresh stags come in, insistent on establishing a territory, the first stag will have too much to do to keep the whole place and all the hinds for himself. Here are some actual figures from observation in a Ross-shire forest in 1934 (Darling *op. cit.*). A big, dark stag with wide-spreading antlers had 77 hinds and followers in a corrie at 1,700–2,000 feet on September 28. These deer were grazing on an area of about twenty acres and the stag was running round them continuously, roaring every minute or less, scraping the ground with his fore feet, lying down for thirty seconds, up again and running round the group with his muzzle outstretched and roaring as he ran. Two or three hundred yards away on each side of the group were some youngsters and a few rutting stags. The young stags took no notice of the central group of hinds and either grazed or lay quiet. The others were in no way equal to the big stag who was with the hinds, and though roaring occasionally, they made no positive challenge. If they came a little too near, within two hundred yards of the hinds, the master stag would run towards them at a swift trot, muzzle far extended. They did not stay to meet him and he never ran so far as to lose touch with the hinds. Two days later this stag had 46 hinds and followers and three other stags had the rest in much smaller territories well below him. They were closer to each other than to him. On October 4 the big stag had only 23, and 11 on October 7. Then he disappeared. By this time the volume and persistence of roaring had increased among the other stags, for there were now ten harems in the area, and other rutting stags were roaring in the periphery.

I had not had the experience of watching bird flocks at the breeding season at this time, and had not begun to think of the theory of social stimulation in breeding activity which I put forward later. But in my notes relating to the territories described above, I find that I did say how much greater was the activity on that side of the glen where there were ten harems near together than on the other side where there was one stag with a few hinds. Many other observations confirmed this and, at a later date, when I came to watch the Atlantic grey seals, I found the same phenomenon—namely, much more show and activity where harems were near together than where a bull had two or three cows in an isolated place. I also noted that the calves were earlier in those parts where the cow seals were crowded, but I cannot say that deer calves appeared any earlier in the following season in places where there had been crowded harems the year before.

It is a common thing to hear of great fights between stags at the rutting season. Nature fictionists and artists like Landseer find such fights a source of perennial interest. Sometimes there are such fights, pursued with terrific vigour, and occasionally to the death, but they are not common. Broadly, it may be said that fighting occurs more frequently later in the rutting season than at the beginning. The vast majority of encounters are no more than challenges and a sparring of antlers. After all, it may be to the interest of the species that the stronger male should be dominant and therefore the sire of calves, but the species does not benefit by heavy fighting among the males in which one might be killed and the other exhausted. The whole subject of fighting has received far too much attention in popular natural history, probably because man is naturally a bellicose species—it is at once a virtue and a fault, and there can be little doubt that the great task before our species is to lift war from the physical plane and between men to the intellectual level where immense problems of science, health and sociology await the combative spirit. In animal life the rule is much more " he who fights and runs away lives to fight another day."

Encounters between stags are most interesting to watch, for they are occasions of formality and punctilio, or, in biological terms, threat display. There are definite forms : two stags will roar at each other across what they conceive to be a boundary of a rutting territory. They will walk up and down each side of that imaginary line, occasionally trying to take a dig at each other's ribs or flank. But both of them know the game quite well ; the one thus attacked whips round head on with antlers lowered. The attacker does not waste time driving in, so the watchful march up and down begins again. Perhaps they will face

John Markham

LOCH ABHAINN, Cairngorms, Banffshire. The summer home of the red deer
June 1945

John Markham

… with Braeriach beyond, Strath Spey, Inverness-shire, May 1945

up, stretch their hind legs—which depresses the rump—lower the head and tuck in the muzzle so far that the antlers are extended forwards, and then fence with the tips of the antlers as lightly and cleverly as two men with foils. While fighting remains at that level and so far formalized, it is stimulation, analogous with that of blackcocks.

The activity shown by the stags in the rutting territories cannot be maintained by the same animals for the whole six weeks of the rut. As it is, stags eat very little at this time and show the same nipped-up appearance of the abdomen as a racehorse in training. Rests are necessary, and it seems that certain high corries are the places chosen for recuperation. The stags are quiet up there, feeding on *Lycopodium* moss and lichens, and though they do not feed in the close group seen earlier in the summer, it is noticeable that there is no display of animosity or of challenge. They rarely even roar. Those high corries are neutral territories where the animals rest and where advertisement would not be to their advantage. Movement into and out of these high grounds usually occurs at night, but occasionally the observer may see a stag in the neutral corrie become restless and then trot away towards the hind grounds two or three miles away.

The rut ends soon after the end of October and the stags resume life in their companies, coming on to the low ground of their territories for the winter. The interrupted but not disrupted matriarchy of the hind groups continues normally again. Had we wished to see how apparent rather than real was the temporary dominance of the stag in the rutting territories, we could have shown ourselves instead of keeping in hiding, and then we should have seen the leading hind go off with her group in good style ; the stag might have bundled along with them or he might have struck a course of his own and sheered off, not to return to that particular territory.

The senses of the red deer are acute, particularly that of scent, upon which it relies for much that a human being might ascertain by sight and touch. The tactile organ of the deer is the muzzle ; I have occasionally seen it pressed to the ground as if to listen through the ground. Hearing is acute and may be looked upon as the inquisitive sense. The observer may also correctly deduce some of the emotions of the deer by studying the movements of the ears and the angles at which they may be held. Hearing is also highly selective. The deer will hear the sounds of an observer's approach through the sedge and heather even in a high wind when he can barely hear his own movements. In saying that hearing is the inquisitive sense, you may squeak and make whistling sounds which may draw hinds nearer to you, for they like to know, but if you try scraping the metal of your shoe against the rock, the deer will move away—because if they do not *know* what that is, they have a very good idea. The sight or sound of flushed grouse will make deer move quickly without waiting to find the reason, and if the deer hear the explosive hiss of a disturbed sheep they will move immediately. Wild goats also hiss with an explosive snort through their nostrils, but the sound carries farther than that of the sheep. The deer take note from as faraway as half a mile if it happens to be a still day in a high corrie where the sound is carried and amplified.

The sense of scent is linked with a great deal of the behaviour of a herd of red deer ; weather much affects the acuteness of this sense and therefore is one of the primary stimulating influences to action of one kind or another. The state of the weather may make the deer either hypersensitive or apparently tame. It would seem that the interaction of humidity and temperature are of particular importance. The term relative humidity means the ratio, expressed as a percentage, of the actual amount of moisture in a given volume of air to the total amount of water vapour which this air would contain if it were saturated, under similar conditions of temperature and pressure. If you run a thermograph and hygrograph, you notice that as the temperature rises, the needle of the hygrograph falls accordingly. If these rises and falls do not correspond inversely, there has been a change of relative humidity. Suppose our hygrograph shows a relative humidity varying from 20 to 40 per cent at intervals of from 2 to 3 hours ; this is a fairly dry atmosphere which might occur during a light east wind in February. We should expect to find the deer fairly tame on such a day, that they would stand still to satisfy themselves of the nature of a possible disturbance before moving. But suppose there is a warmish southwesterly breeze with a hygrograph showing minute to minute variation in relative humidity of 60–100 per cent. This would mean that the deer would be in a highly nervous state and very irritable. It is common after such weather for the wind to veer to the north, with a possible fall in the temperature but a decided steadying of the hygrograph record. We should also find a tendency in the deer to steady from their irritable condition and not to gallop away as we passed along a well-known path at 500 yards range. If there is a state of constant saturation, as in frost, or super-saturation, as in mist, a close

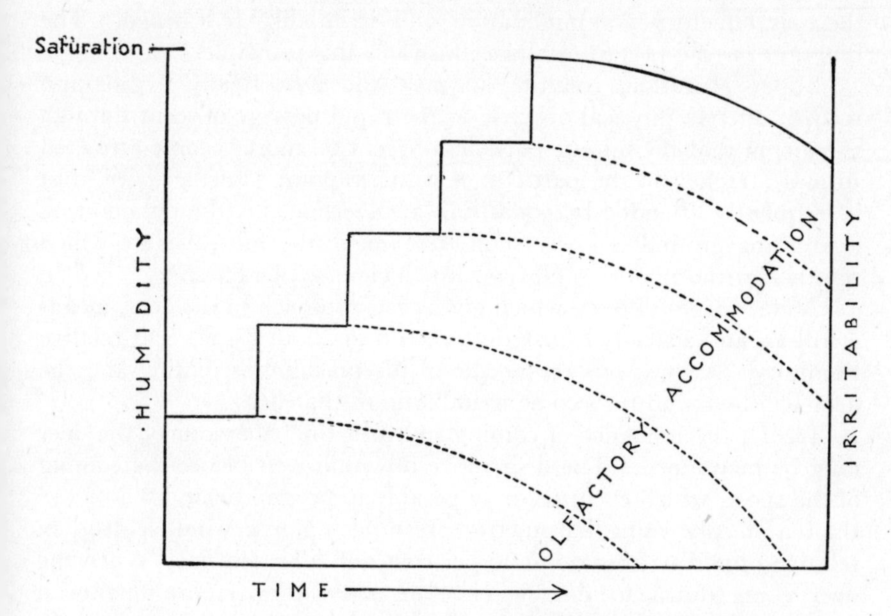

By permission of The Oxford University Press

FIG. 8.—Diagram showing irritability to movement consequent on disturbance in relation to humidity of the atmosphere.

approach is possible, though in the latter set of conditions, hearing an intruder without the steadying influence of sight may cause a panic among the deer.

A warm moist atmosphere conducts scent better than a dry cold one. The olfactory system of animals needs a moist outer receptive surface if it is to function properly. It is known that the thing called "scent," that which is smelt, consists of minute droplets of volatile oil exuded by the animal smelt. These droplets carry much easier in a damp atmosphere and volatilize sooner if it is warm. Scent will reach an animal from a greater distance in a moist warm air than in dry. The same scent reaching an animal's nostrils from the same distance under different degrees of humidity will give different strengths of stimulus to the olfactory senses, and will therefore result in different degrees of the type of behaviour induced. If there is a stepped increase in humidity there will be a comparable stepped reaction of the deer to a disturbing factor involving scent. If humidity remains steady, there is olfactory accommodation and irritability is lessened. The diagram on the preceding page illustrates this principle.

Super-saturation, resulting in mist and dead-steady hygrograph record, offers a physical obstacle to the rapid passage of scent through the air, in that the minute particles of scent oil must become attracted to and attached to the particles of water vapour. Furthermore, mist is frequently attended by conditions of inversion, i.e. the temperature nearer the ground is lower than that above the mist, a state which results in atmospheric stability or low incidence of eddies.

A clear night of frost, which gives easy approach to the deer, means a still air and a steady hygrograph record at about 95 per cent relative humidity. A thaw sets the needle of the machine oscillating and the deer will be found to become irritable immediately.

Lastly, the influence of coming snow on the behaviour of the deer may be mentioned. The deer move downhill well before the coming of the snow, which event we may be able to prognosticate by no more than a steeply rising barometric pressure, a north wind, a drop in relative humidity from 90 to 60 per cent and a leaden sky. When the deer come down to the glens before snow they ignore territorial boundaries. The deer begin to flock and long strings may be seen steadily making their way down the hillsides. The straths fill with hundreds of deer, and when it is remembered that the average density of red deer on the forests of Scotland is about one to thirty or more acres, the deer of large areas of country are to be seen together at these times. The observer, as surely kept in the glen as the deer by the heavy snow, feels a sense of oneness with the animals, and there is real enjoyment to be had—in which the animals join—when the drifting by the east wind ceases and frosty weather follows. Then the snow will carry us, the sun shines, and despite the cold the still air gives the illusion of warmth. The deer go up to the patches drifted clear on the hillsides. As long as the frost holds it will be safe to go high, and when a thaw is imminent they will come down again beforehand lest they be isolated on those bare patches by a sea of soft snow. But if they have been kept low by soft snow and a thaw is imminent, the deer go up again beforehand, knowing that the snow will soon disappear and they will have newly washed grazing.

PLATE 17

John Markham

THIN PINE COVER. Abernethy Forest, Strath Spey, Inverness-shire
September 1944

PLATE 18

John Markham

BLAEBERRY (*Vaccinium myrtillus*) in the pine forest. Strath Spey, Inverness-shire. September 1944

THE PINE FOREST, BIRCH WOOD AND OAK WOOD

THE DESTRUCTION of the old Wood of Caledon has been bewailed at sufficient length already in earlier chapters of this book. Let us now study those small portions of it which are left. The largest piece is in the basin between Aviemore and the Cairngorms comprising Rothiemurchus (Pl. 16, p. 125), Abernethy (Pl. 17, p. 128) and Glenmore Forests, from about 700 feet altitude at the level of the Spey to the tree line at 1,500 feet. The stretches of undisturbed pine forest are very much smaller than the few thousand acres of the whole.

Then again, on the other side of the Cairngorms, the old trees appear in the Forest of Mar, occurring in several patches down the valley of the Dee. There are some fine examples at Ballochbuie on the King's ground, and Lord Glentanar conserves a few hundred acres on the slopes south of Aboyne. The rainfall in this region is fairly low and the greatest danger to the trees—apart from another timber shortage—is fire.

There is the Black Wood of Rannoch on the south side of Loch Rannoch which is still within the Central Highland zone. The term black wood means the same as dark wood—which is pine as opposed to oak and birch. Some stretches of pine exist in Forestry Commission ground on the south side of Loch Carron in Ross-shire, where the old trees' greatest danger is from the Forestry Commission itself which in the past has been obsessed with monocultural methods of non-native conifers. Farther north still, at Rhidorroch near the Sutherland border, there is a wood of native pine above the Old Lodge. This wood lies higher than a birch wood, a result no doubt of earlier cutting of the pine and colonization of the ground by birch. There is no regeneration of any kind now because of the stocking of sheep in the area. Many old pines occur in the Inverness-shire glens, but are not thick enough anywhere to form pine forests and its associated flora. Nor is there regeneration.

Other small areas of old pine still existing precariously are on the south shore of Loch Tulla, Blackmount ; Crannog Wood, on the east side of the railway crossing Rannoch Moor; a patch south of the railway near Tyndrum; and in Glen Affric, Glen Cannich and Strath Farrar.

Tansley (1939) has drawn special attention to the fragment of old forest on the south-western shore of Loch Maree, at Glas Choille Leitir, for at this point there is free regeneration of old pine, comparable with that occurring in Rothiemurchus. Such a condition presupposes (*a*) limited access or absence of deer and sheep; (*b*) a sufficiently vigorous and long growth of *Calluna*, *Erica*, and *Vaccinium*; and (*c*) absence or very light density of bracken (*Pteridium*); (*d*) rapid drainage or absence of dense moss. These conditions in fact are fulfilled at Glas Choille Leitir, though in the surrounding countryside there are many places where they are not. Tansley gives a diagram in another portion of his big book representing a terrace in Glas Choille Leitir on which the rainfall is caught up and held. On this bit of ground the pines are absent and *sphagnum* becomes dominant, with some *Carex* spp., *Drosera* spp., *Potentilla erecta*, *Juncus* spp. and a little *Calluna* and *Erica tetralix*. Dwarf pines appeared on rocky islands in this terrace. They could exist in conditions too dry for them but were absent where it was too wet. Such terraces are very common in the Highlands, particularly on the Torridonian formation.

One factor which would appear to be of great help to regeneration of native pine forest is a breaking of the ground surface which tears up the moss and lays bare the soil. The visitor to Loch Tulla can see for himself how freely the pines regenerate on the roadside where, unfortunately, they are continually eaten down by deer and rabbits. The proprietor has enclosed a small area with deer- and rabbit-proof fencing, of about half an acre's extent to one side of a mature stand of trees. The bottom pad of moss was slashed in places to allow the seed from the mother trees to reach the soil. This half-acre, fenced about 1938, is now dotted with seedlings of up to eight years old. The grazing-off of seedlings by sheep, deer and rabbits occurs in the Black Wood of Rannoch. Here, also, the breaking of the ground by the haulage of timber has allowed the germination of many pine seeds. But without fencing the seedlings are doomed.

Typical untouched and regenerating pine forest does not show a great variety of plant species. The complex is one of large, adult pines which are many-branched, flat- or round-topped; young pine trees which are still conical in habit and whose needles are longer than those of the adult trees ; juniper (*Juniperus*), some of which is tall and conical (10 feet) and some spreading and low (4 feet) ; there are occasional birches and rowans, and birches and alders become thicker along the sides of the burns. The ground vegetation is dense *Calluna* and *Erica cinerea* where the shade is not too great and juniper not dominant, but under the trees the heather thins out and its place is taken by *Vaccinium myrtillus* and *V. vitis-idaea.* Where the trees (even of the old pine) have been planted and stand in loose formation they lose their round-topped form, grow long trunks and provide a general shade which precludes regeneration. The undergrowth becomes almost a pure *Vaccinietum* (Pl. 18, p. 129), with some *Hylocomium* moss.

Other plants characteristic of the pine woods but thinly distributed therein are *Linnaea borealis* (in South-Eastern Highlands only) ; some of the wintergreens (*Pyrola* spp.) ; that arctic-boreal relic allied to the loosestrifes, *Trientalis europaea* ; coral root (*Corallorrhiza trifida*) in the Black Wood of Rannoch and on the east side of the Highlands ; and lesser twayblade (*Listera cordata*) generally. Some plants of the pine woods, such as lesser twayblade, are found much higher on the hills and may reach into the alpine zone. Those which are shade lovers, such as the common wintergreen and the wood anemone (*Anemone nemorosa*) occur in the treeless gullies seemingly far outside the habitats in which we are accustomed to see them. *Trientalis europaea* also occurs locally in the northern birch woods.

The birds of the pine forest may be bound to it completely, or they may be of those species which have greater latitude of habitat or powers of adaptation. The Scottish crested tit (Pl. XV, p. 108) is an example of a bird whose fortune rests on that of the pines. The headquarters of the sub-species which is found only in Scotland is the Spey Valley. Outliers are in the Aird district of Inverness, in Easter Ross and in Banffshire. It also occurs at Glengarry and Achnacarry in the Great Glen, and as noted earlier, I have seen it at Fort Augustus, but cannot say whether it was breeding. The bird is never so obvious as the other tits. Its food is mainly insects and larvae found on the pine itself, but pine seeds are also eaten and juniper berries.

The second bird bound to the pine forests is the Scottish crossbill. But it would seem more able to take advantage of plantations of pine than can the crested tit. Its range is considerable on the eastern side of the Highlands from Dunkeld to Sutherland, and were observers more numerous in the West I think a good many occurrences would be recorded. The crossbill is certainly resident in the pine woods on the side of Loch Maree and I saw several at Dundonnell. The seed of pine is the main food supply, in gaining which it uses its seemingly deformed bill. The seeds of other conifers are also acceptable, together with such wild berries as rowan. The high nesting habit of this bird tends to limit its occurrence to fairly mature timber, if it is outside the natural forest.

Thirdly, the capercaillie (Pl. XIc, p. 96), though not confined to pine forests, is at least dependent on coniferous forests of some kind. Its food largely consists of the shoots of spruce or larch and the buds of Scots pine, especially during the period October to March. The fruits of associated plants are eaten in summer, e.g. crowberry, bramble, raspberry, rowans and hips.

This very large bird (the cock is as long as an eagle and probably heavier) indulges in a complicated social display. The males meet in small numbers for the display of formalized aggressive postures. Coition does not take place for some time after these meetings, when the display before the female takes on different forms. The capercaillie is a much more rangey bird than the two mentioned above. Males are inclined to pack in winter and go to the moor above the coniferous forests.

The siskin (*Carduelis spinus*) (Pl. XIa, p. 96) is another inhabitant of coniferous woods of open character. It is a fairly common bird on the eastern side of the railway from Perth to Inverness and farther north as well, but there is no doubt that it is breeding in the West Highlands also where conditions allow, and certainly breeds in several places in North and Mid-Argyll. In the summer much of its life is spent in the high tops of conifers, spruce, pine and larch, where it builds its nest many feet from the ground and often at the far end of a branch ; and here it sings and makes its display flight in the space between the tree tops, so that apart from its clear call note it would be little noticed from the ground. But when the young are fledged, family parties come to the overgrown hawthorns and ashes in a hedgerow where such exists, and the male will sing and make display flights there, or the birds will hang on the tall meadow plants such as *Rumex* to feed on the seeds, when the yellow and green plumage of this beautiful little finch can be properly seen.

The British goldcrest (*Regulus regulus*) is another bird of the tree tops and principally of the coniferous woods and plantations. It joins with tits such as great tits (*Parus major*), coal tit (*Parus ater*), blue tit (*Parus

James Fisher

BIRCH SCRUB, persisting along the track of a burn. Coigach, Wester Ross
May 1944

John Markham

PTARMIGAN COUNTRY : Ben Macdhui (4,296 ft.), Cairngorms, Aberdeen–Banff border. June 1945

caeruleus), and long-tailed tit (*Aegithalos caudatus*), and with the tree-creeper (*Certhia familiaris*). All these birds are free of the necessity of pine woods but they are nevertheless commonly found in the old forest. It is interesting to speculate on what exactly confines the crested tits to the pines while the other tits mentioned are ubiquitous, and the willow-tit (*Parus atricapillus*), in the rare places it occurs, is confined to the birches and willow scrub.

The tree-pipit (*Anthus trivialis*), the robin (*Erithacus rubecula*), the wren (*Troglodytes troglodytes*), and the chaffinch (*Fringilla coelebs*) are also found in the forest but not of necessity. As everyone knows, they are just as common in other habitats. The ring-dove or wood-pigeon (*Columba palumbus*) is found in the old pine forest, but not as numerously as in the dense plantations of conifers, which provide it with perfect cover and nesting sites.

The commonest birds of prey of the old pine forest are the sparrow hawk (*Accipiter nisus*) by day, and the long-eared owl (*Asio otus*) by night. The hawk lives very largely on birds, and the owl probably takes more birds than do the other British species. The nightjar (*Caprimulgus europaeus*) is a bird of the edge of this habitat. It is not of the dense woods of pine, oak or birch, but of the fringes with the moor, and of open glades in lightly wooded country. Its association with the trees is not concerned with their species, but with their value as perching places at convenient intervals. Although the nightjar occurs throughout the mainland Highland region and in the Inner Hebrides, there are several patchy places where it is extremely scarce, e.g. West Inverness.

This habitat of old pine wood, in comparison with some deciduous woods on good soil, lacks shrubby secondary growth of that dense habit beloved by small birds such as warblers and finches. The wood-warbler, however, prefers a wood of high mature trees with light, low ground cover where it can build its domed nest hidden among leaf debris and moss, and where the male can sing his two contrasting songs or make song flights from branch to branch high above. Earlier than this summer visitor to the woods comes its relative the willow-warbler (*Phylloscopus trochilus*) which is found in vast numbers all over the Highlands wherever there are trees or bushes of any size. It arrives at the end of April or a day or two later in the far north, and suddenly one morning one wakes to the song of many of these birds. Another warbler, the whitethroat (*Sylvia communis*) occurs in the pine wood but is not common, and some of the smaller patches of old forest are quite without it.

The song thrush is commoner than the blackbird (*Turdus merula*) in the pine forest ; indeed, the blackbird is comparatively rare, while the ring ouzel, though occurring on the forest streams, is more numerous on the moorland waters above. The redstart (*Phoenicurus phoenicurus*) is plentiful in the pine forest. Like the siskin it tends to sing in the tops of the trees so that the beauty of its plumage is lost to the observer on the ground.

The grey wagtail is not usually considered to be connected with trees, but in the Highlands certainly occurs more often along burns where there are trees than on those completely barren and bare of tree growth, and in Rothiemurchus is the reverse of the ring ouzel, for it disappears from the upper courses of the streams above the line of the forest.

The jay (*Garrulus glandarius*), that noticeable predator of small birds in deciduous woodland, has now made its appearance in the Black Wood of Rannoch.

We cannot say there are any distinctive mammals of the pine forest, for even the pine marten has taken to the open hill and is now a very rare inhabitant of the old pine woods. Squirrels are certainly commoner in coniferous woods than in deciduous ones, and, in fact, these animals are entirely absent from the birch woods. The roe (*Capreolus capreolus*) is there, and the red deer, but they are in no way bound to these places. The long-tailed field mouse (*Apodemus sylvaticus*) is much commoner in the old open pine wood than in birch, but this fact is probably concerned with the drier ground of the pine woods.

The artificial close coniferous plantation is an anomalous thing which has a chequered natural history. At first, as we saw in the last chapter, there is the period of unchecked graminiferous growth in which the young trees are in danger of being choked. This is the period of intense vole colonization with its attendant predatory fauna of stoat and weasel, and kestrel, short-eared owl and buzzard. Then the ground cover becomes choked by the growing trees and for a few years there is a spell of summer colonization by willow-warblers. As the trees get still higher and the ground cover disappears entirely, the willow-warblers give it up and the upper surface of the trees becomes a field trodden only by the goldcrest and tits, and by the vast flocks of wood-pigeons which congregate in autumn. The chiffchaff does not occur as in England. The close coniferous plantation is sanctuary to the pigeons. The human being attempting ingress may find such a monstrous wood impenetrable, or, if it has been properly trimmed and thinned, he will find the floor a dead, quiet, dark place in which there is little joy but that of shelter and stillness.

If these plantations are devastated by fire in their fairly young state, the regeneration which takes place is of birch. Fire rarely burns the trees thoroughly. It runs through them as a scorching flame exploding the tops and more slowly removing any ground cover there may be. The bark splits and peels part way and the exposed living tissue of the cambium scorches and turns orange colour. The fire may have been in the vicinity of each tree no more than a few moments, but the trees are dead. Their black and orange skeletons then form excellent protective cover for the birch which begins to grow in the following year. The cost of a forest fire is not merely in the worth of the trees but in the years lost and the amount of work needed in clearing the ground afresh for replanting.

Before leaving the ecological complex of the old pine forest, it may be noted that it is a habitat in Scotland particularly favourable to several species of ants (Pl. 23b, p. 132). There are more species of these social Hymenoptera present in the Rothiemurchus-Abernethy-Glenmore pine forests than anywhere else in the Highlands. Dryness, depth of highly porous ground layer, the right kinds of detritus and ample supplies of resin enable the forests to hold the following ten species: *Formicoxenus nitidilus*, *Myrmica laevinodis*, *M. ruginodis*, *M. lobicornis*, *Leptothorax acervorum*, *Acanthomyops niger*, *Formica rufa*, *F. pratensis*, *F. exsecta*, *F. fusca*. (Donisthorpe, 1927.)

A large Hymenopteron commonly found in the old pine woods is the wood wasp (*Sirex gigas*), a most striking large yellow and black insect with a very long ovipositor. It is not generally attacked by birds, but its fellow Hymenopterons, the parasitic Ichneumonid *Rhyssa persuasoria* and the Cynipoid *Ibalia leucospoides*, are also present in the pine woods and are foremost as enemies.

One Lepidopteron may be mentioned because the Black Wood of Rannoch is its classic station and it is not found south of there—namely, the Rannoch looper (*Thamnonoma brunneata*). Its larva feeds on the blaeberry (*Vaccinium*) which grows so well at the base of the pines. The moth is small, bright chestnut in colour, and may be seen on the wing in June and July. The juniper which makes the underbrush in parts of the old pine woods is the food plant of the caterpillar of the juniper pug moth (*Eupithecia sobrinata*). This moth shows much variation and an extensive series of variants can be seen in Rothiemurchus.

The birch woods of the Highlands are far more extensive than the pine. Many of them show no regeneration (Pl. 23a, p. 132, Pl. 24, p. 133) and will thus disappear within a few years because birch is a comparatively short-lived tree. The absence of regeneration is practically always caused by over-grazing by sheep, red deer or rabbits. Fortunately, there are still many areas where regeneration is taking place, and in these young woods, such as in Sutherland under the high hill masses of Quinag and Suilven, there is an extraordinary feeling of joyousness among them in spring. The colour of the trees themselves is good ; and the young green of the leaves is pleasant in conjunction with the sound of swarms of willow-warblers. Redstarts are fairly common and long-tailed tits also nest in the birches, the lichen-laden boughs of which provide well-camouflaged nesting sites. It has not been noted elsewhere that some of these far northern long-tailed tits are white-headed like the sub-species *Aegithalos c. caudatus* which occurs in Northern Europe and Asia. These white-headed birds have been seen in the breeding season in West Sutherland and the Loch Broom area, and I have seen an intermediate form as far south as Sunart, North Argyll. Let us hope this statement will not set the sub-species maniacs a-shooting. Other birds of the birch and oak woods are wood-warbler, tree-creeper, great tit and coal tit, the robin and the chaffinch. There is a fair breeding population of woodcock throughout the Highland area, as well as a large winter influx. The bird is found in every type of wood, including young plantations. There is a tendency among the resident woodcock to move upwards to the open moors after the breeding season and before the onset of autumn.

I would not be surprised if, in the future, the redwing (*Turdus musicus*) were to stay and breed in these northern birch woods. This would be one more welcome addition to the Highland fauna which would heighten the observer's impression of being in similar country to the truly boreal region of Scandinavia.

The vegetation of the birch wood at maturity tends to be that of a moist habitat (Pl. 19, p. 140). Rowans occur throughout the birch stands and, as Crampton pointed out in 1911, rowans will arise two miles from the parent tree into the moor, while birches are rarely found more than a hundred yards away from the general stock. The reason is that the rowan seed, for the most part, passes through birds before germination and thus has wide possibilities of diffusion. The birch must depend on wind. Hazel is not nearly so common in the West, except on the tertiary basalt, as in the central zone where this species may form entire thickets. The purple-brown of leafless birches on a hillside merges into the grey-green tops of alders in the glen where they become dominant.

Birch woods in the West Highlands are distinctly different in their undergrowth from those of the Spey Valley where drier conditions and better drainage exist. The birches themselves are different for the most part, *Betula pubescens* being the common species in the West and North and *B. pendula* in the Central and Eastern Highlands. The field layer under birches in the West consists of bent grasses (*Agrostis* spp.), sweet vernal rarely, and rough meadow grass (*Poa trivialis*) and other species occasionally. But the main floor tends to be largely of mosses. Spleenwort is common and bracken is also fairly common. Wood sorrel is always present ; primroses and violets are characteristic and patches of large woodrush frequent. None of the heathers grows in a close birch wood. I have seen an extremely close stand of 20-foot-high birch under which grass had entirely disappeared and the ground was given up to mosses though the wood was on a well-drained shelf. The birch woods of the Spey are sometimes so dry as to carry a field layer of *Vaccinium* with juniper at shrub level. Birch woods in sheltered glens carry a richer flora approaching that of some of the better oak woods.

The Highland oak woods occur for the most part in the glens running into, or not far from, the Great Glen, e.g. Glen Garry where the woods are particularly fine and should be preserved. The North of Scotland Hydro-Electric Board has a scheme for damming the waters of the Garry which would submerge these woods and a great deal of lovely scenery alongside Loch Garry. The electric works will certainly come to the Highlands and whether we like them or not the fact must be accepted. Instead of attacking on principle every hydro-electric scheme as it comes along, it would be better to reserve our fire and concentrate it on opposition to selected schemes where the damming would remove a priceless possession of natural history and an asset to tourism which may be worth more, monetarily, than the hydro-electric power. There are still some good oak woods in the Southern Highlands as, for example, in the Pass of Killiecrankie, between Loch Tay and Dunkeld and in Strath Tummel up to Loch Rannoch.

The oak woods run on through Loch Eil to Arisaig and again along the north shore of Loch Sunart as far as Glenborrodale. The colder south shore is covered with birches. More oaks are to be found in strength on the north shore of Loch Leven. There is a bit of oak wood left on the north shore of Loch Maree, but north of this there are no stands of oak on the west side of the country. Nowhere in the west do we find the oak going far up the hill, hardly ever beyond 500 feet and usually not so high as that, but in the South-Eastern Highlands they reach 700 feet, and a few at Kenmore reach 1,000 feet. The oak wood fades off into birch and rowan and if there is any clearance of the oak it is birch which takes its place, or, in the Southern Highlands, Scots pine. I am not quite clear in my own mind whether, even with cessation of grazing pressure, there would be ample regeneration of oak. Oak wood is a climax. The tree needs good feeding and is not remarkable as a builder of humus. It is probable that the maintenance of pure oak stands in the West Highlands will need management. From the fact of the sparseness of the oak in the Northern Highlands and the marked preference of this species for the north (and therefore sunward) shores of lochs and sides of glens, it is obvious that its habitat is a limited one in the Highlands. As Tansley says (*op. cit.*) : " In ascending the hills, this valley oakwood evidently once passed over everywhere to pine and birch wood which was thus zoned above the oakwood both latitudinally and altitudinally."

Probably because the oak occupies a favoured situation, its associated flora is often of richer type, and includes the ash (*Fraxinus excelsior*) which appears to be a truly wild tree in the Highland glens of the better sort, especially above granite. The holly (*Ilex aquifolium*) is also relatively common at all levels of the oak wood, and gean (*Prunus avium*) occurs locally. The species of oak in the Highlands include both *Quercus petraea* (=*sessiliflora*) and *Q. robur* and apparent hybrids between the two. An oak wood in the Highlands is very different in associated flora and in appearance from those of Southern Central England. The bark of Highland oaks is heavily bemossed, sometimes so much that the trunks are entirely green and the branches festooned with lichens and spleenwort. Ivy is relatively uncommon. The ground cover tends to moss and open bracken, with some brown bent grass (*Agrostis canina*) and *Holcus* spp. Bluebells (*Scylla nutans*) grow under the oaks where the ubiquitous sheep do not graze them out. This plant must have been far commoner before the rise of sheep farming. As it is, large sheets of bluebells are almost confined to policy woods. Bramble (*Rubus* spp.) is common in the Highlands but not as an undercover of oak woods as may be seen in the south. The yellow pimpernel or wood lysimachia (*L. nemorum*) and cow wheat (*Melampyrum sylvaticum* and *M. pratense*) grow among the moss. Wood anemone (*Anemone nemorosa*) is common and yet curiously local.

The lepidopterous fauna of the oak wood is generally richer than that of the birch, and in North Argyll and West Inverness-shire includes the rare shade-loving butterfly, the speckled wood (*Pararge aegeria*). This insect apparently survived the last glaciation and has, since Pleistocene times, preserved a separate existence from the populations farther south. This is but one more example of the fact which is becoming clear, that a study of Highland natural history, particularly of plants and some insects, can further world knowledge of evolution and greater detail of our island's history.

The birds of oak and birch woods are not very different as a group. They are possibly more numerous in oak, but a comparative census of Highland oak and birch woods has never yet been made, so the above suggestion must be taken as being tentative. The great spotted woodpecker, as already noted, has come back into the Highlands after virtual extinction and is rapidly colonizing. It is generally reckoned to prefer coniferous woods, but on the west side of the country north of the Great Glen I should say it preferred these valley oak-and-birch woods. Decaying birch stumps are the chosen nesting sites.

The uses to which human beings put the oak woods in past days were for fencing-stakes, charcoal, domestic fuel and boatbuilding. I have seen a native oak at Dundonnell which was of no great size, but, having had room, had grown short-trunked with a large number of boughs going off almost at right angles. I was told that £90 was offered for this single tree by the Gairloch boatbuilders towards the end of the 19th century. Such a tree provided many " knees " of great strength.

If there is one mammal above another which might be associated with the Highland oak woods it would be the badger (*Meles meles*) (Pl. XVI, p. 109). Its occurrence is much commoner than is generally thought. The slopes of the Great Glen hold many badgers and they are coincident with the oak along to Arisaig and on Loch Sunart. A few badgers were taken to the north of Sutherland some years ago and they have done well among the regenerating birch woods. The squirrel does not appear to be a permanent inhabitant of the oak wood. It prefers to have conifers in its habitat.

The oak woods are a favourite habitat of Daubenton's bat (*Myotis daubentoni*) when these are in close proximity to water. The pipistrelle (*Pipistrellus pipistrellus*) is common in these oak woods and throughout the Highlands even where there are no woods at all, as far afield as the Outer Hebrides. Natterer's bat (*Myotis nattereri*) is a local species found in heavily timbered land in the vicinity of water. It occurs down the west shore of Loch Fyne. The whiskered bat (*Myotis mystacinus*) has been found in the open birch wood near Kinlochrannoch. The long-eared bat (*Plecotus auritus*) is common in many parts of the Highlands, more particularly in the wooded areas but in treeless country as well. Millais (1904) records it at Balranald in North Uist flying round farm buildings and hawking round some dwarf alders.

The insect fauna of these woods is abundant, so much so that one wonders why the small-bird population is not more varied than it is, or even more abundant. Probably the answer to this question is partly to be found in the preferences of birds for particular niches in the habitat, and partly from the fact that these woods are all too often islands in a sea of dead moor. There is a numerous population of moths of the Geometrid group. The caterpillars of these moths feed on sallow, birch and alder and oak, also on bedstraw and bent grasses. A few of these moths may be mentioned : the clouded border (*Lomaspilis marginata*), the common white wave (*Cabera pusaria*), the Gallium carpet (*Xanthorhoë galiata*), the common carpet (*X. sociata*), the yellow shell (*Euphyia bilineata*), the green carpet (*Amoebe viridaria*) and the early thorn (*Selenia bilunaria*). The beating of the leaves of these trees in summer disturbs a large variety of diptera and of lacewings as well as froghoppers and Pentatomid bugs. The lacewings are predatory on the aphids which swarm on the birch and sallow leaves. It may be mentioned that the oak woods of the Highlands do not feed the oak leaf-roller (*Tortrix viridiana*) which is so largely eaten in the larval stage by woodland birds in southern oak woods.

In concluding this section on the woodlands of the Highlands, I am drawn for a moment to discuss the question of cover. By this term or its more gamey version of covert, we usually mean vegetative shelter. What are the functions of cover ? It protects the organism from an inclement climate, whether it be woods to a roe deer or the snow above a lemming on the tundra. Cover also protects an animal from

John Markham

ALPINE MEADOW on 4,000-ft. plateau, Cairngorms, Inverness-shire
June 1945

John Markham

WILD CAT COUNTRY: Loch an Eilean, Rothiemurchus, Inverness-shire
June 1945

F. Fraser Darling

CARPET OF MOSS on 4,000-ft. plateau, Cairngorms, Inverness-shire
July 1944

John Markham

SPHAGNUM Moss and rushes : peat in the making
Cairngorm region, Inverness-shire. September 1944

its predators, whether it be a rabbit going into the bushes from a fox or a black guillemot dropping like a stone into the sea when the peregrine falcon stoops at it. But it must not be forgotten that cover is not merely protection and seclusion for the preyed-upon, but hiding for the predator as well. Cover also gives animals a chance to live a private life and do some idling. Cover may also be the means of creating micro-climatic needs in a habitat in such matters as shade, temperature and humidity. All these factors are of great importance in the Highlands and Islands. The fox uses cover quite definitely when stalking a deer calf; the wild cat lies on a low branch of a tree ready to drop on an unsuspecting bird or rabbit and creeps through the heather when stalking grouse. Plate 21b (p. 144) shows typical country in the Spey Valley with wild-cat cover.

The concept of cover has been discussed by Elton (1939) in an interesting and thought-provoking paper. As he says, cover may provide food, e.g. tree browsing by red and roe deer. If cover-eating animals exceed a certain density they denude the cover and deprive themselves of the protection from weather and predators which it also gave. Examples are found in a vole plague when the animals eat the ground bare instead of merely making channels through the grass, and when red deer prevent the regeneration of the birch woods. If there is one reason above another for keeping deer down to the natural density of one to 40 acres, I repeat that it is this urgent one of regeneration of natural woodland.

Elton impresses the need for the naturalist to enlarge his notion of cover beyond that of vegetative cover. Darkness and mist are cover—even noise, as of a torrent, can be cover unless an organism has a highly selective ear. I have known myself, during the years in the deer forest, move away from a waterfall before taking my midday meal because the noise destroyed part of my awareness of what was going on. My eyes could not do it all. Elton suggests that cover should be studied not alone, but as one factor in human warfare in relation to wild life. He says, "We are going through a period in which there is some doubt whether even the enormous power resources at our disposal can produce enough cover to shelter the human race from itself." But to come back to woods, it may be mentioned that before the second German war the Russians cleared a strip many miles wide of all forest growth along their western frontier.

The biological consequences were profound.

THE SUMMITS OF THE HILLS

IT HAS BEEN the theme of the last few chapters that the wild country of the Highlands is not untouched, virgin or unalterable country. Much the larger part of it shows the influence of man's hand and of the mouths of his domestic animals. Even the deer forest, we saw, was affected in the character of its vegetational cover through the 19th-century practice of feeding deer in winter, and thus throwing a greater grazing strain on the low ground by increased stocking, which prevented sufficient regeneration of tree growth to replace losses.

The summits of the hills stand clear of the influence of man, at least if we confine our notion of hill-top conditions to that ground which lies above 3,000 feet. In the first place, the herbage of this zone is scanty and it grows extremely low to the ground without great density. Such country cannot be burnt. Secondly, it lies under snow and frost, or constant intermittency of these conditions, for several months of the year ; and thirdly, man's domestic animals do not graze land over 3,000 feet except occasionally, though on the high plateaux of the Cairngorms herds of deer may graze for several weeks at 3,500 feet and above.

The country of the summits is, in the Highlands, an immense archipelago of biological islands holding relic communities of a past age—that of the last glacial epoch. When the topographical zones of the Highlands were being described in Chapters 2 and 3, the northern area was said to have certain sub-arctic affinities in its vegetational complex. Some botanists might qualify this description and say boreal as a more correct adjective. But when we come to the summits, arctic affinities are obvious and beyond quibble. Even that common arctic phenomenon of frost action is found on the summits of several Highland hills, of polygons of assorted sizes of rock granules and coarse sand.

The alpine flora as it appears on any one hill top strikes the observer by its great stability and by its sharp exclusions. For example, no Gymnosperm or dicotyledonous tree goes beyond the 3,000-foot contour in Britain. The nearest approach is by the dwarf juniper

(*Juniperus communis* var. *sibirica*=*J. nana*) which spreads over exposed rocks at high altitudes.

What are the conditions obtaining on the summits which render them a distinct habitat? The tops are a country of extremes and of paradox. First in the matter of temperature: for a large part of the year the atmospheric and soil temperatures are low, frequently below zero Fahrenheit. The soil temperature is particularly low when there is a frost without snow—a common occurrence, especially on the western hills. The Ben Nevis Observatory figures are the only ones we have, unfortunately. Summer temperatures are also low as compared with those at sea level, but occasionally the temperature of the barely-covered granular soil may be much higher than most places at sea level. Only in certain spots such as sandy beaches and cliff edges, upon which we shall have occasion to remark again, are similar conditions found of periodic unduly high soil temperatures. There are also sharp alternations between day and night temperature until July, when day and night temperatures on the tops come much closer to each other, and there may then be adiabatic inversion—that is, the temperatures at night on the higher levels may be higher than they are down below. Day temperatures on the tops are frequently higher than in the glens and on the coast. I have lain on the summit of An Teallach, 3,483 feet, in brilliant sun and still air, watching the water vapour rising from a patch of *Rhacomitrium* moss, and then, looking through the telescope out to sea ten or twelve miles off, have seen the waves, big and white-capped under the force of a strong south-easterly wind. These differential and sometimes inverted temperature conditions and the related condition of relative humidity account for some of the most beautiful landscape effects; for example, in late summer, when an observer who spends the night on a high summit may wake to see the sunlit tops brilliantly clear as blue islands in a level sea of white mist. Soil temperatures of the summits also vary widely according to the slope. A northern gully will be cold even when the southern face is extremely hot, as much from the rapid evaporation of the moisture from such a place into the surrounding dry air as from the difference between shade and sun temperature. There are climates within climates.

Second, there is the matter of moisture. The summits endure a higher precipitation in Scotland than any other part of the countryside. They are, indeed, the focal points for that part of the rainfall caused by the moisture-laden air being cooled by contact with the hills. The plants and animals of the summits exist for days and weeks at a time in a super-saturated atmosphere. But at other times they suffer drought conditions from the action of several factors. A period of frost imposes a physiological drought. High temperature, which may overheat the soil even for these deep-rooting plants of the tops, may impose a physiological drought, and may cause excessive transpiration, despite the adaptations of the leaves of alpine plants to prevent this. Straight drought conditions of lack of precipitation are not at all uncommon in the Highlands, especially in the second quarter of the year. There is also the factor of slope which helps to drain water away rapidly, and lastly the nature of the soil. The peat, except in rare instances, has been left behind a thousand feet or more below and the soil of the tops is little more than a conglomeration of fairly large granular particles of rock extremely deficient in humus. This means that such soil has very little sponge-like quality. Despite the high precipitation, therefore, the plants of the tops are not able to use it fully, but are limited in expression and development by the frequent periods of actual and physiological droughts.

Third, the plant communities of the tops have a severely curtailed period of exposure to light and free air. On the Cairngorms and on Ben Nevis a few places may have no more than a month of exposure, and large tracts fail to get six months of light in the year. Nevertheless, the extensive snowfields do provide much shelter and are in themselves a factor ameliorating drought, for their gradual melting in a hot dry time irrigates a large surrounding area.

Fourth, we should not forget the frequent incidence of high wind above the 3,000-foot contour. The 13-year average of 261 gales per annum of more than 50 m.p.h. on Ben Nevis has already been quoted.

Tansley (1939) warns the observer of arctic-alpine vegetation against laying too much stress on zones of altitude expressed numerically. He points to the fact that on the Atlantic side of the country arctic-alpine species are found at a much lower level. This brings us to the point that certain species of plants appearing on the higher plateaux and slopes have a habit of cropping up again at sea level or on cliff faces. Sea pink (*Armeria maritima*) and roseroot (*Sedum roseum*) may be taken as examples. The intermediate zone does not carry these plants. Both of them are drought resisters in a high degree and both need good drainage from their root systems. Drought at the sea's

James Fisher

OLD BIRCH SCRUB, with no regeneration ; doomed to disappear unless protected from grazing. Coigach, Wester Ross. May 1945

John Markham

NEST OF WOOD ANT in Caledonian Forest, Inverness-shire September 1944

John Markham

Isolated Birches. Spey Valley, Inverness-shire
June 1945

edge is brought about for these plants in but a minor way by straight absence of precipitation : the main cause is a physiological drought brought about by a high salinity. These plants may be drenched by the very salt Atlantic water for days on end and *Armeria* growing in a tidal gravel has a diurnal immersion in salt water. The dwarf juniper, essentially a light-loving plant, is another member of the 250-foot stratum nearest the sea on the more northern Inner Hebrides, and on the Summer Isles.

The arctic-alpine flora of the Highland summits is much affected by the geological formations which form them. The Torridonian and quartzite tops of the North-West have a poor flora compared with Ben Lawers, 3,984 feet, which latter hill is composed of a metamorphic schist rich in basic elements. The relatively flat granite tops of the Cairngorms also have some beautiful stretches of alpine grassland which are not unlike downland when one is up there and forgetting the mighty glens below.

The stable quality of the vegetational complexes of summits has been noted. This is because they are climaxes which are not subject to disturbance of the conditions which have pertained for some thousands of years. The opinion of botanists who have studied the flora of Scottish summits, however, is that the purely arctic species are dying out slowly as the last glacial period recedes in time and in its effects. It may be further remarked (though the fact must be obvious) that the vegetational complex is much more distinct and characteristic than that of the animals. Indeed, few animals can be said to be confined to the high tops, and among the higher forms the tops may only be visited as an incidental or seasonal event in their lives, and not because of any special predilection for such altitudes ; among these may be mentioned such mammals as the red deer, the fox, the wild cat, the weasel, the stoat and the field vole. Even the pygmy shrew (*Sorex minutus*) was observed at the top of Ben Nevis in the Observatory days, and many of us who have had much to do with the high grounds in winter can admit our surprise from time to time at finding this tiny creature running about on the top of the snow. The mountain hare occurs much lower than 3,000 feet, of course, but in the West Highlands where it is now a scarce animal (since 1913) it is almost confined to the area above 2,500 feet, living on stony ground that one would scarcely imagine held enough food. In such places the mountain hare has been observed to burrow on occasion.

The birds of the high tops (Pl. 20, p. 144) do emphasize the quality of the summits as relict areas. The snow bunting (*Plectrophenax nivalis*), for instance, breeds in Scotland only among the tumbled boulders and screes at or above the 3,000-foot contour, whereas in Greenland it is a common breeder near sea level. The ptarmigan (*Lagopus mutus*) (Pl. XVIIb, p. 148) is a bird of the tops also in Scotland, but inhabits much lower levels in more northerly regions. The dotterel (*Eudromias morinellus*) (Pl. XVIIa, p. 148) breeds in the Highlands above the 3,000-foot level but may be found at an altitude of 200–300 feet on the Arctic tundra. The food of these birds of the tops consists of coleopterous and dipterous insects and spiders. The ptarmigan is almost wholly a vegetable feeder on the shoots of blaeberry, heather, willow and crowberry. All of them take the crowberry fruit in season, even as nearer the sea on the little islands it is taken by birds as diverse as grey lag geese, gulls and meadow pipits.

The golden eagle (Pl. XIIIa, p. 100) is very often seen about the summits, but it cannot be said to be characteristic of them. Its breeding site is usually below 2,000 feet. This phenomenon of arctic shore level birds being alpine nesters in Britain is part of a great stratification of species in relation to altitude and latitude. The lesser redpoll (*Carduelis flammea cabaret*), for example, nests in low country in Britain, but as an alpine species in southern Europe.

Invertebrates show much less specialization : for example, among the 52 recorded species collected by W. S. Bruce (1896), on the summit of Ben Nevis in the Observatory days, it was said that thirty could have been found in an English parish, and it was doubtful if any of them could be looked upon as true mountain species. Bruce also collected many Hymenoptera, including Ichneumons and Braconids, and some Hemiptera, from the summit of Ben Nevis. The ptarmigan, though mainly a vegetable feeder, consumes a fair quantity of Tipulid Diptera which are of normal occurrence at 3,000 feet. The deer, which go high to escape from the Tabanid Diptera in June, certainly get out of the main density of these insects, but I have found *Tabanus* on the summits and especially *Chrysops* ; *Haematopota* occurs only very rarely as high as 3,000 feet. The nostril fly (*Cephenomyia auribarbis*), which affects deer, is mostly to be found at the higher levels, and Grimshaw (1895) says that the males are usually to be found at the summits of high hills.

There are a few species of Lepidoptera which seem disposed to inhabit the tops. The moths *Crambus ericellus* and *C. furcatellus* are mountain species though they are also found on moors at mid-height. They are daylight fliers. The larvae feed on mosses, particularly under club moss (*Lycopodium* spp.). The Eastern Cairngorm tops and Lochnagar are the only British station of the mountain burnet moth (*Zygaena exulans*). The caterpillar feeds on such characteristic mountain plants as moss campion, cyphel and *Loiseleuria*. This moth, like so many others of the open hill, flies in sunshine, and may be found in July. The netted mountain moth (*Fidonia carbonaria*) has a much wider distribution, being found on many summits north of Perthshire. All the same it is local in its appearances, a characteristic of many Lepidoptera which it is not always easy to explain. The caterpillar of the netted mountain may be found on the highest-growing dwarfed birches, on red blaeberry and on bearberry. An interesting point is that this sunshine-flying moth appears in April and May, a time of year when the upper thousand feet of the hills are often still under snow. The small mountain ringlet butterfly mentioned in Chapter 5 is found on the upper reaches of some Central and West Highland hills, south of the Great Glen.

Spiders apparently show a slightly greater tendency to specialization. Such species as the following occur at over 3,000 feet in the Cairngorms and other hills in the Central Highlands : *Lycosa amentata*, *Oligolophus morio* var. *alpinus*, *Trochosa biunguiculata*, *T. andrenivora*, and *Pedanstettius lividus*.

An interesting and important paper on spiders collected from West Coast islands and hill summits by Bristowe (1927) points to the great advantage in altitudinal range possessed by those spiders that live under stones and which walk abroad only when conditions are optimal. Such spiders are not subjected to anything like as wide a *range* of temperature as are web-making species. Bristowe is thus led to emphasize the factor of exposure as of equal importance with actual lowness of temperature in limiting the range of spiders into arctic-alpine conditions. He remarks that the numbers and species of spiders increase rapidly on the lee side of mountains just below the summits ; thus two extremes of altitude for spiders exist in any given locality :

"1. The extreme altitude at which a species will occur at the summit (limiting factor ' exposure ').

"2. Extreme altitude below a summit (always greater than the last owing to the limiting factor here being ' temperature ')."

This chapter cannot become a catalogue of species found at high altitudes in the Highlands, but the relict quality of the summits may be emphasized once more by the discovery by Murray (1906) of specimens of both arctic and antarctic species of those primitive and microscopic arthropods, the Tardigrada or water bears, in moss on the summit cairn of Ben Lawers.

The plant communities of the summits are a fascinating study in which there still remains much to be done. Tansley (1939) implies that the work of W. G. Smith in his chapter in *Types of British Vegetation* (1911) must still be considered standard for this habitat. The digression may be forgiven to mention that W. G. Smith was the brother of Robert Smith who, dying in 1900 at the age of 26, was a botanist Scotland could ill afford to lose. His industry was immense and he was one of the first to develop the ecological aspect in regional botany. His second and last paper on the *Botanical Survey of Scotland*, that dealing with North Perthshire, was published a few weeks before his death, and reads now, nearly half a century later, as if it were contemporary with us. The section on the alpine region should not be neglected by the student to-day.

Many of the arctic-alpine species which occur above 3,000 feet in the Highlands are found practically at sea level in the Arctic, but not until about 8,000 feet in the Swiss Alps. Such is the effect of latitude, but as has been mentioned before, some species reach down the hillsides on the Atlantic side of the country and even appear at sea level. Such is the effect of climate and slope.

All the plants of the tops are low in growth form. Apart from the shriving influence of wind, low growth is probably an adaptation ensuring the plant—or its perennating buds—remaining below the snow during the very cold weather. Some follow a cushion-like habit, like the sea pink (*Armeria maritima*) and the moss campion (*Silene acaulis*) (Pl. XVIII, p. 149). The rosette form, as in some saxifrages, is also common.

Vivipary, i.e. the floral axis proliferating vegetatively on the parent plant instead of forming seed, is common among the alpine grasses, such as sheep's fescue (*Festuca ovina*) and alpine meadow grass (*Poa alpina*). It is one more functional adaptation toan exacting climate.

Mosses (Musci) and liverworts (Hepaticae), collectively known as Bryophytes, and the lichens which are composite plants of fungi and algae, are extremely common on the summits, and associations of these

Eric Hosking

DOTTEREL, a plover of the highest moors
Cairngorms, Inverness-shire. June 1940

John Markham

PTARMIGAN (hen), the game bird of the high tops
Cairngorms, Inverness-shire. June 1940

PLATE XVIII

John Markham

Moss Campion, *Silene acaulis*, on Ben Macdhui, Cairngorms, Aberdeen-Banff border. June 1945

form almost the entire flora of some areas. There are over two hundred species of mosses on Ben Lawers alone, and together with the larger lichens such as *Cladonia* and *Cetraria*, the Cryptogamic flora may be sufficient to tempt the deer up to graze it. Cushion moss (*Grimmia*) is greedily eaten by deer, and many a stag, after being shot on the high ground, has been found to have little but club mosses of various kinds (*Lycopodium alpinum*, etc.) in his rumen. One of the commonest mosses of the high tops is woolly fringe moss (*Rhacomitrium lanuginosum*). It is a great colonizer, spreading itself over boulder slopes which would appear to offer no nutriment whatever. Eventually this moss may form enough of a bed of organic matter—in fact, a peat of sorts—to allow the colonization of other species. Or the *Rhacomitrium* may grow just too well so that the wind can get underneath it, and then away it goes and has to start all over again. Even on the seemingly barren summit of Suilven there is a large alp of *Rhacomitrium* heath with alpine grasses growing within it. The luxuriance of the growth of mosses on the high grounds may be gathered in some small measure from the coloured plate No. 22a (p. 145), which represents less than a square yard of a carpet of moss found on the plateau between Ben Macdhui and Carn Lochan, at 4,000 feet in the Cairngorms. The liverworts grow either by themselves in damp places or among mosses, which latter give them both shelter and more constant moisture. These alpine hepatics often adopt a tufted form, e.g. *Marsupella confirta* which may be found at 4,000 feet. Others of common occurrence at 3,000 feet and above are *Frullania tamarisci*, *Lejeunia serpylliflora*, *Diplophyllum albicans*, *Pressia commutata*, *Bazzania tricrenata* and *Jungermania cordifolia*, which last may be found in the little wells of water which surprisingly occur at high altitudes and produce a tiny oasis of plants typical of a lower altitude. A very full list of mosses, liverworts and lichens of the arctic-alpine zone appears on p. 790 of Tansley's big book.

Those places which are subject to a long period of snow cover are often characterized by a deposit of fine silty soil in which a liverwort, *Anthelia juratzkana*, is the common pioneer. The moss *Polytrichum sexangulare* follows on the liverwort and eventually the minute willow *Salix herbacea* may get a hold. Seton Gordon (1944) mentions patches of moss in the Cairngorms which probably see the light for no more than one season in ten and yet survive. He found that *Saxifraga stellaris* could endure longer eclipse by the snow than any of the grasses common to the tops.

The flowers of the summits are probably the best-known feature of this habitat. They are often of delicate colouring and beauty and remote enough from everyday life to make them prized. Some high hills such as Ben Lawers have certainly suffered depredations on their flora so that some species are getting very scarce. Alpine pearlwort (*Sagina nivalis*), an arctic plant found in the courses of tiny streams near the summits, is but one example. Another alpine, *Menziesia caerulea*, occurs on one summit only and is in danger.

Some of the fairly common and most beautiful flowers of the tops are the saxifrages : *Saxifraga oppositifolia*, *S. cernua*, *S. stellaris*, *S. nivalis* and *S. hypnoides*. Other flowers of great beauty are mountain avens (*Dryas octopetala*), roseroot (*Sedum roseum*) which also occurs at sea level, moss campion (*Silene acaulis*) (Pl. XVIII, p. 149), alpine lady's mantle (*Alchemilla alpina*), mountain azalea (*Loiseleuria procumbens*) and alpine fleabane (*Erigeron alpinus*), which last is not found on the western summits of the Highlands at all. Several hawkweeds (*Hieracium* spp.) occur on the high tops. *H. alpinum* var. *nigrescens* is common in the Cairngorms, *H. angustatum* on Ben Lawers and *H. callistophyllum* on the Argyll summits. The Breadalbane range of hills between Cruachan and Ben Lawers is so much richer geologically than many Highland summits that, as might be expected and has been mentioned earlier, their flora is richer, especially along the strata of sericite schists (Macnair, 1898), but in addition it is found that plants will be found at higher stations on these hills than on others of poorer geological formation. R. Smith, for example, found common wintergreen (*Pyrola minor*) at 3,700 feet, and sheep sorrel (*Rumex acetosella*) at 3,300 feet in Breadalbane.

Lastly, a few words must be said on the alpine meadow or alp (Pl. 21a, p. 144). Such stretches of continuous green herbage play their part in maintaining the deer from the end of June until almost the end of the year, so long as the weather remains good. Many of the flowers mentioned above are found in these alps, but their most prominent constituents are the arctic-alpine grasses, sheep's fescue, alpine meadow grass and mat grass ; alpine foxtail (*Alopecurus alpinus*) and alpine cat's-tail (*Phleum alpinum*) are found on the richer summits. Alpine rushes such as *Luzula spicata*, *Juncus castaneus*, *J. triglumis* and *J. trifidus* also occur.

The common alpine sedges are *Carex capillaris* and *C. rigida*. Some lowland species of grasses and sedge are often present in an alp, particularly sweet vernal, wavy hair grass, purple molinia and tufted sedge (*C. goodenovii*). Some of these plants are intrusions into the alp, being characteristic of the peaty ground much lower down. Among the main complex of grasses of the alp are found several berry-bearing plants. The common bearberry (*Arctostaphylos uva-ursi*) goes very high and is found on dry places. Its leaves are obovate and a glossy dark green, and the berries are bright red and smooth. The black bearberry (*A. alpina*) is very much an arctic plant and is found in the Highlands only on the eastern and far northern tops. The bog blaeberry or whortleberry (*Vaccinium uliginosum*) is commonly found in the high meadows but does not entirely replace its congener the common blaeberry (*V. myrtillus*), though the latter may assume a dwarf form when occurring at 3,000 feet. The red whortleberry or cowberry (*V. vitis-idaea*) is also present. That mountain member of the bramble family the cloudberry (*Rubus chamaemorus*) is unlike the other mountain berry-bearing plants in having rather large orbicular or reniform leaves. The drupes are large and red. And finally there is the crowberry (*Empetrum nigrum*) which is common in alpine grassland. Its leaves are tiny and heather-like in texture and the fruits black, globular and shiny. This is another plant found on many a low island of the Minch as well as on the high tops, but often completely absent from the intermediate zone. It is a most fragrant plant underfoot when the warm sun is shining, and the fruit becomes a staple of diet for a large number of varied species of birds. It is refreshing to ourselves if we crush a handful of the berries in the mouth, swallow the juice and spit out the numerous small flinty pips.

To recapitulate: the high grassland is an extremely stable complex, growing on soil consisting of large particles of the mother rock, well drained but often watered from springs rich in basic salts, free from peat, and forming very little humus in the course of growth. The alp or patch of mountain grassland is an old climax and worthy of study as something which remains unaffected by the hand of man. By escaping the blanket of peat it is floristically much richer than the middle levels of the hills. The grazing provided by the summits is much preferred by the deer to that of the peaty levels. When plants grow with an adequate balance of basic compounds, their protein metabolism is on a higher plane than when they grow on acid land. Thus the alpine herbage is richer in protein and has the effect of flushing the milk-flow of the hinds when they go up to it with their calves during the last fortnight in June.

A word may be said about the delight of the high tops, and particularly of the arctic-alpine grasslands, for the human observer. The deep and precipitous corries and the spiry summits of some geological formations may cause awe, and may even depress some people by the immensity of spoil and waste devoid of a regular cover of vegetation. But the high grasslands on a summer day have an idyllic quality. They are remote and quiet. They are green and kind to the eye. They are ease to the feet. Far below are all that foot-slogging and the exhausting peat hags. The acid, locked-up humus of the peat grows poor stuff compared with this washed, granulated rock of the higher slopes. The flowers made a poor showing for two thousand feet or more, but here they appear again in greater variety and a new beauty. The very pebbles among which they grow have a sparkle and show of colour. To climb to one of these alps of grass and descend again in a few hours is not enough. Take a little tent and remain in the quietness for one night at least. Carry enough food for a few days so that it does not matter if the mist should keep you high for a day or two. It is a magnificent experience to rise in the morning in such a place and feel fresh, knowing that your enjoyment of the peat-free plateaux is not to be spoiled by a gruelling climb and the necessity of going down the same day. The only sounds breaking the silence, if you get the best of the early July weather, will be the grackle of the ptarmigan, the flute-like pipe of the ring ouzel, perhaps the plaint of a golden plover or a dotterel and the bark of the golden eagle. These are good sounds and do not disturb what is for the moment a place of peace. See how the deer, now bright-red-coated, lie at ease in the alpine grassland. Listen, if you have stalked near enough, to the sweet talkings of the calves who are like happy children. Here is new herbage over which no other muzzles have grazed ; the very soil has been washed by fifty inches of rain since the deer were here before, in November. On this short nutritious grass the deer are growing their clean bone and the good condition which will help them to face the winter. Of your charity disturb them not in their Arcadia.

THE SHORE, THE SEA LOCH AND THE SHALLOW SEAS

The Shore Line and the Intertidal Zone

NOT ALL Highland coasts are wild and forbidding. There is an extreme contrast, however, between the western points such as Ardnamurchan, Greenstone, Rhu' Mor Coigach, Stoer, Cape Wrath, the Butt of Lewis and Barra Head, and the sheltered sea inlets of Loch Broom, Loch Carron, Loch Sunart and Loch Fyne. The one means ocean, the others little more than salt water without storm. The winds met on the outer coasts render the habitat comparable in many ways with the summits of the hills. The outer coasts are washed with driven spray and rain so that what little grass they grow is sweet and clean, and much liked by the sheep and cattle which graze there. The main difference between the summits and the outer coasts is in winter temperature and the effects of snow-lie. Apart from that the rigour is similar. Many plants of the shore, the cliff face and the top of the cliff have to endure drought conditions caused by lack of humus acting as a sponge for water, from extreme paucity of soil for their roots and from the physiological drought caused by salt water. It is common, therefore, to find plants with tightly rolled leaves such as viviparous sheep's fescue which we found on the summits ; some plants have deeply ribbed leaves, very stiff, such as marram grass (*Ammophila arenaria*) ; some have polished glossy leaves, like scurvy grass (*Cochlearia officinalis*) ; there are little linear crowded leaves like those of sea pink, and fleshy ones like roseroot and stonecrop (*Sedum anglicum*) which absorb moisture and store it. All these plants are more or less drought resistant, achieving their end by one means or another. Then there are others such as orache (*Atriplex patula*) and bladder campion (*Silene maritimus*) which are common on shore and cliff and yet do not show any particular adaptation of leaf to a droughty or salty habitat. Orache, indeed, is a common weed of gardens and arable land far from the sea. The curled dock (*Rumex crispus*) has a leaf form which enables it to resist some measure of drought and it is in fact often found on shingle beaches below the line of the highest spring tides, and on cliff faces. This plant occurs as far afield as North Rona, nearly fifty miles from other land, but only in certain cliff faces. One of the reasons why it is found in such situations on this and many other islands off Highland coasts is that, being a weed of corn land, it gets picked up by the gulls at seeding time on the crofts, when the birds are already roosting at their gulleries on the cliffs. The gulls cast up the indigestible husks of the oats as a bolus, and the dock seeds, untouched in their hard shiny coat, germinate easily.

The orache, bladder campion and curled dock all show in their foliage from time to time a common effect of drought in the way their leaves turn red. Another common plant of the cliff edge and shingle beach which is highly salt- and drought-resistant is scentless mayweed (*Matricaria inodora*), but it does not turn red in drought. Sea milkwort (*Glaux maritima*) is very closely linked with the spray zone, or the intertidal area of low shingle beaches where wave action is not too great to disturb its rooting. Its rather fleshy leaves turn bright yellow in conditions of extreme drought. Silverweed (*Potentilla anserina*) comes down as far as the high-tide mark but not below, and achieves its drought resistance by a fine hairiness which calms the air near the stomata of the leaves and thus slows down transpiration. Such hard-surfaced, glossy-leaved xerophytes as sea holly (*Eryngium maritimum*) do not occur generally on West Highland coasts, though this species is recorded from Arran, South Argyll and Skye.

Salt marshes are not of considerable extent in the Highlands and cannot be compared in richness of flora with those of England, which are generally on a much more muddy base. The estuarine salt marshes of the Highlands are on an alluvial base of gravel from which the finer particles have been washed away long ago. Also, the Highland salt marsh is always heavily grazed by sheep, which type of grazing in itself is an impoverishing factor on the flora. There are other patches of salt marsh in the Outer Hebrides where the sea reaches into the low " inner " coast of the ramifying sea lochs.

The salt-marsh zone of the shore stretches from the high-water mark of neap tides to the high-water mark of spring tides. Generally speaking it is a form of close grassland intersected by channels and studded with shallow holes where the grassland stops abruptly, and the mud or gravel is there tinged with the green and blue-green algae, and quite different from the vegetational complex of the shingly and rocky shore line described above.

The occurrence of definite periodic immersion in salt water is, of course, the outstanding ecological factor in the life of the salt marsh. Immersion varies from regular twice-daily periods of some hours to fortnightly occasions of possibly less than an hour. The plants are halophytic, i.e. having a high tolerance of salt. Their cellular structure is similar in some respects to the xerophytic or drought-resistant plants. These two kinds of plants—of the salt marsh and of the cliff edge and mountain top—maintain a higher osmotic pressure in their cells than normal mesophytic plants. Salt-marsh flora are also subject to considerable fortuitous changes of salt concentration in their root medium, depending on such factors as rainfall and hot sunlight during periods of emersion.

The vegetational complex of a Highland salt marsh is commonly made up of the following plants. Dominant members of the flora are marked with an asterisk.

Sea pink	*Armeria maritima**
Sea aster	*Aster tripolium*
Sea milkwort	*Glaux maritima*
Seablite	*Suaeda maritima*
Sand spurrey	*Spergularia salina*
Sea plantain	*Plantago maritima*
Buck's-horn plantain	*P. coronopus**
Red fescue grass	*Festuca rubra**

There is another type of coastal vegetation in the West Highlands which must have special mention—namely, the *machair* (Pl. XIXb, p. 156) already described in its physical features. The *machair* starts with the florally sterile tidal zone of shell sand, then there is the bank of unstable dunes, on the seaward edge of which the marram grass begins to grow thinly. The marram is locally called " bent " but should not be confused with what is botanically referred to as bent (*Agrostis* spp.). The importance of the marram cannot be overestimated ; it is one of the first plants to stabilize sand along with sea purslane (*Atriplex portulacoides*). Were it not for this spiky-leaved marram grass with its dense network of roots, there would be no rich *machair* behind it, and if the bent is cut or lost from the primary dune above the tidal zone the sand begins to blow. The wind makes a throat in the sand and fans out on the landward side of it, removing sand and potential grassland. There should never be grazing in the marram zone, nor should leave be given to cut "bents." This was done some years ago at Dunfanaghy, Co. Donegal, with alarming results. A large bridge on a main road and some houses were enveloped. Inspired work on the part of the Eire Department of Lands not only stopped further trouble, but caused the displaced sand to be blown back to where it had come from. Artificial dunes were started with whin bushes and wire fencing and as these developed, bents were planted a few inches apart all over them, and they were stabilized. Landowners of the past knew the importance of marram and in the Tiree leases of the Dukedom of Argyll it was specially stated that if a man should find a hole in the dunes, he should fill it and plant a bent therein. It is doubtful whether such care is being taken anywhere in the West Highlands now. At certain points in Tiree many acres have gone, leaving isolated dunes held together by their dense cap of marram. The floor of these blown-out areas is of pebbles and boulders and provides nesting sites for little terns, and also for the arctic and common terns which nest elsewhere as well.

Sea sedge (*Carex arenaria*) does its best in these places along with marram. There is something almost purposive to the eyes of the human observer in the contemplation of a rhizome of sea sedge moving forward and thrusting up a shoot every few inches. The *machair* behind the marram has developed from the primary colonization by hop trefoil (*Trifolium procumbens*) and bird's-foot trefoil (*Lotus corniculatus*) among the marram. These nitrogen-fixing legumes create conditions for other flowers and grasses to strike; and soon a shell-sand grassland is developed which is heavily grazed by crofters' stock. The extensive *machairs* of Tiree (Pl. 25, p. 212) are too heavily grazed and the sand is showing through the grass in many places. Again, cart tracks develop over the *machair* and the wear of the wheels breaks the turf and the sand begins to blow. Then, when the ruts are inconveniently deep, the cart takes a new track and eventually more land goes. Here and there, notably at Balevoulin, the dunes are increasing and giving promise of new land.

The flowers of the *machair* and the profusion of common blue butterflies make it a brilliant place in July, offset by the blue of sky and sea, the white edge of surf and the cream expanse of shell-sand beaches. The *machairs* of Coll are *much* less heavily grazed than those of the heavily populated island of Tiree. Here is a short list of flowers found on the Coll *machair* in July :

PLATE XIX

F. Fraser Darling

DUN CRUIT, the Harp Rock of Lunga, Treshnish Isles, Inner Hebrides
September 1937

Robert M. Adam

MACHAIR. Vatersay, Outer Hebrides

John Markham

RINGED PLOVER. Inverness-shire
May 1939

John Markham

OYSTERCATCHER. Allt Mor, Inverness-shire
May 1940

BIRDS OF THE SHINGLE AND SEA-SHORE

Buttercup	*Ranunculus bulbosus*
Milkwort	*Polygala vulgaris*
Mouse-eared chickweed	*Cerastium vulgatum, and C. semidecandrum and tetrandrum*
Heartsease	*Viola curtisii*
Cathartic flax	*Linum catharticum*
Blood-red cranesbill	*Geranium sanguineum*
Red clover	*Trifolium pratense*
Wild white clover	*T. repens*
Hop trefoil	*T. procumbens*
Bird's-foot trefoil	*Lotus corniculatus*
Kidney vetch	*Anthyllis vulneraria*
Wild carrot	*Daucus carota*
Ladies' bedstraw	*Galium verum*
Daisy	*Bellis perennis*
Spear thistle	*Cirsium lanceolatum*
Creeping thistle	*C. arvense*
Cat's ear	*Hypochoeris radicata*
Sow thistle	*Sonchus oleraceus*
Bog pimpernel	*Anagallis tenella*
Forget-me-not	*Myosotis versicolor*
Germander speedwell	*Veronica chamaedrys*
Eyebright	*Euphrasia officinalis*
Redrattle	*Bartsia odontites*
Wild thyme	*Thymus serpyllum*
Selfheal	*Prunella vulgaris*
Ribgrass	*Plantago lanceolata*
Frog orchid	*Coeloglossum viride*
Marram	*Ammophila (Psamma) arenaria*
Yorkshire fog	*Holcus lanatus*
Meadow grasses	*Poa* spp.
Woolly-fringed moss	*Rhacomitrium lanuginosum*

In short, the *machair* may be considered as a natural grassland of calcareous type, consolidating land initially stabilized by marram. Moderate and always controlled grazing helps to perpetuate it by adding organic matter and keeping a clear sward. The people of the country have in the past effected this control by each crofter having a given " souming " of stock, and in the old days the township constable, appointed from among themselves, saw to it that the souming was not exceeded. The Crofters' Act of 1886 did away with the constable and there is evidence that the souming is now often exceeded,

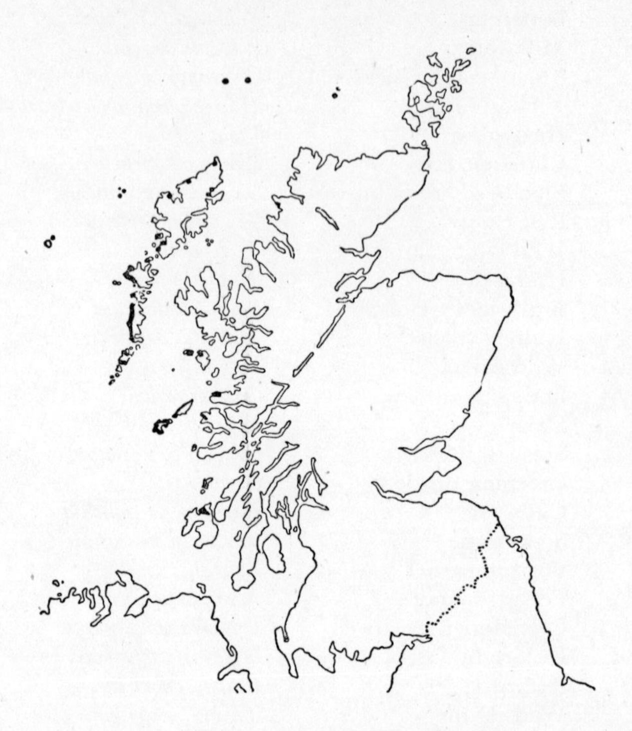

FIG. 9.—Distribution of *traigh* and *machair* on Highland and Island coasts

to the detriment of the *machair* which is the basis of existence on the Atlantic coastal strip of several islands.

Mankind is not the only species confined to this strip, or at least showing a marked concentration on it : the distribution of snails is interesting. The dunes, being still unstable and receiving the force of the prevalent high winds, have an extremely scanty population of Mollusca ; but as soon as the stable *machair* vegetation is reached, full advantage is taken of the lime-rich conditions, and snails abound in such quantities that there may even be inter-specific competition. *Helix aspersa*, *Hellicella itala* and *Cochlicella acuta* are found, and several slugs (*Agriolimax* and *Arion* spp.). The inner edge of the *machair* bordering the peat moor is also prolific in the smaller land molluscs, but once the peat is reached, snails disappear and slugs only are found. Shell production limits the range of environment.

The sea's edge is a frontier, a place of action, whether it be the quiet shores of a sheltered sea loch or the cliff face of an outer coast. There are tides twice a day, there are sudden changes of salinity through the action of heavy spates which occur so often in the West Highlands and there is a constant reaching up and reaching down of species from the one element or the other. The very beaches are often in a state of change ; a spring tide will put up a bank of wrack (Fucidae) and the next tide may so affect the gravelly floor that a layer of sand is put on top of the weed. When the weed rots there is for the year a highly fertile seed bed which some of the plants mentioned already may colonize and find a footing for a season or two. If that band of drifted weed is a thin one it will dry and the broken line may give arctic and common terns a zone for their nests where camouflage will be extremely effective. If the band is very thick there will be a wet malodorous rot of weed and within it will be found millions of larvae of dipterous flies.

The fucoid seaweeds themselves, growing in relatively sheltered situations, may contribute to a gradual change of shore. Bladder wrack (*Fucus vesiculosus*) and knotted wrack (*Ascophyllum nodosum*) will each grow on a piece of stone and when the plants get large enough they will almost float the stone. At least, wind and wave action are sufficient then to make the weed carry the stone ashore and deposit it near the high-tide mark. The weed, thus removed from its optimum habitat in the intertidal zone, dies, and the stone is left. The writer's harbour on Isle Tanera was filled several feet in a hundred years by this means alone.

The optima for the fucoid weeds are quite closely defined, as may be seen if the stratification is studied at low tide. First, there is the channelled wrack (*Pelvetia canaliculata*) which forms a narrow band near and just below high-tide mark. It may reach slightly above if there is sufficient wind and wave action to cause a fair amount of splash. This is the weed which is most liked by grazing animals such as sheep, cattle and ponies. It constitutes a factor in winter subsistence for them in the Hebrides, the Shetland Isles and on many another stretch of Highland shore. The channelled wrack usually grows on bed rock. Second, there is flat wrack (*Fucus spiralis*) which is out of the water for more time than it is in. It fastens itself to bed rock and large boulders. If the intertidal zone is muddy enough, quiet enough and large enough, there may occur in the exposure stratum of the flat wrack a fairly rare seaweed called *Ascophyllum mackayii.* It occurs in several West Highland estuaries such as Cona Glen, Loch Linnhe, and Strontian, Loch Sunart, and is of outstanding interest in that it is unrooted and unanchored. The several plants intermingle their short fronds and form a mat which floats in a waterlogged condition at high tide and sits lightly on the mud at the ebb. Third, there is the wide zone of the knotted wrack (*Ascophyllum nodosum*) which plays an integral part in intertidal ecology by providing cover. This weed grows only in sheltered positions, but otherwise its range of salinity is a wide one. It forms such a blanket when seen at low tide that the boulder shore on which it grows may be entirely obscured. At high tide when the bladders hold the fronds upright, the weed forms a marine inshore forest which has considerable effect on quietening the water there and thus providing conditions for animals which could not otherwise subsist. Not only is the water quietened, but it is darkened at half-tide when part of the fronds float flat on the surface ; and the rock surfaces are insulated against great heat and cold and desiccation by the blanket of knotted wrack. Lower down still, the serrated wrack (*Fucus serratus*) at low tide falls with all its fronds one way and being fairly short, forms a dense thatch which enables some animals to withstand diurnal emergence from the sea.

Below the serrated wrack we are into the region of another group of seaweeds, the Laminarias, of which there are vast beds off the West Highland coasts. The wrack weeds are used by man for manure, especially on the eastern side of the Hebrides where sheltered inlets are numerous, but the Laminarias are of much greater importance for this purpose, especially on the Western Atlantic side where immense quantities of the weed are torn from the sea floor and washed ashore in spring. This is in effect a natural thinning of the beds and forms a natural resource in Hebridean economy. The carts are going busily in spring carrying the torn weed from the tide mark on to the ploughed ground and meadow land of the crofts. Most of this ground on the west side of the Hebrides and some of the Inner Hebrides is *machair*. When ploughed, this limy, sandy soil must be kept well supplied with organic matter if it is to remain in good heart. The annual casts of *Laminaria* provide exactly what is needed. Crofting agriculture on the *machair* land immediately falls to pieces if the labour supply gets too low to gather enough weed. The writer has heard not very large farmers speak of carrying six hundred cart-loads in a spring. One may make a wry face at carting so much water from the beaches, but there is nothing else to substitute. As the Aberdeenshire farmer said of the turnip's 90 per cent of moisture, "It's damn' good watter."

The main species of *Laminaria* found are *L. digitata* at the upper limit, i.e. visible at low spring tides, the crimped *L. saccharina* a little lower, and to a lesser estent *Alaria esculenta,* which latter has a midrib to the leaf. *L. bulbosa,* visible usually only at the equinoctial low tides has a large expanse of flat leaf, and a short stem growing from a large, hollow, papillated swelling which looks rather like coarse tripe turned inside out. It is at low spring-tide level also that carragheen (*Chondrus crispus*) and dulse (*Rhodomela*) are found. Both are red algae, gelatinous and edible. Carragheen is in general use in the islands and on the outer coasts as a thickener of milk to make a blanc-mange-like mould. Dulse is gathered by the inshore and lobster fishermen and chewed occasionally as they go about their work.

A striking seaweed to be found at this lower level, especially in the lower pools, is thong weed (*Himanthalia lorea*). From its holdfast, a short neck widens into a concave disc about two inches across, and from the centre of this bud forth the thongs and their branches. The colour is a rich deep green, and the surface of the disc is beautifully glossy. Thong weed grows in the region of the coralline weeds which are lime-encrusted and bright pinky-purple in colour. *Lithophyllum* lies flat to the rock and completely covers it, as if an artist had worked it on with a palette knife. It makes a striking lining to a rock pool, as may be seen in the coloured plate No. 26a (p. 213) of the lobster.

There can be few amusements so absorbing as wandering among the Laminarias at the equinoctial low spring tide. For these few hours we see something of a world normally hidden. I was on Colonsay and Oronsay recently and was so fortunate as to be poking about the many channels among the skerries between Oronsay and Eilean nan Ron just at this moment of the September low tide. Here were sheltered low-tide levels in a wholly Atlantic situation and the array of sub-littoral marine life was one of amazing variety and beauty. There are sponges and sea anemones that most of us do not know, there are brilliantly striped red and blue long-armed squat lobsters (*Munida banffica*), only two or three inches long, or even an inch long, that seem to be half-crab and half-lobster. There are silver tommies (*Gibbula cineraria*), pellucid limpets (*Patina pellucida*) and half a hundred more forms of invertebrate animal life. One should look under large boulders for there may rest a lobster (*Homarus vulgaris*) (Pl. 26a, p. 209) waiting for the tide to return. Perhaps a " hen " lobster may be found to be " berried," carrying her 10,000 eggs glued among her legs. The lobster fishermen are supposed by law to return berried hens to the sea as an obvious measure of conservation, but all too many are taken. Sometimes a fisherman may pluck a few hundreds of the tiny black eggs between his thumb and first finger and put them in his mouth. He says they are fine for combating tiredness in the boat. The taste of these eggs is most delicate ; it is almost a strangeness. The larger lobsters usually have a few acorn barnacles (*Balanus balanoides* and others) stuck on their big claws or their carapace, otherwise the barnacles inhabit a rather higher zone of rock face, sometimes so thickly that the nature of the rock cannot be seen. The ship's barnacle (*Lepas anatifera*) with shells almost an inch across and with fleshy stalks over a foot long, is not seen unless a floating log comes along from far out in the Atlantic. Acorn barnacles are free-swimming larvae in April, at which time a fisherman is wise not to bring his boat into a harbour where it will dry out with the tides, because on such a surface alternately wet and dry the barnacle takes its stance, and by the end of the summer has grown crusty enough to retard the speed of the boat as she is pulled or driven through the water. And yet, if the boat remains always in the water at a mooring, young *Laminaria* and other algae will begin to grow on the bottom of her so that she must be dried out, scraped and dressed with copper anti-fouling paint.

Perhaps side by side with the lobster under that big rock we may see the head of a large conger eel (*Conger vulgaris*) which fish is able to live quite well for a spell out of water if the atmosphere is damp and cool. The congers which live inshore among the rocks are black and full of fight. To see a battle between an Atlantic seal and a six-foot conger is a most exciting experience. Both are masters of their element, and being in the water thay have three dimensions for their movements. The grey congers off shore are not nearly so vigorous if caught.

Down there under the stones and weeds are little stout fish like the shanny (*Blennius pholis*) and the longer butter fish (*Centronotus gunnellus*) ; they leap about when discovered and are difficult to pick up in the hand.

The rock or black goby (*Gobius niger*) and the speckled goby (*G. rhodopterus*) are common where fresh water falls to the sea in most sea lochs. Bullheads (*Cottus* spp.) are seen in the rock pools. These fish—they are also known as cobblers or sea scorpions—are like tiny dragons and are feared by children. Their eyes are very large and prominent and the heavily spined fins are so large as to be out of all proportion to the size of the fish. Yet the whole creature is not more than three to four inches long. The bullheads are related to the gurnards (*Trigla* spp.) which are called *crunan* in Gaelic from the habit these fish have of emitting a croaking sound or croon as their lips appear above the surface of the water.

One of the most important things to remember about West Highland and Hebridean shores is the fact of the Atlantic Drift. An organism which emphasizes the phenomenon of this warm current lapping some of our British shores and not others is the sea urchin (*Echinus esculentus*). D. M. Reid (1935) wrote a most interesting paper which not only took credence from formerly held beliefs, but explained its present distribution as an almost direct consequence of the Atlantic Drift. The sea urchin is absent from the Channel coast and from Wales and the East Coast of Ireland as a littoral form but is very plentiful on the West Coast and off the West Highland coasts. It occurs in Shetland and all the way up the Norwegian coast as far as the North Cape. The brilliant red and purple sea urchins are found attached to the rocks and cliff face at about low spring-tide level, or on large leaves of tangle below the surface of the sea, for they are vegetable feeders. Their temperature range is very great—from 4·2° C. in deep waters to 17–18° C. off the north of Spain. It is worthy of note also that where they are commonest in Britain—off the West Highland coast—the low spring tides fall in the early afternoon when the atmosphere is warmest, so the sea urchin must occasionally undergo considerable warming. Its range in salinity is also great, for West Highland seas are salt and those in Norwegian fjords are much less so. The only constant feature in the animal's littoral distribution is the Atlantic Drift.

The influence of the Drift is again apparent in the occurrence of crabs of western Irish distribution in the Inner Hebrides. These were discovered by Nicol (1939) off the west side of the Isle of Muck, and were *Xantho incisus*, *Pilumnus hirtellus*, and *Pirimela denticulata*. The strong current from the west of Ireland evidently carries the planktonic larval stages of these crabs north-eastwards.

Rock pools vary in type, from those at lowest tides to those which are but faintly salt, receiving only splash water from the ocean. Green algae are commonly dense in these brackish pools and become scarcer as the salinity rises. Three-spined sticklebacks (*Gasterosteus aculeatus*) may be seen in these higher pools. This is a fish with a wide range of salt tolerance. The orange-red belly of the male may be seen to advantage if he has just chased another away from the nest which he guards so assiduously. At other times it is paler. The larger fifteen-spined stickleback is more truly a salt-water species, and may be found in the larger and lower rock pools off West Highland coasts. One might think that the landward three-spined stickleback would be absent from very small islands long severed and far from other land, but the species was present in the rock pools on Leac Mor Fianuis on the northern promontory of North Rona, sometimes in pools that could have been no less salt than the ocean itself. This extreme accommodation to a varying range of salinity is a character probably developed by natural selection in an environment which through storms, splash, rainfall and drought is peculiarly liable to sudden and continual changes of salinity.

The tolerance and powers of resistance of most of the forms of life found in these brackish rock pools are very wide. Fraser (1935) working on the life history and ecology of the copepod *Trigriopus fulvus* found that this species and two others persisted for two years in a sealed bottle of water taken from a pool above high-water mark, though they were stunted in size. An active Turbellarian worm was also present. The blue-green algae went into a resting stage, but regained colour and grew when the bottle was opened, after which event there was a new surge of activity and growth in the species present.

In order to get a clear picture of the teeming life and action present on a rocky shore it is necessary to take a close look at a vertical cliff face between the high and low spring-tide levels ; then at a different exposure where there may be a gradient of 45° or less. Looking at the vertical cliff face where there may be a fairly large amount of wave action, we are aware that the last landward plants are lichens in the spray zone, principally *Usnea barbata*, the grey-green beard-like lichen which may make a whole cliff appear a different colour from what its geological formation would indicate. Almost at the top of the spring-tide mark there are shells of the barnacle *Chthamalus stellatus*, which shows whiter than *B. balanoides*. The upper extent of *B. balanoides* overlaps the lower level of *C. stellatus* and is the zone of the lichen *Lichina pygmaea*. This latter barnacle is not found usually in sheltered places, only where there is considerable wave action. Kitching (1935) in a paper on the ecology of intertidal rock faces on the coast of Argyll states that *C. stellatus* is plentiful on most wave-beaten coasts but is almost absent in the Sound of Mull. It occurred in the unusually sheltered waters of Loch Sween, but on the underside of overhanging rocks. Kitching suggests that some unknown ill effect of emersion may be responsible for the restricted range, but this is overcome by plentiful splash or the protection offered by an overhanging surface.

It will be readily seen from examination of rock faces that the barnacles like a fairly clear field. The presence of much wrack, especially *A. nodosum*, inhibits close colonization by them. But we may be arguing from the wrong end and the reason may be that the fronds of *Ascophyllum* damage or sweep off the young barnacles which settle almost everywhere in the spring of the year ; because live specimens of *B. balanoides* may be found close to the holdfasts of *Ascophyllum* where they would escape mechanical disturbance from the fronds.

The lower end of the barnacled stratum is part of that occupied by the common limpets (*Patella vulgata*) and the colonies of dog whelks (*Purpura lapillus*). It is known that limpets have their own places on the rock face, returning to their stances after food-gathering journeys. Such limpet homes are obvious after the swarming of the barnacles, for in the pinky-purplish texture given to the rock by the millions of tiny barnacles are those completely clear patches exactly the size of a limpet's foot.

Closely packed beds of small mussels (*Mytilus edulis*) (Pl. 26b, p. 213) are also common in this band of the rock faces. They do not make up to any great size in these situations and it would seem necessary for the mussel to have a fair amount of fresh water coming past it, with the varied small life which brackish concentrations encourage. The beds of large mussels are to be found at the mouths of burns on the sea lochs, but single large specimens commonly occur in the higher rock pools which must receive a lot of rain water and are not scoured out by wave action very often.

The common winkle (*Littorina littorea*) is very common where there is even moderate shelter. Its zone is lower than those species already mentioned ; it is found feeding on serrated wrack and particularly on the *Laminaria*. The period of emersion is never a very long one, but at low spring tides on hot days in spring and summer the winkles may be seen in large numbers feeding on the sunward side of the tangle as it lies above the surface of the water, their shells dry and warm. On a dull or wet day, the winkles would have to be sought on the undersides.

The fauna of a sandy shore is very different from the rocky ones to which we have given more particular attention. Where a sandy shore is well sheltered from wave action and possibly much surrounded by land, it tends to become muddy in the intertidal zone through the accumulation of terrestrial detritus, and by the decomposition of fucoid seaweeds and possible casts of *Laminaria.* In such places the sand may appear black if the condition is extreme, but quite often the blackness appears at a depth of two or three inches and there is an objectionable smell. The smell and the blackness are caused by the generation of hydrogen sulphide (H_2S) from the decay of the sulphur-rich weed, and the deposition of iron sulphide in the sand. Wave action would cause aeration and dispersal of the products of decomposition. The detailed life histories and ecology of the fauna of the burrowing life of sandy and muddy submarine soils is not well known, so that explanations of why and wherefore tend to be more hypothetical than factual.

The intertidal zones of the Outer Isles are so extensive and of such exceptional interest that they cannot be passed by without special mention of the work that has been done on them. The earliest investigator on scientific lines was W. C. M'Intosh (1866), though that observant man Martin Martin (1703) made special mention of the interesting phenomena of the brackish-water lochs of North Uist, which he visited in 1695. For example, Martin records that these lochs, reached by spring tides only and therefore but slightly brackish, may contain cod, ling and mackerel. A. C. Stephen (1935) investigated the North Uist sands in the course of a quantitative survey of sandy and muddy intertidal areas of Scottish coasts in general. He found that the sandy shores subjected to considerable wave action contained no molluscs and but few Polychaete worms. Where the strands were sheltered, four molluscs were found, *Macoma baltica* and *Cardium edule* in great abundance. The well-known lug worm *Arenicola marina* was common on the Vallay strand and other places but not everywhere. The most remarkable of Stephen's findings in North Uist was the virtual absence of that other bivalve mollusc so extremely common on Scottish coasts, *Tellina tenuis.* The co-occupant of the zone, *Donax vittatus*, was also absent. These molluscs usually occur at and lower than the lower end of the *Cardium-Macoma* stratum which reaches three-quarters of the way down to low-water mark. Stephen says :

"This almost entire absence of the *Tellina-Donax* zone would seem to lie in the physical conditions of the shores. A glance at a map will show that most of these areas are very extensive and covered only by a few feet of water at high tide. In many cases also the incoming tide enters through one or more narrow channels, and does not overflow from these to cover the main portion of the strand until a considerable period after the turn of the tide. In warm weather, the water flowing over the strand is very considerably heated; . . . On less extensive beaches the main body of sea water is not so far removed from the intertidal water and more mixing can take place."

Stephen also says that the cockle (*C. edule*) though maintaining itself, does not thrive specially well, judging by size of shell, but *M. baltica* flourishes particularly, the specimens taken in North Uist being the finest met with during the whole Scottish survey.

Dr. Edith Nicol (1936) made a survey of the brackish-water lochs of North Uist, those which reach in from the east coast of the island and which receive salt water at varying states of the tide. Salinity varied from 30 per thousand down to 2–3 per thousand. The fresh water of the island has a hydrogen-ion concentration of about 5·4 but in the brackish-water lochs it rose to 7·8–9·9.

Nicol found the brackish-water lochs of North Uist to be extremely rich in species compared with other brackish-water areas in Britain. She points out that the greater number of species present are marine in origin, and that there is a wide variety of substratum. This latter factor is in itself of high importance, equal to that of salinity in controlling distribution. The burrowing Amphipod *Corophium volutator*, for example, occurs only where the bottom is of sandy mud or mud. It is also surmised that the salinity of these lochs remains relatively constant, at least through the spring and summer season. There is a rapid drop in the number of marine species between the salinities 35–25 per thousand and the fresh-water species disappear when a salinity of 5 per thousand is reached. The greatest number of brackish-water species occurred at 25 per thousand. Summarized, Nicol's numbers of species found in the lochs were 59 marine, 24 fresh- and 25 brackish-water forms, as well as five euryhaline forms, such as the salmon, which are at home in any salinity.

The sandy shores of the Highlands do not merely reflect the rock of the district. They are varied in type. The most important sandy shores, as indicated above, are those immense stretches of shell sand on the western sides of the Outer Isles and some of the Inner Hebrides

—Barra, the Uists, Harris, Tiree and Coll. Their influence is benign on the adjacent land and their cream expanse is a joy to the eye. The dead-white silica sands of Morar are not nearly so pleasing, nor do they so profoundly influence the coastal strip. At Gruinard Bay, near Loch Broom, and at several places farther north on the west coast of Sutherland there are bays of Torridonian sand under rocky shores and cliffs of archaean gneiss. Sometimes these sands have a shelly and therefore calcareous patch at the low spring-tide level. The Kentra sands between Ardnamurchan and Moidart are calcareous to an extent of about 50 per cent, but at the seaward end of these sands and at low spring-tide level there is a bank of almost pure shell sand.

Lastly, there are the few banks of coral sand which are emersed for but a short time at low spring tides. They occur at Tanera Beag of the Summer Isles ; at Claggan and near Staffin, Skye ; at Duncraig Island, Loch Carron ; and at Erbusaig near the Kyle of Lochalsh. Few people know that such sands exist in these parts and that beautiful pieces of pink and purple-tinted coral, much branched, can be picked up in quantity. This coral is not made by the coral polyps of sub-tropical seas but by a plant, a seaweed called *Lithothamnion*. This weed lives a few fathoms out from shore in not too exposed places and forms a semi-circular cushion about four inches across. Bits break off and are cast up to make the coral sand beach. It would be good to discover the ecology of this seaweed with a view to transplanting it elsewhere along our coasts, for it is obviously an efficient extractor of lime from sea water and can go on manufacturing the wherewithal of agricultural fertility while we sleep.

The fauna of these coral sands is extremely poor and they carry no flat fish on them. The size of the fragments is much too large for that superficial and subterranean life of the intertidal sands described already. But these few beds of coral sand have had a great influence on the aspect of parts of the surrounding countryside. The old folk knew the fertilizing value of the coral and thousands of tons were carted to the crofting townships for the inbye land. To-day an observer may see black and green ground sharply demarcated here and there, and it was the sand that made this possible. In any policy of rehabilitation of the Highlands, the strands and banks of shell and coral sand must play an important part as a natural resource.

The birds of the shore line are mostly waders. The rock pipit (*Anthus spinoletta petrosus*) is a notable exception. A distinct sub-species (*A. s. meinertzhageni*) occurs in the Outer Hebrides and is darker in colour than the mainland form. Also, it differs in behaviour in that it goes to the inland moors, whereas the typical form keeps strictly to the shore zone.

One of the most striking things about the bird life of the littoral zone on the West Highland and Hebridean coasts is its paucity compared with that of the East Coast and its muddy firths. Clean sand is beautiful, but if you want numbers and variety of shore birds there is nothing like mud. Mud means a rich invertebrate fauna, the staple food of so many of the waders. The oystercatcher (*Haematopus ostralegus*) (Pl. XXb, p. 157) is found almost everywhere, whether the shore is sheltered or open, and it has a liking for the cleanest of sand even though its food consists very substantially of the limpets, mussels, cockles, periwinkles and small crustacea which are found on mud and not on the Atlantic shores.

The curlew (*Numenius arquata*) is also common on most coasts because the immature and non-breeding birds make the shore line part of their habitat, whatever its characteristics. They feed in the intertidal zone if it is suitable, but otherwise get their food inland. There is a good number of curlews on the estuaries and saltings of the West Coast all the year round. The whimbrel (*N. phaeopus*) is seen on spring passage most years, but is not strictly a shore bird at all.

A certain number of turnstones (*Arenaria interpres*) come to the clean beaches of the Hebrides in winter, but North Rona is a station occupied for most of the year, where the birds work in the sea of mud churned up by the seals. The knot (*Calidris canutus*) is not seen generally on the West, but occurs on migration on the oceanic islands. The dunlin (*C. alpina*) occurs commonly, sometimes in vast flocks, but it is nothing like so common as on the East Coast, where it is considered most plentiful of all shore birds. The winter dunlins on the West are probably all of the northern race (*C. a. alpina*). It is a most diligent feeder, following the receding waves and quartering the estuarine grounds. The purple sandpiper (*C. maritima*) is a constant winter resident on the more exposed shores of the West. This bird works singly or in small parties, following the wash of the waves down the barnacled rocks, picking up those small specks of marine life which are sieved by the rough surface of the barnacles.

The sanderling (*Crocethia alba*) is rarely seen on western mainland shores, but a number of these birds takes the western migratory route, and they are fairly common on the strands of the Outer Isles in autumn and winter.

The redshank (*Tringa totanus*) is a bird of curiously local distribution in the West Highlands and Islands, and is not essentially a shore bird though it is so commonly found there. Several estuaries of the western mainland are devoid of redshanks, others have several all the year round. Islands which have stagnant gull-haunted pools or places where a great mass of decaying seaweed accumulates are likely to hold a few redshanks. This bird is very scarce in the Outer Hebrides. The greenshank (*T. nebularia*) appears on the coasts during migrations, and when its breeding haunt is within reasonable distance of an estuary the greenshank comes out of the deer forest and down to the estuarine flats in the very early morning and late at night.

The ringed plover (*Charadrius hiaticula*) (Pl. XXa, p. 157) agrees almost equally with the oystercatcher in its ubiquity. It occupies precisely the same habitat, but lives on rather different food than the oystercatcher—smaller mollusca and crustacea, insects and annelids. The oystercatcher and ringed plover will nest in very close proximity on shingly shores.

Free-swimming Fauna of the Sea Lochs and Shallow Seas

If one wishes to have a full list of the fishes found in the inshore waters of the Highlands and Islands reference should be made to the *Vertebrate Fauna of Scotland* series, particularly the Outer Hebrides volume (Harvie-Brown & Buckley, 1888) and the Shetland volume (Buckley & Evans, 1899). Further additions have been recorded in such publications as *Scottish Naturalist* and *Annals of Scottish Natural History*, and in *Reports of the Fishery Board of Scotland*. No attempt is made here to repeat or supplement these lists, but some comment can be made on the commoner fishes in relation to the general economy and natural history of the Highlands.

The shark family and other Elasmobranch fishes are common off-shore in the Highlands. The small blue shark (*Carcharius glaucus*) occurs in shoals, but is not fished at all now. A hundred years ago their livers were an important source of oil in the Hebrides, but the subsequent fickle appearance and population of the shoals caused the fishery to die out. The same remarks apply to the basking shark (*Selache maxima*) the second biggest fish in the sea. Both species were called *cearban* in Gaelic and were fished with special heavy tackle and harpoons. In recent years the basking shark has been very numerous off the West Highland coasts and a new fishery is being started not by natives, but by individuals to whom the capture of these 40-foot monsters offers a challenge as well as a livelihood. Major Gavin Maxwell has bought the island of Soay to the south-west of Skye and is conducting work from there and Mallaig. He is having much to learn of the habits of these great fish. They can rid themselves of a superficially-planted harpoon by sounding to the bottom—in possibly 70 fathoms—rolling over and over and either twisting or snapping the shank of the instrument until free. They are strong enough to pull a 76-foot fishing boat for several hours. With all this power the basking shark or sail fish is yet a quiet, inoffensive fish. They appear off the Irish coasts at the end of March on a northern migration from Mediterranean and North African waters. By the beginning of May they are of general occurrence off the West Highlands and are reaching up to Shetland by the latter end of the month. One stream of the fish comes into the Firth of Clyde and can get no farther than Loch Fyne. The rest work their way up the Minch, and outside it as well, and ultimately migration takes the sharks to the North Cape by the end of July. The latter part of July and all August are a time when few basking sharks are seen off Highland coasts, but they appear again in September, this time on their southward run, for a much shorter time than in the spring, and they do not bask so leisurely with their great dorsal fin flapping lazily in the sunlight as they do in spring and early summer.

The basking shark comes very close inshore. I once saw one rub his side along the end of the stone quay on Tanera, in about twelve feet of water, and off the Summer Isles I have been among them in a canoe within fifty yards of the shore. They progress at about two knots, feeding on the small surface life of the sea. The water containing the food is taken in through the almost constantly open mouth and is sieved out through the multiple gill slits, the relatively small quantities of food being left behind to be swallowed. Major Maxwell says that the contents of the stomach are almost indistinguishable in scent and appearance from shrimp paste ! One or more of these sharks will hang round a chosen bay for several days and if a salmon bag net or a herring net should happen to be set there, it is almost inevitable that it will be damaged, not because the shark wishes to eat fish, but simply because the nets happen to be in its way. Herring drift-net fishermen have told me that herring will not afterwards go near a net which has been damaged by a basking shark. They say that the slime from the fish's skin causes a permanent contamination to which the herring are sensitive. The point needs further investigation. The coloured plate (No. 27a, p. 220) of two basking sharks is the result of one of those happy moments when everything was right. I had spent most of a Sunday afternoon trying to get a good photo at sea level as the fish came round the Anchorage of Tanera. Then I gave it up and went up to a 40-foot cliff on my way somewhere else. It was then that the sharks passed through the calm water below me, the sun being at my back and not reflecting off the water. One shark is completely submerged and the other has part of the dorsal fin above water in characteristic fashion.

There is another shark which visits West Highland waters sporadically in some numbers—namely, the thrasher or fox shark (*Alopecias vulpes*). They were unusually and unpleasantly common in the summer of 1938. The thrasher is about 12–14 feet long, extremely savage in attack on such a creature as a whale, and given to suddenly springing out of the water and coming down a " belly-flopper " which resounds like a gunshot. In attack they use the tail as a weapon of offence at the end of one of these leaps from the sea. Harvie-Brown (1888) cites an account of a battle between thrashers and swordfish on the one hand and a large whale on the other. The whale, apparently, had much the worst of it and the sea was red with blood.

The six-gilled shark (*Notidanus griseus*) is fairly common in deep water and is carnivorous, but it is seldom seen, being a ground feeder. It reaches 10–12 feet long. Sometimes it is taken on deep-sea lines, and may be recognized by the iridescent eyes and the six gill-slits.

Several species of dogfish (Scyllidae and Spinacidae) are common throughout the region. They are wolfishly carnivorous and are a constant nuisance in the cod and ling fisheries and even in haddock fishing with short lines. Skates and rays (Raiidae) are also common off most West Highland shores, and are at times the subject of direct fishery.

Mackerel (*Scomber scomber*) occur in vast shoals in summer, sometimes penetrating to the heads of the long sea lochs such as Sunart, Hourn and Broom. Their play (or is it display ?) of breaking water with their dorsal fins and making a tiny crackling concert, is a sound far-reaching and characteristic of calm summer days in these parts. The related and much larger tunny (*Orcynus thynnus*) also occurs in movements of the herring shoals.

The common cod (*Gadus morrhua*) is of general occurrence on suitable banks between ten and forty fathoms such as round Dhu Artach, off Gairloch and Coigach, near Canna and at several places off the Outer Hebridean coast. There are good banks round St. Kilda and very rich ones round Rockall. After the herring, cod form probably the next most important fishery for the dwindling number of professional fishermen of the West Highland coasts. March is the most common month for this work and quite small boats of 20-foot keels take part in it. The haddock (*Gadus aeglefinus*) is fished, of course, but it is too uncertain in most parts to be the basis of the regular fishery.

The coalfish (*G. virens*) is exceedingly numerous throughout the region. The young ones, about a foot long, are called cuddies and frequent certain skerries off shore in May and early June. In the late dusk the shoals begin to jump and the sound is like heavy rain. At this time of year and time of night, West Highlanders who never go to the sea at any other season may be seen rowing little boats out to the skerries, where the cuddies are fished from bamboo rods. The occasion is a social one ; vast catches are taken and much time spent in giving away the fish to friends in the township. The lythe or pollack (*G. pollachius*) is another rock fish taken all through the summer. At one time the lythe was fished for its liver oil by the people of the West.

The hake (*Merluccius vulgaris*) is found wherever there are herring shoals, but is not regularly fished *ad hoc* on this side of Scotland. Ling (*Molva vulgaris*) used to be an important fish in Highland affairs and could be again if a new fleet of small boats were forthcoming for the Hebrideans. There is fine ling ground west of the Outer Isles, and at one time the salt fillets of ling were a staple of export from the region. Incidentally, this filleting of the fish ashore in the Atlantic townships of the Hebrides meant the accumulation of a large quantity of backbones of these long eel-like fish, and in the closely ordered social life of the islands there were women whose task it was to grind up these bones into a meal. The women were known as the *cosnaiche cnamh* —bone labourers. The dried meal, consisting largely of calcium phosphate, was fed to the cows in winter. These folk had anticipated the findings of research in mineral nutrition. The pity is that the ling fishery is gone and that the bone women no longer grind the meal, for how common it is to see cows beachcombing West Highland shores, exhibiting every sign of pica, i.e. a craving for bony material.

The halibut (*Hypoglossus vulgaris*) occurs in many parts of the West Highland seas, but is not regularly fished. Harvie-Brown (*op. cit.*) says: " Plentiful and of great size off St. Kilda, where an attempted cod fishing was partially frustrated by the immense takes of this fish that they could not dispose of." Specimens of 2 cwt. are sometimes taken.

The herring (*Clupeo harengus*) is still immensely important in West Highland economy, but not to the extent it used to be. The largest part of the drifter fleets fishing herring in the Minch or about the Hebrides is owned by East Coast men from the Buckie-Peterhead region. The herring is still a fish of which we do not know enough about its various clans and movements. There are some herring dealers who can say where a catch of herring came from, and the feeding grounds seem to be quite important, although the fish are feeding so largely on the free-swimming copepod *Calanus*, which itself is feeding on the superficial diatoms. It must be that the micro-plankton differs much in quality, depending on salinity of, and the origin of, the nutritive salts in the water. It is reckoned that the best herring come from outside the West Hebridean coast. They are better than Minch herrings, and much better than those from the North Sea.

Broadly, the herring migrate from west to east round the Scottish coasts but in addition to this vast movement there must be smaller groups which do little more than travel in and out of a sea loch, though the young herring may grow to their first spawning season a good way out in the Atlantic or as far north as the Arctic Ocean. The main shoals of herring seem countless and show no signs of lessening despite the constant fishery through hundreds of years. But it is different with the herring of the lochs which also seemed numberless in the second half of the 18th century. Loch Fyne still has a considerable herring fishery, but not equal to what it was. Loch Sunart, Loch Creran, Loch Nevis, Loch Broom and Loch Glendhu of the mainland, and Loch Roag and Loch Maddy in the Hebrides were all prolific of herring years ago. Now there are but few. The writer used to think the decline had to do with a changing course of migration taken by the herring, but now leans to the idea that these were small and local races of the fish, and that the intensive fishing worked them out.

Take Loch Broom for example: the rich herring fishery was discovered by the Dutch, who showed the Scots how to fish herrings.

They fished from sailing busses and apparently made quite long trips to and from the netting grounds. The English speculative companies who were so common in the Highlands in the latter half of the 18th century, saw that the sailing trips to and fro could be shortened by building herring curing stations on the outer coasts, such as at Isle Martin and Isle Tanera. Now the busses had to go less than a mile into the mouth of Loch Broom or into Badentarbet Sound, through which latter the herring came into the loch, and the boats came back inside an hour sometimes to clear their catch. But from 1820 onward the herring got less in numbers and by 1880 the Loch Broom fishery was finished as a serious pursuit.

THE HERRING AND ITS PREDATORS

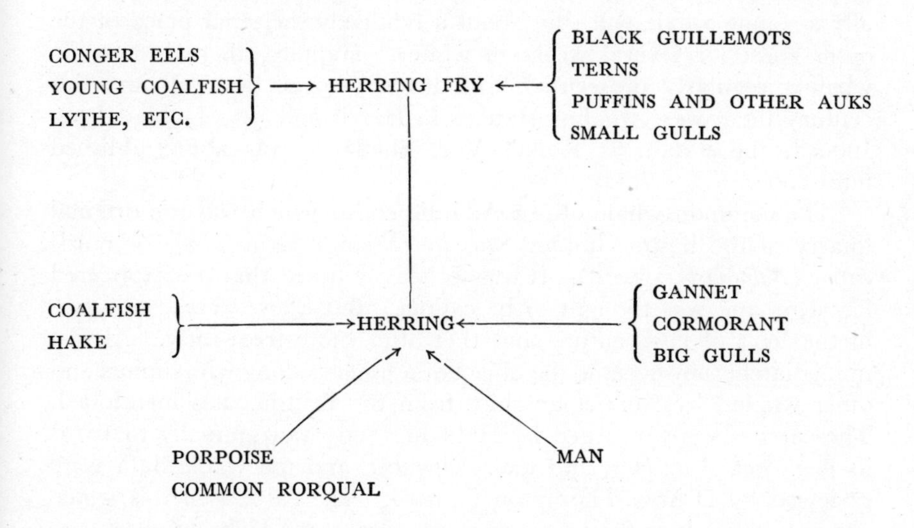

The herring is one of the staples of the sea. We catch the adults ; so do other animals like the dogfish, the tunny fish and the coalfish. The bigger gulls take adults also, and they are a food staple of the gannet ; and down the scale we go, till we find terns catching immense numbers of herring fry and quite inconsiderable little coalfish will be found to be packed with fry. Large coalfish appear to hunt almost as a pack sometimes and manœuvre a shoal of herring into a small space. The herring seem to panic and pile up together in the sea to such an extent that there is actually a pile of herring lying above the surface of the sea. Gulls come from far and near to swallow to repletion and the coalfish and dogfish are snatching at the outside of the herring "pan" and gorging themselves. Humanity joins in this free-for-all, whenever opportunity offers.

The Mammalian Fauna of the Hebridean and West Highland Seas and Sea Lochs

Whales are common migrants along the West Highland and Hebridean coasts. It would be better to say migrants rather than residents, for whales are seen more often in summer than in winter, and there seems little evidence of any stationary population. Occasionally a young whale will stay about a relatively sheltered place of the outer coast for several weeks in winter. Happily, there is now no whaling regularly prosecuted from British shores, but well into this century there were whaling stations in Harris and the Shetland Isles. Indeed, the station at Rona's Voe, Shetland, was not established until 1903.

The common whale of our Atlantic coasts which was the original quarry of the Basque hunters was the Atlantic right whale or nordcaper (*Balaena biscayensis*). It was so heavily fished that it disappeared for years and was thought to be extinct. But a few were seen again in the '80's of last century and thereafter more frequently. Almost immediately they became the object of a fishery, along with finners and other whales, by Norwegian ships from the British bases mentioned. The catches were recorded by Haldane (1905 and annually to 1910) in *Ann. Scot. Nat. Hist.* and *Scot. Naturalist*, and the whole data were reviewed by D'Arcy Thompson in 1918. The catches of this whale were commonest to the west and south-west of the Hebrides and were round about a score a year, but after a few years numbers fell rapidly again and it is good to know that such of these whales as now exist are left alone. They are inhabitants of the temperate seas, ranging from the Spanish and North African coasts in winter to Norway in high summer. This is a truly oceanic whale, of which the western Atlantic stock performs a migration up and down the American coast comparable with ours. D'Arcy Thompson thinks it possible that the two

James Fisher

DOLPHIN, off Cape Wrath, Sutherland; probably the white-sided dolphin
May 1939

James Fisher

STAC AN ARMIN from the top of Boreray, St. Kilda
June 1939

PLATE XXII

R.A.F. Crown Copyright

ROCKALL, Leonidas rock beyond
April 1942

stocks may mingle in mid-Atlantic in early winter, in the latitude of the Azores.

The sperm whale (*Physeter macrocephalus*) is another global oceanic species which appears west of the Hebrides in August, mainly north and west of St. Kilda and out to Rockall. It also has made a northern migration, but much remains to be learned of the habits of these creatures; the sperm whales seen off the western Scottish coasts in summer are almost invariably males.

The blue whale or Sibbald's rorqual (*Balaenoptera sibbaldii*) is also found in all the oceans of the world and one stock appears west of the Hebrides in summer. It formed a large part of the early 20th-century whale fishery from Harris, but its pursuit is now more profitable in Antarctic waters, and those visiting Hebridean seas are left in peace. Once more we may be thankful that though the profit motive starts exploitation, there is hope for an animal's continued existence when profit sinks to a low level and the species is a widely dispersed one. During the North Atlantic fishery many of the blue whales killed were pregnant females. As is well known, this is the world's largest animal and it was not possible to hunt it successfully until the invention of the harpoon bomb, which could kill the whale when struck.

The common rorqual (*B. physalus*, sometimes *B. musculus*) is common off West Highland coasts. It is one of the finners and, seen end on, appears to have a very stiff dorsal ridge. It is greyish in colour with white underparts which are deeply grooved or furrowed longitudinally. The whaler's term for this type of undersurface is "plaited." The whale formed the largest part of recent temperate North Atlantic fishery. Though a baleen whale, it does not live on small crustacea, exclusively, as does its larger relative the blue whale. It is known as a fish eater as well and is often called the herring whale.

Rudolphi's rorqual (*B. borealis*) is a very common whale to be seen from the shore in the north-west. It is between the common and the lesser rorqual in size and may be distinguished by its high dorsal fin. It is an active fast-moving whale and when coming up for air may blow no more than once or twice.

The lesser rorqual (*B. rostrata*) is probably the commonest inshore whale of the West Highlands. It has little fear of man and quite often comes nosing about the cliffs. The writer himself has had several chances of closely observing it from such vantage points, and it is one more great sea creature which so far honoured his handiwork as to scratch itself along the end of the quay of Tanera at high tide. Looked at from above they are dark-coloured, of course, but they are immediately recognisable by the broad band of white across each flipper on its upper surface. If the observer should happen to be in a launch and a small school of these whales blows within a boat's length of him, he will notice that the lesser rorqual is greyish white in colour. I examined one in January, 1944, which was washed ashore at Polbain in the north-west corner of Ross-shire, after apparently being injured about the head. The skin was now steel blue on the upper parts and extremely beautiful in texture, so smooth to touch. The whale was 26 feet long. Several of the larger gulls were trying to tear the skin of this whale, entirely without success and without making any mark at all on this wonderfully smooth surface.

It is not necessary to say much about the porpoise (*Phocaena communis*) for it is so common, especially so when food in the shape of small fish is plentiful. Large schools will stay in a bay or sea loch for a week or more and then disappear. They are often ready to play with a boat. I have had them leap from the water round my launch, cross and recross its path and swim round and round it at what seemed an incredible speed. The best opportunity for watching the speed was one flat-calm night in a wide anchorage, when the bottom could be seen clearly several fathoms down. Sometimes in such flat-calm weather the explosive sound of blowing porpoises may be the continual and only noise to be heard. For a week or two in 1939 when a very large school of two or three hundred porpoises were in Badentarbet Sound, there was one which made a barking sound every time it blew. Unfortunately, I wasted an opportunity which a good naturalist should not have lost—of measuring the incidence of blowing through a period of time, for it would have been easy having such a distinctive sounding beast.

The killer whale (*Orca orca*) or grampus, is really the largest of the dolphins, reaching to rather over twenty feet in length. It has an extremely long dorsal fin which is not very broad at the base. A full grown bull's fin appears to stick up about six feet when the whale rises to blow. Usually a party of four to six travels together, and as they all blow at the same time the very long fin of the bull is quite clear.

The killers are the terrors of the sea. They will attack the largest whales, or porpoises and seals. I have occasionally seen grey seals jump right out of the water in obvious fear, not upwards and downwards, but in a low forward parabola, trying to get away from something behind. This seemed to me different from the quite common habit of common seals of flinging themselves far out of the water. This action in the common seal is thought to be encouraged by changes in weather conditions, but no one really knows. Once I saw a young grey seal hydroplane along the surface of the water for nearly a hundred yards, a feat which I scarcely thought it could manage. I thought a killer must be the cause, but I never saw any break of the long fin. Common seals would be a much likelier prey for the killers.

The pilot whale (*Globiocephala malaena*) is a small toothed cetacean which moves in large herds, usually of hundreds of animals together. In my opinion it is not so common as it was years ago, and as far as the West Highlands are concerned it is only to be seen off the Hebrides and the North Scottish coast with any regularity. When a herd of these whales gets into a Shetland voe, everyone turns out in small boats to hunt them, but the terrain is not so good in the Hebrides and the pilot whales go their way.

The bottle-nosed dolphin (*Tursiops tursio*) is probably commoner in occurrence off Highland and Hebridean coasts than the common dolphin (*Delphinus delphis*) which tends to keep farther out in the ocean. I was lucky enough one day to see, from the northern cliffs of Priest Island, something of a sporting match of dolphins a few hundred yards out. I had my glasses with me and from watching them leaping high out of the water and generally having fun for about three minutes I reckoned it was the bottle-nosed dolphin I was seeing. The dolphin which James Fisher photographed off Cape Wrath in May 1939 (Pl. XXIa, p. 176) may be a white-sided dolphin (*Lagenorhynchus acutus*) from the shape of its fin.

It is difficult to learn much of the natural history of these small cetaceans for they are not to be seen regularly and with much chance of identification. Even dead ones are uncommon to find in good condition. Once on Priest Island I fetched in from the sea a fresh, dead porpoise calf, newly born. I tested its lungs to see if they had breathed, but they had not. Its bones were cartilaginous and its skull very thin, but the ear bones were densely ossified and the semi-circular canals were of extremely hard dense bone. This is very different from what we find in ordinary land mammals. The ear bones of the grey seal are also ossified at birth and will be the only remains of this animal visible on the nursery grounds in the following year if it dies as a calf. This ossification of the ear bones of water-going mammals is an adaptation to allow them to balance perfectly in the water immediately after birth, the semi-circular canals being organs closely linked with balance and orientation of the body.

The Atlantic grey seal might well come in this section but as its breeding grounds in the West Highlands and Islands are almost exclusively insular, its life history is described in the chapter following that on the oceanic island. There can be no question where the common seal (*Phoca vitulina*) should be mentioned, for it occurs particularly in sheltered and inshore waters, and lives a life separate and different from that of its larger relative. As far as the West Coast is concerned the name common seal is not the best, for it is the less common seal in numbers, though there are but few places up the coast where it does not appear. It is sometimes called the firth seal and that would be a good name for it anywhere in Scotland. It is in the Firth of Clyde, it is in Loch Linnhe, finding its way to the brackish head-waters of almost every sea loch of the Highlands, and it occurs in small numbers in the sheltered parts of island groups on exposed coasts; for example, I have seen it in the northern half of the Treshnish group, west of Mull, in the strand at high tide between Colonsay and Oronsay, and in the sounds between the inner Summer Isles and about the islands out from Loch Inchard. Nowhere in the Hebrides or off the West Coast is it as numerous as in Shetland where hundreds at a time may be seen from the steamer between Lerwick and the north isles.

Many people find it difficult to distinguish our two British seals in the water. Here are some points: the common seal has a much shorter face than the Atlantic seal, as well as being much smaller. As the common seal raises itself to look at you its nose seems almost to turn upwards. The grey seal never gives that impression for in both male and female (Pl. XXXa, p. 229) the face is distinctly roman-nosed. Common seals vary a good deal in colour from black, through blue and brown to fawn and greeny cream, but the mottling over all is small and uniform, quite unlike the harlequin splashings of the throat and belly of the female Atlantic seal. The times when the two species may confuse a fairly practised observer are when the Atlantic seals are newly gone to sea at six weeks old (but then they are still near the nursery and not mixing with common seals) or when they are about nine months old, at which time they are particularly to be found well inshore and far from where they were bred. They will even mix with common seals at this time, and I have seen a common seal and a young Atlantic playing together at the back of Tanera. The Atlantic seal is fawn coloured at this age and looks greeny cream when it is hauled out and dry. If observation can be close enough, the longer nose of the Atlantic is noticeable at this age and its mottlings are not the regular ovals of the common species. Sometimes a bull common seal can look quite convex in the face and rather impressive, but if you have once seen the great head and the sad eyes of an Atlantic bull come above water at close quarters, you will not make a mistake again.

I think the common seal is much more intelligent than the Atlantic seal, and that the striking differences in its breeding habits render it almost immune from the extinction which could face the Atlantic seal at any time civilized man cared to hunt it and, in Britain, to lift the protection now given it by law. The common seal is hunted with vigour in the estuary of the Tay where the species does much damage to salmon coming up the river, but it is quite alive to the hazards and successfully overcomes them. It is said that the seals hauled out on the sandbanks of the estuary know quite well the individual sound of the engine of the Commissioners' launch which hunts them and will slip into the water in plenty of time. Contrarily, a common seal will become tame on its own account, like the one that used to come out on the wharf at Ayr and accept fish from anyone who cared to offer them. A young common seal is easily tamed and will live quite happily about the house if it can also get down to the water for a swim and to feed. The grey seal calf is not easy to quieten. It has its own stock reactions of hostility which it repeats time after time, and because of its way of being reared you cannot offer it anything which it would like better than to be left alone. I tried handling one grey seal calf for a while every day from birth to a fortnight old. At the end of a week it was at least quiet in my arms, but I cannot flatter myself that it found any pleasure in my company or looked forward to my coming.

The fundamental difference in the life history of the two British seals is that the common seal is better adapted to a wholly aquatic life than the Atlantic. The young are born ashore on a rock or a sandbank. The pup sometimes has a white coat of a sort at birth but usually it has not, having shed the white coat *in utero*. This fact is not generally realized, that the young common seal is most often born with a short sea-going coat. If it is clothed in a white coat, this is short—and short-lived—and no handicap to the young animal in the water. The young common seal will happily go off with its mother as the tide envelops it, but the Atlantic seal calf does not last more than two or three hours in the open sea if it should be so unfortunate as to be there on its first day. It cries pitifully in such circumstances and its mother is rightly much worried. The young common seal with its mother forms one of the most delightful sights in a June day's watching among the islands. The disposition of these seals is much more amiable than that of the Atlantic species, so they are not constantly bickering and fighting among themselves when hauled out on their usual rock. The babies will play and when the mother and pup go into the water, the pup may be often seen sitting on the back of the old one and holding on by its hands. There is a certain amount of segregation of the sexes in early summer, but it is far from absolute and where the numbers are few, one favoured rock in a sea loch will hold old males, mothers, immatures and pups, perhaps a dozen animals in all. The lactation period in the common seal seems to be at least two months and this fact alone is important in creating family cohesion.

The oil of this seal is still used in the Hebrides and elsewhere for cattle food, but much less so than formerly. There are some pedigree cattle breeders who use seal oil particularly because it gives such a bloom to the cattle for spring sales. Seal oil should never be used for stitched leather work such as harness and boots. It rots the stitches in a very short time and has no great preservative action on the leather. The present time is certainly easier for British seals than that when their skins and oil were staples of remote island life.[1]

The ringed seal (*P. foetida*) is not a normal inhabitant of Scottish waters but it does occasionally occur in the north and west and possibly oftener than we think, because, not expecting to see it, we can easily confuse the animal with the common seal. Lord Dumfries says he has seen it at St. Kilda, at which place one would not expect the common seal to be plentiful. It is improbable even that the Atlantic seal ever breeds there, for the shores and caves are unsuitable.

Common seals are not migratory to any appreciable extent off the West Highland coasts. As long as food is procurable—and in this case

[1] I am wrong. Dog-racing means red meat of any sort in constant supply, and at the present time when any sensible country would be cutting down its stock of luxury carnivores, Britain's racing greyhounds are being kept going on the country's wild fauna, mostly sea birds, and on such seals as can be killed.

they have a catholic taste in fish, crustacean and starfish—they stay about their own place. The Atlantic seal, as we shall see, is in part migratory. The common seal will often move considerable distances solitarily, in an exploring sort of way; for example, it may go some miles up a river into fresh water, or it may go up a burn from the sea and enter a fresh-water loch to fish sea trout or salmon.

THE SUB-OCEANIC ISLAND

OCEANIC Islands are remote places for human beings: they are reached only after a good deal of trouble and labour, and the mighty swell of the ocean may prevent landing even when the islands are there before one's eyes. Knowledge and technique are often a necessity before an observer can get ashore from a small boat, and yet there will be occasional days in summer—and in winter also, but rarely—when the swell will drop and the sea will seem scarcely to lap those worn shores. Swell is a phenomenon not immediately connected with storms overhead. Many are the serene days of sunshine in summer when within a quarter of an hour the swell will rise and an island's coast will be lashed white for a hundred yards and more out to sea and the great boom of it will be sounding. Whatever disturbance created that swell, it was far away.

The islands are remote, but they have a habit of acquiring importance for human beings who cannot make a permanent habitation on them. An island may be a key in a communication system, it may be a means of yielding some of the resources of the ocean, it may provide the biologist with a field for the study of evolution if it carries isolated populations of animals and plants, and what should not be disregarded, an oceanic island fills the romantic heart of man. He wants to see and feel.

Oceanic islands have an immense significance for animal and plant life. There are those animals which cannot recruit their numbers from outside, such as the long-tailed field mice of St. Kilda and the pygmy shrews on many a Hebridean island far from other land. We in Britain have no flightless birds such as are found on some islands of the southern hemisphere, but the wren of St. Kilda is an anchored species whose population is not augmented from elsewhere. It is in the nature of islands that they tend to be poorer in numbers of species of animals and plants than are larger masses of land nearest to them. This phenomenon has been given attention by Lack (1942) in a recent paper describing the number of species of birds on the mainland, in Orkney and in Shetland. The islands do gain a few species not to be found on the mainland, but they lose more. I found similar trends between the mainland opposite the Summer Isles, the inner Summer Isles of which Tanera (Pl. 4a, p. 45) was the largest, and the outer ones such as Priest Island and Glas Leac Beag—all in a distance of not more than ten miles.

TABLE OF BREEDING BIRDS

Mainland Loch Broom Parish	*Tanera, largest and innermost of Summer Isles*	*Priest Island and outer Summer Isles*
Raven	Raven	Raven
Hooded crow	Hooded crow	Hooded crow
Starling	Starling	Starling
Greenfinch	—	—
Lesser redpoll	—	—
Twite	Twite	Twite
Bullfinch	—	—
Chaffinch	Chaffinch (1 pr.)	—
Corn bunting	Corn bunting	—
Yellow bunting	—	—
Reed bunting	—	—
Snow bunting	—	—
House sparrow	House sparrow	—
Skylark	Skylark	—
Tree pipit	—	—
Meadow pipit	Meadow pipit	Meadow pipit
Rock pipit	Rock pipit	Rock pipit
Grey wagtail	—	—
Pied wagtail	Pied wagtail	—
Treecreeper	—	—
Great tit	—	—
Blue tit	—	—
Coal tit	—	—
Long-tailed tit	—	—
Spotted flycatcher	—	—
Goldcrest	—	—
Willow warbler	Willow warbler	—
Wood warbler	Wood warbler (once)	—
Whitethroat	—	—
Missel thrush	—	—
Song thrush	Song thrush	Song thrush

TABLE OF BREEDING BIRDS (*Continued*)

Mainland Loch Broom Parish	*Tanera, largest and innermost of Summer Isles*	*Priest Island and outer Summer Isles*
Ring ouzel	—	—
Blackbird	Blackbird	—
Wheatear	Wheatear	Wheatear
Whinchat	—	—
Stonechat	Stonechat	Stonechat
Redstart	—	—
Robin	Robin	—
Hedge sparrow	Hedge sparrow	Hedge sparrow
Wren	Wren	Wren
Dipper	—	—
Swallow	—	—
House martin	—	—
Sand martin	—	—
Nightjar	—	—
Kingfisher	—	—
Great spotted woodpecker	—	—
Cuckoo	Cuckoo	Cuckoo
Long-eared owl	—	—
Tawny owl	—	—
Barn owl	—	—
Merlin	Merlin	Merlin (once)
Kestrel	Kestrel	—
Golden eagle	—	—
Buzzard	Buzzard	—
Sparrow hawk	Sparrow hawk	—
Heron	Heron	—
—	Grey lag goose	Grey lag goose
Sheld duck	Sheld duck	—
Mallard	Mallard	—
—	Eider duck	Eider duck
Goosander	—	—
Merganser	Merganser	Merganser
—	—	Cormorant
—	—	Shag
—	—	Storm petrel
—	—	Fulmar
Slavonian grebe	—	—
Little grebe	—	—
Black-throated diver	—	—

TABLE OF BREEDING BIRDS (*Continued*)

Mainland Loch Broom Parish	*Tanera, largest and innermost of Summer Isles*	*Priest Island and outer Summer Isles*
Red-throated diver	Red-throated diver	—
Wood pigeon	—	—
Rock dove	Rock dove	Rock dove
Curlew	—	—
Woodcock	—	—
Common snipe	Common snipe	Common snipe
Common sandpiper	Common sandpiper	Common sandpiper
Redshank	Redshank	—
Greenshank	—	—
Ringed plover	Ringed plover	—
Golden plover	—	—
Lapwing	Lapwing	—
Oystercatcher	Oystercatcher	Oystercatcher
—	Arctic tern	—
Black-headed gull	—	—
Common gull	Common gull	Common gull
—	—	Herring gull
—	—	Lesser black-backed gull
—	Great black-backed gull (once)	Great black-backed gull (many)
—	—	Razorbill
Corncrake	Corncrake	—
Moorhen	—	—
Coot	—	—
Black grouse	—	—
Red grouse	Red grouse	—
Ptarmigan	—	—
Totals : 85 species	43 species	29 species

Similarly, the flora of North Rona (Pl. XXIV, p. 193) is as low as 43 species, and some of those, such as the curled dock (*Rumex crispus*), are cliff dwellers obviously brought by birds.

Sub-oceanic islands are most remarkable for their place in the lives of migrant and semi-migrant fauna. The numbers of species may not be large but there is often an amazing numerousness of individuals of those which are present. Sometimes, as at Fair Isle (outside the area of this survey), there may be waves of small land birds passing through in spring and autumn ; or a species may come to an island to breed in such numbers that, as at St. Kilda, the island becomes the biggest gannetry in the world. So also with North Rona where the Atlantic seal, the rarest of the world's total of 25 species of seals, congregates in larger numbers than anywhere else, and holds at one time what must approximate to almost half the world's population of the species. It is necessary to keep in mind that an oceanic island is a metropolis in the animal world and usually an important port of call in the systems of communications which animals establish. Every naturalist at some time of his life wishes to visit such places, and fortunately there are some in reach of all, but others, like Sule Stack, are so inaccessible that this rock has had but one naturalist ashore in the last half-century—Malcolm Stewart—and he knows he was lucky.

The number of such islands and rocks off West Highland and Hebridean coasts is not very large, and it is difficult to set a criterion for what is and what is not an oceanic island in the sense they are being considered in this chapter. The biologist's general meaning of the term oceanic island refers to those islands far from any continental land, such as the Galapagos, the Azores and Tristan da Cunha, where evolution has gone its own way for a long period of time. But in this book the term " sub-oceanic "is used rather loosely to describe a small island washed by uninterrupted ocean seas, and in the area under survey. In general, they are uninhabited by man. It is worth while making a list giving their position and one or two items of information :

St. Kilda (Pl. XXIX, p. 228) lies 40 miles west of the north-west corner of North Uist, Outer Hebrides. The name alludes to a group of islands and stacks, seven in all, of which Hirta (Pl. VIIIa, p. 61) is the largest, extending to 1,575 acres and reaching a height of 1,397 feet. The other small islands are Soay, 244 acres, 1,225 feet ; Boreray, 189 acres, 1,245 feet ; Dun, 79 acres, 576 feet ; Stac an Armin (Pl. XXIb, p. 176), 13 acres, 627 feet ; Stac Lii, 6 acres, 544 feet ; Stac Levenish, 6 acres, 185 feet. No permanent human inhabitants on St. Kilda since September, 1930. Largest gannetry in the world.

Rockall (Pl. XXII, p. 177) is just a protruding rock 70 feet high above a reef, lying 184 miles almost due west of St. Kilda. Has been landed on in 1810, possibly in 1887 and 1888, and in 1921. No plants on the rock.

Flannan Isles (Pl. XXVIa, p. 197). The group consists of 7 main islands and a large number of skerries lying 17 miles WNW. of Gallan Head on the west side of Lewis. The largest island is 39 acres in extent and the highest point 288 feet. All the Flannans are cliff-bound. There is a lighthouse on the largest island.

North Rona (Pl. XXIV, p. 193) lies 47 miles NE. of the Butt of Lewis and the same distance NW. of Cape Wrath. The island is 300 acres in extent, cliff-bound and reaching a height of 355 feet.

Sula Sgeir (Pl. XXIII, p. 192) is 12½ miles WSW. of North Rona. It is a rock of a few acres but is about half a mile long with a sea cave running right through it in the middle, and reaching a height of 229 feet. Large gannetry.

Sule Stack (Pl. XXV, p. 196) is 30 miles north of Loch Eriboll off the north coast of Scotland ; about 6 acres and 120–130 feet high. Gannetry.

Sule Skerry rightly belongs to the Orkney group. Lies a few miles NE. of Sule Stack. A flat reef half a mile long ; 35 acres, 40–45 feet at highest point where there is a lighthouse.

Haskeir is a low islet of a few acres of gneiss lying about 7 miles NW. of Griminish Point, North Uist. Atlantic seals.

Oidhsgeir, 6–7 miles south of Canna, and 7–8 west of Rum. Over half a mile long, 38 feet at highest point. Two low reefs of columnar basalt. The sea leads up to a small lagoon in the middle of the island.

Monach Isles. These low islands of shell-sand and gneiss lie about 8 miles SW. of Hougarry Point, N. Uist. They became uninhabited, except for the lighthouse on the extreme western tip, in 1942. There are two main islands, extending to about 600 acres in all.

Berneray is the southernmost island of the Hebridean chain, 400 acres and 580 feet in height. The only habitation is the lighthouse at the southern end, Barra Head.

Shillay, the westernmost island in the Sound of Harris. A few acres of low gneiss. Atlantic seals.

Shiant Isles. Not strictly oceanic as they lie in the Minch, 17 miles due east from Tarbert, Harris. There are three islands and some small rocks, totalling 500 acres, composed of tertiary basalt, some of it columnar ; highest point 523 feet.

Skerryvore and *Dhu Artach* are just small rocks lying 10–20 miles SW. of Tiree and of Mull. Both have lighthouses.

The *Treshnish Isles* (Pl. Va, p. 52, Pl. XIXa, p. 156) lying between Tiree and Mull are open to the ocean on the SW. They are of basalt and the two largest islands, Lunga and Dutchman's Cap, have volcanic cones, the latter having such a marked one as to give the island its name, and to make it a well-known landmark. The largest island, Lunga, is 170 acres and 337 feet high. The cone of the Dutchman set on a level platform of rock is 284 feet high.

The natural history of the small sub-oceanic islands off the West of Scotland has been worked out so far by comparatively few men. The first who left a record of his work was Sir Donald Monro, High Dean of the Isles, who wrote in 1549. We need not let ourselves be irritated by his vagaries of size and distance, but can be grateful instead that he wrote at all considering the difficulties of the subject. He tells us much that is valuable about cover, nesting birds, inhabitants and so on. Next came Martin Martin, Gent., whose book was first published in 1703. His work was detailed, accurate, and is invaluable to the student of to-day. In my opinion his work is much to be preferred to that of Pennant (1774), who had much more scientific training but made his tour as an intelligent traveller rather than as the naturalist he was on his own ground. Martin is also more reliable in some branches of natural history than John Macculloch whose high-flown descriptions filled four volumes in 1824. All the same, there is a lot of good fun in Macculloch.

The 19th century was remarkable for the number of men of independent means who were both interested in natural history and were keen to visit the out-of-the-way corners of their own country. There was the group which centred round Harvie-Brown and who are perpetuated in the *Vertebrate Fauna of Scotland* series: T. E. Buckley, J. Swinburne, R. M. Barrington and M. E. Heddle. Their description of remote islands in the series are sometimes a little breathless but there is always enthusiasm and a feeling that they hoped to come back again later and do better.

The bird migration work of Eagle Clarke on these remote islands is well known, that of J. Wilson Dougal in geology and in general observation much less so.

The next move was the modern one, which came after the first German war, consisting of young men who worked alone or in pairs, though they all knew each other and were ever ready to share their knowledge and results. There is Malcolm Stewart, who has visited most of the remoter islands and rocks and has recorded his observations in a book (1933) and in papers. He was also responsible for gathering together a group of modern scientific papers on St. Kilda and publishing them as a volume, copies of which he has placed in many libraries in

England and Scotland. George Waterston has given special attention to Fair Isle and the bird migration to be observed there. He has now established a bird trap and ringing station on the island and hopes to make it easier for enthusiasts to visit the place. Tom Harrisson, James Fisher and Gwynne Vevers have also wandered through the islands and have published scientific papers. Robert Atkinson and John Ainslie spent five weeks on North Rona in 1936 and in addition to spending their nights working out the habits of Leach's fork-tailed petrel, recorded in a classic paper (1937), Atkinson in this and later visits made a list of the flora of the island and discussed changes since the previous hurried visit of Barrington in 1886. Atkinson and Ainslie have also visited Sula Sgeir, the Flannans and the Shiants and have recorded their findings. J. W. Campbell has put in many years of study in the Outer and Inner Hebrides, particularly on birds, and is preparing a book. His sister, Miss M. Campbell, has published several papers on the flora of the Hebrides. Happily, all the members of this modern group have survived the second German war and we may hope for further results from them. Heslop Harrison and his group from Durham, working in organized expeditions, have done valuable collecting in the Inner and Outer Hebrides. University expeditions from Edinburgh and Glasgow have also worked in fairly large groups in Barra, South Uist, Canna and Raasay. But these expeditions have not studied the small oceanic islands with which we are specifically dealing.

The phenomenon of paucity of species on these small sub-oceanic islands has been mentioned already. It must be admitted that the number of habitats is severely limited, but even so the reduction of species is striking. I remember quoting Barrington's figure of 35 species for North Rona to Miss M. Campbell and her comment was that he could not have made a detailed study, as there must be far more. However, Atkinson (1940) found that four of Barrington's species had dropped out by 1939, and he found only twelve more than Barrington had seen. The final tally, therefore, is 43 species. On Sula Sgeir, a much smaller island, a dozen miles away, Atkinson finds there are only 7 species. St. Kilda has about 140 species, but here the size and number of habitats are much greater. The Flannans have 22 species of flowering plants.

The vegetational complex of sub-oceanic islands is a distinctive one and the flora of North Rona as recorded by Atkinson (*op. cit.*)

will be given in full as a basis for description and discussion.

Lesser spearwort	*Ranunculus flammula*
Creeping buttercup	*R. repens*
Scurvy grass	*Cochlearia officinalis*
Sea pearlwort	*Sagina maritima*
Mouse-ear chickweed	*Cerastium triviale*
Chickweed	*Stellaria media*
Water chickweed	*Montia fontana*
Wild white clover	*Trifolium repens*
Silverweed	*Potentilla anserina*
Marsh pennywort	*Hydrocotyle vulgaris*
Lovage	*Ligusticum scoticum*
Angelica	*Angelica sylvestris*
Daisy	*Bellis perennis* (2 plants only, 1939)
Scentless mayweed	*Matricaria inodora*
Autumnal hawkbit	*Leontodon autumnalis*
Sea milkwort	*Glaux maritima*
Buck's-horn plantain	*Plantago coronopus*
Sea pink	*Armeria maritima*
Orache	*Atriplex babingtonii*
Sorrel	*Rumex acetosa*
Cotton grass	*Eriophorum angustifolium*
Needle sedge (Marsh club rush)	*Eleocharis* (*Scirpus*) *palustris*
Needle club rush	*Eleocharis* (*Scirpus*) *acicularis*
Tufted sedge	*Carex goodenowii*
Yorkshire fog	*Holcus lanatus*
Matgrass	*Nardus stricta*
Red fescue	*Festuca rubra*
Meadow grass	*Poa pratensis*
Adder's tongue	*Ophioglossum vulgatum*

Atkinson's new finds were:

Sandspurrey	*Spergularia salina*
Yarrow	*Achillea millefolium*—single specimen
Eyebright	*Euphrasia officinalis*
Orache	*Atriplex patula*
Curled dock	*Rumex crispus*
Knotweed	*Polygonum aviculare*
Broad-leaved dock	*Rumex obtusifolius*

R.A.F. Crown Copyright

SULA SGEIR, north of Lewis, Outer Hebrides
May 1942

Robert Atkinson

BOTHY on Sula Sgeir, used by gannet-hunters
August 1939

F. Fraser Darling

THE WEST CLIFF, 300 feet
July 1938

F. Fraser Darling

FIANUIS, the northern peninsula
July 1938

NORTH RONA

Jointed rush	*Juncus articulatus*
Toad rush	*J. bufonius*
Creeping bent grass	*Agrostis stolonifera*
Annual poa grass	*Poa annua*
Decumbent triodia	*Sieglingia decumbens*

The losses from Barrington's list are :

Greater plantain	*Plantago major*
Sheep's sorrel	*Rumex acetosella*
Field woodrush	*Luzula campestris*
Early hair grass	*Aira praecox*

The grassy mound of Rona is made up of *Holcus*, *Nardus*, *Eriophorum* and *Carex*, but as the sea is approached, *Plantago*, *Armeria*, *Festuca* and *Cerastium* increase. *Trifolium* is abundant on what was once the arable ground. *Potentilla* forms exclusive beds about the village site. (This plant was once used for food by Highlanders.) *Stellaria* forms acres of luxuriant growth on Fianuis, where *Poa annua* and *Atriplex* also occur in thick patches. The cliffs show such plants as *Rumex*, *Ligusticum* and *Angelica* in among the luxuriant *Festuca*. *Cochlearia* grows to enormous size near where kittiwakes are breeding. It is interesting that plants of cultivation such as *Plantago major*, *Bellis* and *Ranunculus repens* seem to be dropping out.

But here comes a most interesting point on which I am able to throw some light. Two weeds of cultivation, *Stellaria* and *Atriplex*—and *Poa annua* for that matter—are thriving on Fianuis and have apparently greatly extended their range over ground previously covered with *Armeria* ; Atkinson draws attention to this extension and remarks on the recession of *Armeria* as shown by the " peat " the old cushions have formed. He was told that the oil from the skin of the seals destroyed the vegetation when they came ashore to breed, but he aptly remarks that *Poa*, *Atriplex* and *Stellaria* seem to be unaffected. The fact is that the whole area occupied by these three plants is thickly populated by the seals when they come ashore, and in two or three months of wallowing about at a wet period of the year all this area and a good part of the northern face of the hill are in effect cultivated in that the ground is churned up ankle-deep in mud—black, squelchy mud, in which no green leaf can be seen. This is the autumn ploughing for the crop of *Stellaria*, which is top-dressed in May and June by the large flock of greater black-backed gulls. One thing that *Armeria* cannot stand is being continually trodden, and there can be no doubt that it is the weight of the seals' bodies passing to and fro which is killing the *Armeria* on the flattish smooth parts of Fianuis (Pl. XXIVb, p. 193). And the truth is that the seals have greatly increased in the last fifty years as a result of cessation of hunting. Down at Sceapull, the south-west corner of the island, the density of seals at the breeding season is low, and as Atkinson points out, the vegetation is very different from that of Fianuis, which it topographically resembles. He says: "The vegetation leaves no bare patches as on Fianuis, being a close seaside turf of *Festuca*, *Armeria*, *Plantago*, *Matricaria*, *Leontodon*, and *Cerastium*. . . . *Atriplex*, *Stellaria* and *Poa annua* do not occur."

The vegetation of those portions of the cliffs which are not sheer and have some covering of soil is much affected by the birds which use those portions for nesting purposes. They are the puffin principally, and the fulmar petrel to a slight extent. The puffins burrow into the *Armeria-Festuca* sward and cause such excessive drainage that the whole deposit will slough off and fall over the cliff. The fescue is not grazed in these situations and grows long and luxuriant under the heavy manuring from the birds. Among the waving fronds of the fescue the fulmars hollow out a place for their nests. Sometimes the fulmars are quite hidden among the grass. The puffins where they are present must be a considerable influence on the denudation of soil from sub-oceanic islands.

The vegetational complex of North Rona has been discussed in some detail as typical of a northern British uninhabited island of no great size. St. Kilda with its five times larger area and almost four times greater height has room for many of the plants of hill ground, such as *Festuca ovina*, heather (*Calluna*), bell heather (*Erica cinerea*), blaeberry (*Vaccinium myrtillus*) and even cowberry (*Vaccinium vitis-idaea*) on the summit of Conachair (1,397 feet). Since 1931 much of the grazing of the moorland which had formerly taken place at a heavy density has stopped and it will be interesting through the years to see what happens to the moorland complex.

The flora of the high cliffs of St. Kilda is much richer than that of Rona, for in addition there are the following species (Petch, 1933):

Common polybody	*Polypodium vulgare*
Lady fern	*Athyrium filix-foemina*

Dwarf willow	*Salix herbacea*
Broad shield fern	*Lastrea dilatata*
Bladder campion	*Silene maritima*
Primrose	*Primula vulgaris*
Honeysuckle	*Lonicera periclymenum*
Dandelion	*Taraxacum palustre*

Petch says that the cliffs of St. Kilda still do not show a definite and distinguishable rock community, a condition which he associates with the gabbro rock of which they are composed. This formation tends to give a poor flora in Scotland. The flora of the low cliffs as described by Petch shows but little difference from what has been given for Rona.

The flora of the Flannans grows on a well-drained tableland on top of the sheer cliffs and is predominantly green and grassy. The cliff edges give the same complex as has been given already for other islands (Traill 1905, Bennet 1907).

The avifauna of our sub-oceanic islands is characteristic, and many species not confined to islands breed only on fairly remote sea cliffs on the mainland. Only a few breeding species may be said to be common to a mainland habitat near the sea; for example, the meadow pipit and the rock pipit. It will be as well to run through a list of these sea birds and briefly note their status on our oceanic islands.

First, the gannet or solan (*Sula bassana*), a species about which we know a good deal, thanks to the interest the bird has aroused in man for centuries, and finally to James Fisher and Gwynne Vevers who organized the world gannet census of 1939 and who themselves visited many of the colonies. The species is confined to the North Atlantic. Of the twenty-one extant colonies, thirteen are in waters of the British Isles, eight of these in Scotland, and of the Scottish gannetries three fall within the scope of this volume if we exclude Ailsa Craig. The bird has been used as a source of food since time immemorial, the toll being taken when the young birds have reached their limit of growth on the nest and are being deserted by the parents. Sula Sgeir is the only British gannetry from which young birds are taken nowadays. It is not every year that the rock can be visited and landed upon, but roughly 2,000 young birds or "gugas" are taken when the trip is made about September 1. Sula Sgeir (Pl. XXIII, p. 192) is apparently the only British gannetry where numbers are decreasing. The species as a whole endured a period of vast reduction during the 19th century which is directly referable to the activities of man. Before that, several colonies in Britain had been finished by over-hunting, including those on Rum and Eigg which seem to have flourished in the 16th century. Then we come into the era of cheap food, and however much we may deplore its effects in other quarters of the globe, it must be realized that American wheat, Argentine beef and New Zealand mutton have saved several British animals—the gannet undoubtedly. This easing of the pressure has brought about a growing difference of outlook as Fisher and Vevers say in their exhaustive paper (1943–44) : " . . . the twentieth-century recovery is largely due to the relaxation of his [man's] predation, to the control of it, or to positive protective measures. In the story of the gannet man appears in the different roles of mass-destroyer, harvester, conservator and protector. . . . By mass destruction man reduced the gannet population by about two-thirds in 60 years."

We are back again on an old truth, as yet but little realized, and not at all by those concerned with the predation, that a species which has a very wide feeding distribution, but which must gather for reproduction to a few isolated places, is in very great danger. These gatherings are very large, or at least they seem so to predatory man, and he goes hard at them, wastefully and thoughtlessly, and suddenly the resource disappears. These oceanic creatures are particularly susceptible to exploitation because they have to leave their element for the purpose of reproduction. The gannet must come to a cliff face, risking casualty of broken wing should the wind change to an onshore airt, and above all the approach of predators from which it is free for the rest of the year ; and the Atlantic seal climbs out of the buoyancy and freedom of water to move heavily and painfully on land. The seal cannot even fly away and each year there are losses over the cliff of seals that could not get back. These oceanic birds and mammals are harvesters of fish and small crustacean life which they convert into fat either in their own bodies or in that of their young. The fat is in effect stored there against an inevitable period of starvation. The seal mother leaves her calf, the hen gannet leaves her chick, so does the puffin and all the petrel family. Man is always wanting fat—to eat, to make wheels go round and to blow up his fellows or himself. When the presence of the fat coincides with the period of the animal being out of its element, man finds it hard to keep his fingers off it.

PLATE XXV

James Fisher

SULE STACK, north of Loch Eriboll
May 1939

Robert Atkinson

PUFFIN BURROWS. Eilean More, Flannan Isles
July 1937

F. Fraser Darling

GUILLEMOT LEDGE: smaller ledges occupied by kittiwakes. North Rona
July 1938

To quote Fisher and Vevers further : " At certain colonies, however, man has continuously harvested gannets for his own use, apparently without endangering the population. This is true of no colony in the Gulf of St. Lawrence, nor in the South-West of Britain group ; but applies to Ailsa Craig up to about 1880 ; to the Bass Rock up to 1885 ; to St. Kilda up to 1910 ; to Sule Stack up to 1932 ; and to Sula Sgeir, Myggenaes (Faroe Islands), the Westmann Islands and Eldey (Iceland) up to the present day.

" There is no doubt that at the majority of these colonies man has acted as an unconscious conservator. Indeed, at Myggenaes the inhabitants carefully plan their takes of birds in each year, and set an upper limit to their bag before they start killing ; here we can justifiably call them conscious conservators. At the other colonies it is perhaps the physical circumstances that have prevented man from taking too many ; the weather does not permit the men from Ness in Lewis to visit Sula Sgeir in every year (and when they do visit it they are sometimes forced to depart prematurely) ; and there is still a danger that improved methods of transport or a greater demand for gannet flesh, may materially alter the situation in Lewis or Iceland. In 1940 Eldey was declared a sanctuary, and all gannet-taking stopped there ; it will be interesting to see whether the human predation in the Westmann Islands alters as a result of this, with consequent effect on the balance of gannet numbers in this colony."

The gannet colonies of Boreray, Stac an Armin and Stac Lii, of the St. Kilda group form the largest gannetry in the world at present. The total population there was about 16,900 pairs in 1939, since when it is unlikely there will have been any reduction ; Sula Sgeir holds close on 4,000 pairs, and Sule Stack 3,500 pairs.

Birds of the auk tribe, the guillemot, razorbill, and puffin are inseparably associated in the mind with these oceanic islands. The puffin probably the most numerous, then the guillemot, and the razorbill far behind. Puffins (*Fratercula arctica*) have a habit of destroying their habitat by so far tunnelling it that the bank slips away and this must be responsible for several mass disappearances of puffins from places where they formerly bred. They are exceedingly numerous at the Flannan Islands (Pl. XXVIa, p. 197) (Atkinson, 1938), much more so than at North Rona where, nevertheless, there must be close on 100,000. They are also present in vast numbers, probably at least a million, at St. Kilda where it is by far the commonest bird. There are very few on Sula Sgeir and none on Sule Stack. Berneray and Mingulay at the foot of the Outer Isles also have large puffinries. Handa, Sutherland, has a good population of puffins, but from there one must go as far as the Shiants before reaching the next colony. The Summer Isles and the cliffs of Wester Ross and Sutherland are quite devoid of them. The tertiary basalt of the Shiants, of Fladda Chuain and Ascrib Islands (Skye), and of the Treshnish group, provide perfect conditions for puffins because the soil is friable, with a good skin of turf. The same rock is found in Eigg and Canna where puffins also breed. There are puffins on the Rum cliffs also, and here and there elsewhere on the coast relatively small colonies may be found. The number of puffins is legion, but the restriction of their breeding haunts should be remarked.

The guillemot (*Uria aalge aalge*) is a ledge builder (Pl. XXVIb, p. 197) and wherever it is found it is almost certain to find the kittiwakes as well, nesting on smaller ledges or projections above or below the wider and slightly inward-sloping ledge which the guillemot prefers. The guillemot is a very social bird on the nesting ledges, and yet likes room to move about even if the ledge is crowded. It breeds on all the oceanic islands mentioned except those which are too low, such as Oidhsgeir. It seems to be the only bird which breeds on Rockall where there is only one ledge near the summit. But one may question whether it manages to do this every year for there must be many a June gale which will send seas green over the rock. The guillemot leaves the cliffs with its young about August 10 and stays with it on the sea, thereby extending parental companionship, if not care, over a longer period than is common with puffins and petrels. My opinion is that the guillemots travel far and fast after this date, because I have seen old and young together on the sea in considerable numbers by August 12–15 off Priest Island in the northern Minch, yet the guillemot does not breed anywhere nearer than Handa 32 miles to the north as the crow flies—and the birds would have to come round Rhu Stoer—or the Shiants 32 miles south-west. It is surprising how scarce is the guillemot on the Torridonian cliffs of Sutherland and Ross-shire. Indeed, there is no mainland colony between Cape Wrath and Ardnamurchan. Clo Mor, just east of Cape Wrath, is a magnificent station.

Mention must be made of Southern and Reeve's work (1941) on the incidence of the ringed variety of guillemot (Pl. XXVII, p. 204). This ring is a white monocle (with cord) appearing on the black breeding plumage. The difference between it and the normal phase—though I have not seen it thus explained anywhere—is that this area of feathering which is white anyway in winter, fails to go black with the rest of the head and throat in summer. The character is thought to be referable to a simple genetic allelomorph, but whether dominant or recessive is unknown. Intermediate forms are so extremely rare as to be negligible. Counts undertaken with the help of members of the British Trust for Ornithology showed that the percentage of bridled birds increased from south to north and, in a lesser degree, from east to west. This phenomenon of increase of incidence of a character in definite fashion along a line drawn within the geographical range of a species has been discussed by Huxley (1939) and its expression given the name of *cline*. The counts of some guillemot colonies in the Highland and Island area show the trend of the cline of increase in bridled birds. The figures are quoted from Southern and Reeve (*op. cit.*) :

Location	*Number of birds*	*Incidence per cent bridled*
Islay	75	8·00±3·13
Canna and Sanday	194 172 (2 yrs.)	9·85±1·54
Shiant Isles	1126	11·10±0·91
Mingulay	4004	12·05±0·51
Haskeir	1246	12·36±0·93
St. Kilda	873	16·50±1·26
Handa	1366 3339 (2 yrs.)	9·96±0·42
Loch Eriboll	111	16·22±3·50
North Rona	3206	13·20±0·67
Foula (Shetland)	233 1143 (2 yrs.)	23·80±1·16

Some English stations show less than 1·0 per cent of bridled birds, and at Bear Island in the Arctic the percentage was 53·30±1·19.

The razorbill (*Alca torda*) tends to choose a place of its own rather than a ledge with others, in a little hole in the cliff face, under an overhanging ledge, or even on a tuft of sea pink growing in the face of a high cliff, as I saw one two years running on North Rona. Although it is much less numerous than the guillemot, it is found almost everywhere where guillemots occur and much farther afield than this bird : for example, there are a few razorbills nesting far up Loch Broom, and a few more in parts of the Summer Isles. There were about 1,500 razorbills at North Rona in 1938 compared with several thousand guillemots, but Harrisson says there were only 12 pairs present at St. Kilda in 1931, despite careful search. There had evidently been a great reduction since Eagle Clarke's day (1912). However, Fisher says there were many more than twelve pairs present in 1939, many being hidden in crevices of the rocks—just the sort of places they choose for breeding.

The black guillemot or tystie (*Uria grylle*) (Pl. 27b, p. 220) is generally present about the oceanic islands, but there are never many of them anywhere. It is a sociable bird on the sea, but nests privately in some deep crack in the rocks. Two eggs are laid instead of the one characteristic of the auks, and these are roundish oval in form, not pointed at one end like the guillemot's and razorbill's. Sometimes the black guillemot is migratory ; for example, it does not winter at North Rona, but it is present all the year round at Priest Island, 85 miles south. At St. Kilda, the Oxford and Cambridge party found only six pairs in 1931, and Fisher and Nicholson saw only one bird in 1939.

The little auk (*Alle alle*) does not breed with us, of course, and at one time its occurrence even in winter was a matter for comment. A change has evidently occurred within recent years, for this bird is now regularly seen each winter about the islands. I would see two or three at a time in the Anchorage of Tanera or on the seas outside, and I have found its remains at a peregrine's eyrie on Priest Island.

There is no point in going through each member of the gull family, for the presence of many of the British species on our oceanic islands is taken for granted. The kittiwake (*Rissa tridactyla*) is always a bird of the cliff face ; the herring gull (*Larus argentatus*) nests on the tops of the cliffs near the edges or in broken ground nearer sea level ; the lesser black-backed gull (*Larus fuscus*) nests much more inland on islands or may join the herring gulls, but it is remarkable that both species, and especially the lesser black-backed gull, fail to reach large numbers on our truly oceanic islands. The common gull (*Larus canus*) is present only on St. Kilda of our group of islands and is not making much headway from a few pairs. Fisher says none was present in June 1939.

When we come to the great black-backed gull (*Larus marinus*) there is quite a different story to tell. This big, handsome, ugly-faced creature is a very important bird in every way, not least in relation to the flora of the islands. Its status is variable. At St. Kilda, 1,576 acres, " Pairs at intervals round the cliffs . . . also non-breeding adults . . . about fifty in all " (Harrisson and Lack, 1934) ; Fisher says there were about the same in 1939, but that a curious feature was the large proportion of non-breeders. North Rona, 300 acres, 500 pairs breeding (Darling) ; Glas Leac Beag, Summer Isles, 34 acres, 120 pairs (Darling). Such figures cause one to think and take note. The North Rona flock is without doubt the largest in Britain, and the one on Glas Leac Beag is surprisingly large considering the position of the island and the fact that there is no harvest of dead young seals to be cleared up as on Rona. This bird increases where man does not ordinarily get near to it at breeding time. The colony on Glas Leac is saved by the swell of the Minch and the fact that the grazing is not used in May and June. It is a colony of long standing and the influence on the flora has been profound. The other isles of the Summer group are heather-covered, but Glas Leac is brilliantly green and heather is found only at the south end, growing small and low in the grass. In August the island is bright with sheep's-bit scabious (*Jasione montana*) truly a heavenly blue. No island in comparatively narrow waters has given me the sense of ocean as has Glas Leac Beag ; after all, there is no land to the north of it this side of the North Pole ! Lovage and angelica grow in luxuriant profusion, their siliceous stems being used the next year by the big gulls for their nests. The western cliffs are covered on their face by the grey-green goat's-beard lichen and on their upper surface by a vivid saffron lichen. The shelving rocks of the east side are golden with it to the sea's edge. Green and gold, these are the colours of Glas Leac. This remarkable enrichment of the herbage by the gulls has a further consequence ; it draws a flock of 300 barnacle geese in winter, and the island is the chosen sanctuary of the whole Summer Isles race of grey lag geese in their flightless time in July and August. They swim there from the other islands.

The eider duck (*Somateria mollissima*) was once a common nesting bird on Glas Leac and on Rona as well. It does not nest on either island now : that is the other side of the picture. A few puffins used also to be found on Glas Leac, but they have gone. There may be a pair of tysties nesting in the fissures of the Torridonian sandstone and there are a few nesting shags. These, with some rock pipits and a pair of wheatears complete the nesting birds of the island. Several workers have remarked that puffins are not nearly so numerous on North Rona as on St. Kilda and other places. The big gulls are the reason for the reduction. Puffins are the rabbits of the avian world, yet they have but one egg a year. Obviously the possible maximum age of a puffin is far greater than that of a rabbit, which in the wild is thought not to exceed two years. The puffin is the great gull's meat and manna for the months of May, June and July, and a few days of August. Then the puffins go from the islands in a night, and so do the guillemots and razorbills, and a lot of the kittiwakes leave the ledges. The island seems a desolate place and the great black-backed gulls are momentarily hungry. If the thousand black-backs on Rona eat each a puffin every other day, the toll must be heavy in a season. The gull stands above a puffin's burrow ; the little bird comes out quite cautiously, but not cautiously enough, for there is a sudden lunge and he finds his whole head in the black-back's mouth. The puffin is skinned and the skin is left as clean as a glove drawn inside out.

Adult fulmars do not appear to be attacked by the great black-back, but by some means I do not know this gull is able to catch some of the night-flying Leach's fork-tailed and storm petrels, birds which are dark in colour, small and exceedingly fast in flight. The black-back itself is not normally active at night, but it was reasonably noticeable on Rona that at the time the Leach's petrels were flying and calling there was a lull among them if the black-backs were roused by something and started their dreadful complaint. This ability of the black-backs to capture the tiny storm petrels is not confined to the large gull colony of Rona where there are also many petrels ; I have found bones and feathers of the little birds in the casts on Priest Island also.

The sudden exodus of the auks and kittiwakes from the oceanic islands causes the black-back population to migrate in search of food. But with an island like Rona, a large proportion comes back again in mid-September for the breeding season of the seals, at which time they act as efficient scavengers. The observer will see many tugs-of-war between them, the rope being the elastic afterbirth from a cow seal. The slack is down the birds' gullets, but in the course of the strife it may not stay there. After the feast of afterbirths there is the crop of dead seal calves which reaches about 10 per cent of the number born. Occasionally they are born dead and some die at a fortnight or a month old, so there is a fair succession of carrion for the gulls when, as on Rona, the total calf crop is about 1,500.

The black-backs on the oceanic islands are joined in winter by a sprinkling of young glaucous gulls. These birds are the same size as the black-backs, but the young of this species are easily recognizable by the much finer and lighter-coloured pencilling of the plumage. The glaucous gulls are more aggressive than the black-backs and a young one will successfully intimidate an adult black-back.

It is worth noting here that neither on the Treshnish Isles nor on North Rona did I see a black-back make an attack on a living baby seal. Several casual observers have said that such attacks are made, but it is not good enough to infer this from seeing a gull working on a carcass. I have heard the same thing said as a result of seeing month-old seals with sore eyes. This occasional suppuration was much commoner among the Treshnish seals than on Rona, and it appeared to clear up when the animals got to the sea. Careful examination made me certain that the suppuration was not caused by traumatic damage. A young seal can exhibit quite an impressive threat display and can be very quick to snap : the black-back is a bird which does not like to face even the slightest threatening gesture.

A heavy population of black-backs *and* a large seal nursery thus means a very heavy manuring with organic matter : the consequent richness of the grazing of such islands is proverbial, and as we have seen, brings about modification of the herbage to a standard far above what would be expected of soil from the parent rock.

Strangely enough, such an oceanic bird as the Arctic tern (*Sterna macrura*) is not a nesting species on the many of our small remote islands. There are two or three small colonies on North Rona, nesting directly among the gneiss pebbles which their eggs so much resemble. They are not present at St. Kilda or the Flannans, nor on the outer Summer Isles, yet the sandy island of Tiree seethes with terns, Arctic, common and little.

The occurrence of geese on the British oceanic islands has always interested me. The barnacle geese (*Branta leucopsis*) come in thousands to the *machairs* of the Outer Hebrides, to the Treshnish Isles, the Summer Isles and many another place in the West Highland area. Rona would provide good wintering for a flock but they are not present; nor do they winter at St. Kilda. White-fronted geese (*Anser albifrons*) are also common on the Outer Hebridean *machair*, Islay and Tiree in winter, but not on the little islands. One of the great goose-wintering grounds of the West Highlands is the island of Islay. Atkinson and Ainslie saw a single specimen of grey lag goose on Rona in 1936, in July. In the summer of 1938 there were four on the island. Their behaviour was exceedingly shy. I used to see the birds lying on the water half a mile out during the day, and only once did I see them ashore, on the south-western peninsula of Sceapull, not where the best grazing was to be had. In the early mornings I would see new droppings in the rank growth of chickweed, where they had evidently been grazing in the night. I saw no sign of these birds during eight days of late June 1939.

The interest of sub-oceanic islands as ports of call for migrant birds is exceptional. Eagle Clarke's *Studies in Bird Migration*, 1912, shows something of the wealth of species which may be observed on the spring and autumn movements. Since his day the interest has been maintained, particularly by members of the Midlothian Ornithological Club on Isle of May and Fair Isle. We have no similar effort to record migration of the West Coast and in the Hebrides. St. Kilda, the Flannans and North Rona get an extraordinary variety of migrants. Birds like spotted redshanks, green sandpipers and little stints are understandable, but it is hard to believe one's eyes when a turtle-dove appears among the seals. The big winter gales bring in occasional specimens of strange birds, quite apart from the regular equinoctial movements. Unless the naturalist is resident, most of these occurrences are missed.

Most of the Scottish oceanic islands carry some member of the petrel and shearwater family, the Procellariidae. St. Kilda heads the list with four species—the fulmar, Leach's fork-tailed petrel, the storm petrel and the Manx shearwater. Rona, Sula Sgeir, and the Flannans lack the shearwater, but are among the few other British stations of Leach's petrel. The islands of tertiary basalt off the West Highland coast are favoured nesting places because of the easily burrowed soil and considerable talus slopes. Manx shearwaters (*Puffinus puffinus*) are found on Rum, Eigg and Canna and the Shiants, on the Treshnish Isles, all basalt, and on the southernmost islands of the Outer Hebrides, which are of gneiss. The Treshnish Isles also have three of the family, the fulmar and the storm petrel being the other two. Only small islands seem to hold the storm petrel (*Hydrobates pelagicus*) and then only the outer ones of a group. There is no record of this bird breeding

PLATE XXVII

F. Fraser Darling

GUILLEMOTS, one being of the bridled form. Rona
July 1938

F. Fraser Darling

FULMAR, incubating among the sea-pinks. Rona
July 1938

Robert Atkinson

ST. KILDA WREN, removing faecal sac from nest. Hirta, St. Kilda
August 1938

on the British mainland, but once on its little island it makes no attempt to keep particularly close to the sea. I have found it nesting in a hole in the peat 200 yards inland on Priest Island. The Manx shearwater will go well inland also and is inclined to nest at fairly high altitudes, as in Rum. The fulmar nests at a high altitude in Spitsbergen and sometimes up to 20 miles inland (J. Fisher in *Handbook of British Birds*) but in Britain it is mostly a coastal nester only. It has been found breeding some way inland in Orkney and in Easter Ross, and six miles inland in Northumberland. On North Rona, it has colonized the village site, where the semi-subterranean dwellings with their devious passages seem much to their liking.

Leach's petrel (*Oceanodroma leucorrhoa*) is probably our rarest breeding petrel and it is usual to look upon it as a rare bird, though its population cannot justify such an impression. Atkinson and Ainslie have done the most painstaking work on the species in Britain, and with a fine patience have ascertained that in 1936 there were 377 pairs on North Rona. There may not be so many on Sula Sgeir, where Atkinson confirmed their breeding, but they are apparently more numerous on the Flannans and St. Kilda. The rareness then is in the remoteness of the few oceanic stations, and in the restricted area in which these lie. It would be interesting to know whether the storm petrel, though wider distributed, is any more numerous than Leach's.

These two petrels—I say it consciously and without shame—are dear little birds. The churring noise of the stormie is one of the comforting things to the human visitor in his nights on an oceanic island. Leach's petrel is larger, about the size of a thrush, and has lovely grey shading round the full black eye. The birds in the air have an arresting, wild, staccato calling, but those in the burrows make an exceptionally sweet ascending trill which is not so often heard. Both species have an aerial display in the summer darkness but that of the Leach's is much more impressive and takes place with larger numbers of birds. To be present at one of the breeding stations on a fine July night is one of the great experiences for a naturalist.

The Manx shearwater's cry when indulging in somewhat similar aerial evolutions is anything but comforting. It is an unearthly shriek which has to be heard to be believed. The breeding habits of these birds have been closely studied and described by Lockley (1941) wherein he shows that the South Welsh shearwaters feed in the Bay of Biscay area during the nesting season. It still remains for someone to pin a flag on a map showing where the West Highland shearwaters feed and to find out exactly how long each sex is away from the nesting burrow in this area.

Lastly, there is the fulmar (*Fulmarus glacialis*), the history and status of which in Britain have been the subject of an exhaustive paper by Fisher and Waterston. Before 1878 this arctic species bred in British waters only at St. Kilda, but at this one station Fisher shows that there was a fairly constant and very high population of about 21,000 pairs. A budding-off from this vast stock or from the even vaster stock in the Faeroes occurred in 1878 when a few birds were seen at Foula in the Shetlands, which island, it may be remarked, was farther away than many another oceanic station it might have colonized. But the fulmar at that time preferred high cliffs for a nesting site, and Foula practically equals St. Kilda in having the highest sea cliff in Britain. The fulmar to-day is less fastidious and will occupy a cliff between 50 and 100 feet. Fisher's work can be studied in detail for the exact dates of the spread of this bird round the British coasts, and for the illuminating statistical analysis he makes. He shows that the oft-repeated theory of the fulmar being able to spread as a result of man taking fewer young ones and adults for food, oil and feathers, at St. Kilda, is not tenable. There was a deeper biological reason. As far as the West Highland oceanic islands are concerned, the following dates of colonization with proved breeding may be given: North Rona (Pl. XXVIIIa, p. 205) and Sula Sgeir, 1887; Flannans, 1902; Barra Head, 1899; Tiree, 1929; Haskeir, 1919; Shiants, 1910; Treshnish, 1925–6; Priest Island, 1937; Fladda-Chuain, 1933–4; Canna, 1933; and Sule Stack, 1928. The directions of spread seem to have been north to Foula, Rona and Shetland, then south to Orkney, along the north coast and into the Minch as far as the Shiants. Another and later stream is thought by Fisher to have struck south to Barra Head and to the Irish coast, along the north coast of Ireland and up the West Highland coast as far as the north of Skye, where they have met the southward-moving stream.

Fisher's statistical analysis of the breeding efficiency of the many fulmar colonies has proved for this species the cogency of Darling's theory of social stimulation as a factor leading to successful breeding condition in colonial-nesting birds, and the presence of a numerical threshold in some species before breeding takes place. This theory emerged from a study of herring gulls, lesser black-backed gulls and fulmars on Priest Island of the Summer Isles. It was found that large flocks of gulls began to lay earlier in the season than small flocks ; and that large flocks—as flocks—laid their eggs in a shorter period of time than small flocks. Later observation showed that this fact appeared to have value for the production of a good crop of fledglings. The larger flocks produced a higher percentage of young ultimately taking to the air. This concept has now been applied by Fisher in both his gannet and fulmar studies and has been found relevant. It is no easy thing for a colonial-nesting species such as these to get going at a new colony unless several sets of ecological conditions are at their optimum or at least generally favourable. There is a threshold of numbers below which breeding does not take place.

So much for the sea birds. Some of the oceanic islands have a rather surprising list of other birds nesting. Finches are not typical birds for these places, but St. Kilda has the twite and had the tree sparrow in the past, though it has now disappeared. The hedge sparrow is also a bird hardly to be expected, but there were three pairs on Priest Island and the species occurs on other shrubless islands not too far out. Ailsa Craig is one, nine miles from Girvan. The hedge sparrow of the Outer Hebrides and of Skye and the Inner Hebrides, has been given sub-specific rank as *Prunella modularis hebrideum*. Its upper parts are darker and the feather edging more rufous. The throat and breast are also a darker grey than in *P. m. occidentalis*. Most oceanic islands support their pair of peregrines if there are cliffs high enough to allow them to nest—that is, over 80 to 100 feet. Buzzards are usually present if there are rabbits. St. Kilda and Rona are free of rabbits, but Eilean Mor of the Flannans and Lunga of the Treshnish are infested with them.

There are no wrens on Rona or the Flannans, but St. Kilda is like a little country unto itself and has its own wren (*Troglodytes t. hirtensis*) (Pl. XXVIIIb, p. 205). The bird was noticed by Martin Martin in his famous visit to St. Kilda in 1697 and by Macaulay in 1764. The ornithologist Seebohm was the first to point out that this bird merited sub-specific rank. The St. Kilda wren is slightly larger than the mainland wren, its nape and head are uniform grey brown, and the rest of the upper parts a brighter brown than *T. t. troglodytes*. The under parts are paler. Barring is more pronounced and there is a whiter superciliary eye stripe. Its song is sweeter and less shrill and energetic than in the mainland form.

Conferring specific or sub-specific rank on a small bird of small numbers on a small island is a doubtful blessing to the bird. It nearly finished the St. Kilda wren—in the interests of science and all that. The number of museums about the world which consider themselves eligible subjects to receive a full range of male, female, immature summer and winter plumage, is large, far larger than the total population of poor *T. t. hirtensis*. But a museum will take no for an answer, collectors will not. These maniacs will go to extraordinary lengths to satisfy their obsession and under the laws of this country they are not certifiable, but must be brought before the summary courts to be fined. In an age when mental disorder of a serious kind is treated during permanent detention in an asylum rather than by punishment in the criminal courts, it is surprising that such humaneness should not be extended to the collectors of eggs and rare birds. This tiny bird was almost extinct by 1888, when Harvie-Brown published the Outer Hebrides volume of his series. He gave the St. Kilda wren but little space and devoted all of that to what he felt about the callous collecting that was going on. The value of those 19th-century country gentlemen who pursued the study of natural history in a varied and often all-embracing form is shown by the later history of the St. Kilda wren. Harvie-Brown himself was one: then Sir Herbert Maxwell of Monreith (who, years before, had done something quite new in making the large lake at Monreith into a sanctuary for waterfowl) made good use of his membership of Parliament by getting passed the Wild Birds Protection (St. Kilda) Act, 1904. This Act was designed specifically to protect the wren and Leach's fork-tailed petrel.

By 1910 and 1914 the species had much increased and Harrisson and Buchan of the 1931 party were able to record the following number of breeding pairs after careful census work: Hirta, 45 pairs; Dun, 11 pairs; Soay, 9 pairs; Boreray, 3(?) pairs; a total of 68 pairs. The species is by preference a dweller in the high cliffs where puffins and fulmars breed. Approximately a sixth of the total number breeds at the village site where, presumably, the conditions of former cultivation provide a food supply which is not available inland on the island at the breeding season. Harrisson and Buchan's paper gives most interesting data on the types of territories found, how the male and female "work" different patches within their territories and how small birds of other species are tolerated in close proximity to their nests. The authors discuss the known autumnal movements of other wrens and suggest that intensive ringing of wrens on migration would show whether the St. Kilda wren tended to leave the island. As it is, the birds are known to move inland on St. Kilda in autumn and to subsist on ground which they shun in summer. Nicholson and Fisher found the population in 1939 to be much the same as in 1931.

The tendency of remote islands to produce differentiated races of animals is further exhibited on St. Kilda by its mice, of which there are two species: the St. Kilda house mouse (*Mus musculus muralis*) and the long-tailed field mouse of St. Kilda (*Apodemus sylvaticus hirtensis*). It is probable that the house mouse was introduced within historical time, but *Apodemus* is considered to be a true relic. A rather similar form of *Apodemus* is found in the Uists. Just as in the American mouse *Peromyscus* there is a well-marked cline between east and west in coat colour, so in *Mus* and particularly in *Apodemus* it is probable that the island races of mice in Britain form steps in a broken cline. The small oceanic islands of the West Highlands, including St. Kilda, have no voles which might have offered other separate races as have Orkney and the islands off the south-west corner of Wales.

M. m. muralis may be described as a robust type of *M. musculus* and having a lighter underside than the normal mainland house mouse. When St. Kilda was inhabited this house mouse was generally found throughout the houses except the post office. Its fate after the evacuation in 1930 was one of the especial interests of the 1931 expedition. Harrisson and Moy-Thomas (1933) carried out a good deal of live trapping and marking, and finally assessed the total population at between 12 and 25 head. They take the view that the St. Kilda house mouse is doomed to extinction as it is unable to adapt itself to a life without home and fireside so to speak. They also mention that about a dozen cats were left in 1930, but by 1931 only three were to be seen. Two of these, females, were shot, and as one of them had kittens the one which got away must have been a tom. So we may hope that the feline population of St. Kilda will not increase henceforth. The authors admit that the cats must have been a potent factor in reducing the house mice between 1930 and 1931, but ignore the future absence of cats, and prophesy that absence of traditional food supply will bring about extinction of the mice. In 1938 Robert Atkinson did extensive trapping in the village, particularly in houses which had been inhabited during summers since the 1930 evacuation; also in lofts, in byres and in cleits, etc. There was no sign of a house mouse; field mice were very common indeed in the houses, as well as walls, turf, byres and cleits, etc. Sometimes the field mouse was seen in the daylight. There was no sign of a cat and he heard no mention of one. Fisher says he saw no sign of the house mouse in 1939.

At this juncture Darling's experience of house mice on Lunga of the Treshnish Isles seems relevant. The expedition was housed in a bell tent on a ledge about 80 feet above the sea and about 20–50 yards from the ruins of the old houses which were of the traditional type, dry-stone and flat-gabled, and now, of course, without roofs. The island had not been inhabited for about 80 years before 1937. Within a few nights of our arrival, mice of some sort were coming into the tents and tackling the stores ; and it was not long before they were showing all the cheekiness of the house mouse and indulging in games. The house mouse is a very playful animal. Trapping was essential as the stores were not rodent-proof and in four months we caught 75 individuals. From the incidence of this trapping it was obvious that there were always more coming in, so the total population present must have been considerable. These mice showed no different features from type specimens, and it was interesting to note that after the years of living as field mice, this island race was ready immediately to take up the traditional existence of house mice again. Vevers found a comparable condition in the Faeroes. In Highland houses, *Apodemus sylvaticus* is often the only mouse to come indoors, usually in October, but this species is always much less obtrusive than the house mouse and *much* less destructive. The Treshnish experience showed that the habits of the house mouse are strongly hereditary and not greatly altered by education ! It will be most interesting to make sure what has happened to *M. m. muralis* when the next expedition visits St. Kilda, which cannot be less than 15 years after the one of 1931. The proprietor of St. Kilda, the Earl of Dumfries, has done his best to preserve the unique fauna of the islands.

The St. Kildan long-tailed field mouse feeds largely on grass and is found almost wholly below 400 feet. It does not occur on areas of very short grass. It is rather larger than the type specimen and sometimes inclined to be yellowish brown underneath. Harrisson and Moy-Thomas suggest that the evacuation (with comparative cessation of grazing) may influence the future of this mouse, for heather (*Calluna*) may be expected to increase and the grasses on which the mice live will regress. However, the proprietor has placed some of the indigenous

Soay sheep on Hirta to replace the domesticated sheep taken off, so a balance may be preserved. The mice occur on Dun, where sheep were not and are not grazed.

Rona and the smaller sub-oceanic islands listed at the beginning of this chapter have no mice or voles. The Shiants are, unfortunately, full of brown rats (*Rattus norvegicus*). Several of the Inner Hebrides and even a small island like Priest Island of 300 acres have pygmy shrews (*Sorex minutus*). Elton (1938) found both *Apodemus* and *Sorex minutus* on Pabbay, one of the outermost islands in the Sound of Harris. He remarks also on the submerged forests of this region and of the remains of birch and hazel in the peat, and says that the mammalian fauna of these islands has a markedly woodland aspect. This, evidently, is the point ; the long-tailed field mouse and the pygmy shrew are relics of an era of woodland now long gone. These would not be carried to such outlying places by means by which the house mouse must have travelled and one can but conclude that they have been there since the islands were cut off from the mainland in post-glacial times. There seems to have been no differentiation of these tiny mammals during their long isolation, but a closer investigation needs to be made than has been done up to now. (Ailsa Craig has a heavy population of *R. norvegicus* which live on birds in summer and shellfish in winter ; they have driven the puffins away. Ailsa also has *Sorex minutus* and a slow-worm.)

It would also be interesting to know how far out from considerable land masses otters will go. They will certainly colonize islands five miles off shore and live entirely from sea fish. There were several otter cairns on Priest Island and throughout the Summer Isles. They were often to be seen playing in the sea or running about the island in the early morning. Otters are common in the Outer Hebrides where they frequent the isolated rocks of the Sound of Harris, and at the southern tip of the Isles extend to Barra Head, which entails a few miles of ocean crossing. No otters have been reported from St. Kilda.

One more island mammal remains to be mentioned in this chapter —the Soay sheep of St. Kilda (Pl. XXIX, p. 228), which must have been brought there a thousand years ago or more by the Vikings. An exactly similar sheep does not now exist elsewhere. It is not as primitive as the wild moufflon, but it is similar to it in type, though smaller, as one might expect from the habitat. The colour is moorit brown, such as is common in the Shetland breed which has similar ancestry to the Soay, but Soay sheep tend to a lighter colour on the underside and on the legs. The horns of the Soay ram are of the same type as in the moufflon, i.e. lifting well up from the head and taking a full, wide curve. Soay sheep grow a short, fine coat of soft wool which tends to rub off in late winter and early spring, whereas the moufflon has quite a stiff short hair with an undercoat of wool. The mane and hair on the throat which is characteristic of the moufflon also appears on the Soay. The tail is short, triangular, and without wool in both sheep. Shetland sheep may be looked upon as an improved Soay sheep of Norse ancestry also. Most of our domesticated sheep are of Asiatic origin, but there is good reason to think that the Shetland, the Soay and the old Manx breed were originally free from the Roman-nosed, long-tailed, Asiatic stock. One characteristic feature of Soay and Shetland sheep is their dished or concave face and the width of the cranium in relation to other facial measurements.

These little sheep with the comparatively large brain-boxes are not so equipped for nothing: they have a great deal of native common sense which the Asiatic type has lost. The Soay sheep were formerly confined to the islands of Soay and Dun and were the property of the proprietor, Macleod of Macleod, not of the St. Kildans of Hirta, who had a mixed lot of small sheep. It is practically impossible to work these sheep with a dog, and if an attempt is made to catch them, they will go into the cliffs and prove a very trying handful. The Shetland sheep which I kept in the Summer Isles and which received very little shepherding reverted to the same hereditary wildness. If they were not got where they were wanted at the first try, they would scatter, not flock, and go into the cliffs; and in such positions the rams do not hesitate to turn against dog or man. These sheep act very much like deer in that they take full advantage of cover which, on a bare island, means the other side of the hill. The sense of smell is acute and well used. The lambs are a dark nigger brown at birth and have a flat hairy coat. When the mothers move away from an intruder, the lambs go on the far side of them, so that it is quite difficult to count the number of lambs in a flock. They are active immediately after birth, and at a few hours old can keep up with their mothers. If a herbivorous ruminant animal of extreme wildness, such as red deer or a Soay sheep, is taken while very young, preferably on the first day of life, it becomes tamer than many other kinds of animals ever do. I have seen Soay sheep thus reared which have been so tame as to be

F. Fraser Darling

F. Fraser Darling

THE ATLANTIC SHORES OF TIREE
Shell sand beaches banked by dunes and *machair*. Inner Hebrides
July 1945

F. Fraser Darling

LOBSTER in rock pool, with *Corallina* and *Laminaria*. Summer Isles, Wester Ross
July 1943

F. Fraser Darling

MUSSELS on a rock, with sea anemone and wrack. Barnacles on the mussel shells
Sunart, Argyll. August 1945

a nuisance. Their human associates do not seem to be able to make them fear. Only strangers can do this.

It would be impossible in the space of this book to deal fully with the invertebrate fauna of sub-oceanic islands in the area. The number of species is vast. Let it be said that though a good deal of collecting has been done, there remains a large ecological field of study for the adventurer. The seal grounds of Rona, churned to deep mud in winter, swarm with dipterous flies in summer. When, in July and August, the swifts were seen hawking hour after hour along the northern slope of Rona, gliding to and fro just a foot or two above the ground, I used to wonder why there, and not along the fine grassy pastures of the southern slope. Apparently the work of the seals on that north face in winter creates a more numerous dipterous fauna. I did some drag-netting in June 1939, over the Fianuis chickweed and over the grazing of the southern slope, and found flies were present in greater density on the former. The Diptera is by far the most numerous order of insects on the islands.

The Diptera do some of those tasks of pollination which normally fall to hymenopterous insects in other places. Gordon Hewitt (1907) remarking on the occurrence of the orchis *O. maculata* on St. Kilda says that this species is usually fertilized by bees, but he saw a dipterous fly, probably an *Anthomyia*, with two pollinia of *O. maculata* on its head.

Hymenopterous insects are limited in type on small Scottish islands. Elton (1938) found two species of bumble bee, *Bombus s. smithianus* and *Bombus distinguendus*, on Pabbay as compared with five species on Lewis and Harris. But on St. Kilda there are no bumble bees nor are they on Rona.[1] Lack (1932) found the ant *Myrmica ruginodis* on St. Kilda, but there is none on Rona. In fact, it may be said that the hymenopterous fauna of these small islands is predominantly parasitic, consisting of ichneumons and braconids, of which there are many species well distributed.

Over 130 species of beetles have been recorded from St. Kilda, but there is nothing striking about the list as most are found on the West Highland coast, though *Harpalus quadripunctatus*, *Homolota excellens* and *Arpedium brachypterum* are uncommon mountain forms. Lack (1932) found many species of the Coleoptera which had been previously recorded were now absent or rare. These were mostly carrion feeders

[1] James Fisher says he saw a black and yellow bumble bee on St. Kilda on June 3, 1939, but was unable to catch it for identification.

and dung beetles, Staphylinidae, Trichopterygidae and Cryptophagidae, and he attributes this shortage to the removal of livestock and consequent absence of dung. He found 21 species new to St. Kilda, and as some were conspicuous insects he thinks they must be fairly recent introductions, or they would have been noticed by Waterston and Hewitt 25 years before. There is no doubt that the appearance and disappearance of man, and his movements hither and thither, have a great indirect influence on the distribution of species and on their survival or extinction. One species of weevil found, *Ceuthorrhynchus contractus*, has hitherto been recorded only from Lundy Island in the Bristol Channel, where it feeds on wild cabbage (*Brassica oleracea*). The only crucifer on St. Kilda now is scurvy grass, near which plant the two specimens were caught. This find points once more to the Lusitanian affinity in West Highland flora and fauna. Some of St. Kilda's insect fauna must be wind-borne. James Fisher says he saw bumble bees ten miles out from the Sound of Harris in calm weather after east wind.

There is quite a surprising list of Lepidoptera from the islands, but perhaps it is not so surprising when the migratory potentialities of butterflies and moths are remembered. For example, the St. Kilda party of 1931 found painted ladies (*Pyrameis cardui*) almost every day from July 24 to August 10. A small tortoiseshell (*Vanessa urticae*) was seen on Rona in August 1938, though there are no nettles for at least 50 miles. Red admirals (*Vanessa atalanta*) also appear on the remotest islands during the autumn migration. The common blue (*Polyommatus icarus*) which is exceedingly common all over the isles and western mainland, does *not* appear on these very remote oceanic islands. It is most surprising that it does not occur at St. Kilda.

One of the commonest insects of the sub-oceanic islands, however small, is the earwig (*Forficula auricularia*). It is everywhere in the drier rocks near the sea, or where there are any human erections of stone. Stewart (1938) remarks on this fact in relation to Sule Skerry and I can echo it from Rona. The living quarters suffered invasion, and chocolate and dried fruits were found to be their favourite food. It was little trouble to them to remove the tin foil from a half-pound block of chocolate. Hewitt (1907) also records the abundance of earwigs on St. Kilda. Woodlice or slaters are also very common and the bristletail of the islands (*Petrobius brevistylis*) also haunts the same habitat as the earwig and is sometimes almost as numerous.

When Pickard-Cambridge (1905) identified the spiders of St. Kilda he said that most species were common on the mainland, but some only in the south of England, which remark might be compared with what was said of the arthropodan fauna of the high tops.

A few interesting findings of the 1905 party may be added. Waterston and Taylor (1905), listing the land and fresh-water molluscs of St. Kilda, record that at the top of the cliff at the passage opposite Dún (Ruaval), 400 feet up, it was surprising to find a large colony of a common shore species, (*Littorina littorea*). Whelks also crawled about the dykes behind the manse. *Purpura lapilla* was also found among loose stones on Mullach Mhor. The saline atmosphere and the frequent drenching with spray probably allowed this change of habit. A marine isopod (*Ligea oceanica*) was also found at 450 feet on top of Ruaval. I am indebted to Charles Elton for the suggestion that the invasion of the land by shore-line forms may be related to the absence of competing forms. The same phenomenon can be observed in Spitsbergen where the tundra is so invaded. The subject of such shifts of habitat by certain species, if others normally occupying that habitat are absent, is of great theoretical interest, and is only now being explored, e.g. by Elton in his recent paper on competition and the structure of ecological communities (1946).

The natural history of Britain's oceanic islands could provide material for a large volume. This inadequate attempt to summarize some of the happiness and good thinking which naturalists through a hundred years have gained and given, can hope to do little more than focus attention on what will still remain a joyous pursuit for all young folk under eighty years. The only thing which can dull enthusiasm for reaching the little islands must be the stiffening joints which may prevent one from getting ashore in the moment of the slackening swell. Seasickness is certainly not enough to keep the naturalist on the mainland, as this poor bedevilled sufferer can testify. There are certain situations which arouse a tremendous feeling of exhilaration and physical well-being. I know of none to beat the approach in a launch to a remote and uninhabited island where the swell is whitening the foot of the cliff. Whether you are at the engine and tiller with a kedge anchor rope running astern, or poised on the fore peak, ready to jump ashore with the forrard rope, it is all the same. You are trying to beat the elements but you are also working with them as the boat lifts and falls in the broken water at the foot of the cliffs. The island is still remote till your foot touches down, and sometimes the swell will beat you. In this way I touched Sula Sgeir with a boathook but never got ashore. James Fisher in the same month did manage to jump on to the rock, and came off again twenty minutes later with no more than a wetting. Robert Atkinson and Malcolm Stewart were luckier.

The islands are a paradox : bare and remote to our eyes, they are nevertheless among the most heavily populated areas in the kingdom and contain forms not found elsewhere ; on the one hand there is the falling off in the number of species, and on the other the immense numbers of those there are ; the vast comings and goings of the creatures, and at the same time the irrevocable isolation of the tiny mammals. We tend to think of these northern islands as storm-bound and mist-wrapped, yet nowhere can there be greater brilliance of colour, the sea so blue, the grass so green, the rocks so vivid with saffron lichen. A meadow of sea pink in June contains all colours between white and deep purple, and the predominantly white plumages of most of the birds reflect the boreal intensity of the summer light.

THE LIFE HISTORY OF THE ATLANTIC GREY SEAL

J. G. MILLAIS wrote in 1904 that excepting the whales the grey seal *Halichoerus grypus* was the British mammal of whose life history we were most ignorant. This lack of knowledge was most surprising when it is remembered how man regularly hunted the poor animal—and almost to extinction. But that often happens : man does not wait to stand and stare ; he takes what is going. The hunters of the Atlantic grey seal contributed nothing to our knowledge of it and the ardent naturalists of the 19th century seemed unable to find the truth, possibly because of the rarity of the seal. The animal did not receive its specific name until 1791, when Fabricius distinguished it from the bearded seal (*Erignathus barbatus*). But for many years after that British writers continued to confuse these two seals. *E. barbatus* is a northern species that does not come south into British waters at all. The Atlantic grey seal, on the other hand, is a beast of temperate North Atlantic waters only. If it is found in a country of sea ice, it is at the limit of its range.

It may be said with certainty, as of the gannet, that the largest part of the world population of the Atlantic seals breeds in the waters of the British Isles. These two facts alone should make the British people proud of their heritage of wild life and determined to uphold it by proper measures of conservation. This small group of islands holds more than half the stock of the rarest seal in the world. They are most numerous off the west coast of Scotland, but despite their increase during the last forty years, there is only one place, the caves of Loch Eriboll, where they breed on the mainland. All the other breeding stations are on uninhabited oceanic islands or on the more distant parts of larger islands. This seal occurs down the whole length of the west coast of Ireland and there is a small colony on the east side on an island not far from Dublin. There seem to be none on the Solway coast of Scotland or on the western side of England and Wales until the islands of south-west Wales are reached. Here again the seals breed in sea caves as they do in western Ireland and at Loch Eriboll. There are more than a hundred Atlantic seals on the north coast of Devon and Cornwall, again breeding in sea caves, and there is a considerable colony on the Scilly Isles. They have received protection here for many years.

The grey seal does not breed in the English Channel nor on the east coast of England until the Farne Islands, Northumberland, are reached. Here there is a colony of about 300, strictly preserved by the Northumberland natural history societies, who now manage the wild life of the islands for the owners, the National Trust. This colony is an old-established one which has had its vicissitudes, but the seals of the Farnes have always maintained their gregarious habit and have bred in the open on the flat rocks of the Brownsman and others of the group. Where they are driven underground, so to speak, their natural sociability is curtailed and the chances of survival in cave-breeding conditions cannot be so good as when they have land room. R. M. Lockley remarks in some of his articles how battered and wounded are some of the cave-breeding Atlantic seals of Ramsey Island after an equinoctial gale and the concomitant high spring tides.

This seal does not breed on the eastern Scottish coast, but occurs in Orkney and Shetland in relatively small numbers. It is found off the Norwegian coasts (Collet, 1881) and, strangely enough, in the Baltic, where it has so far changed its habits as to breed in spring instead of autumn. The calves appear in March, whereas in our waters September is the season. This is where the Atlantic seal is at its limit, calving as the ice begins to melt. It has another station in the Faeroes where again, perforce, it is a cave breeder. There are colonies of moderate size in Iceland, and it is probably by the old Viking route that the Atlantic seal went to the west side of the Atlantic. It has been shot in Greenland, though its breeding is not confirmed there, but it certainly breeds in very small numbers down the Labrador and Newfoundland coasts, into the Gulf of St. Lawrence and south again as far as Nova Scotia, but no farther.

The headquarters of the species, it may be said, are on North Rona. This island is to the British stock what St. Kilda is to the gannet. I estimated that I saw 5,000 ashore there in November-December 1938, and I do not think it is a wild guess to say this was probably half the world population. The Atlantic seal does not breed at St. Kilda or the Flannans and I have yet to ascertain whether it manages to do so on Sula Sgeir. One could practically never get on to Sula Sgeir in winter, but it would be possible to get a fair idea in summer by taking note of the physical and botanical characters of the ground near the low portion at the neck of Sula Sgeir, and seeing if there were any ear bones of the babies to be found. There are plenty of immature and adult grey seals on the skerries round Sula Sgeir in summer, but that means nothing as far as breeding is concerned. The species is increasing and neither I nor anyone else yet knows all the places off the north-west of Scotland where they *may* be breeding. The Sound of Harris is a favourite ground : they breed on Shillay in fair numbers and south of the Sound on Hasgeir, where there were dreadful seal hunts since time immemorial. It is interesting to note that the colony on this island is decreasing rapidly. Worse cruelty can hardly be imagined than to go to the breeding grounds shortly after the cows have calved and to club old and young alike, nor a more complete lack of any sense of conservation. This is what used to happen on Hasgeir and Rona. Unfortunately, as this book goes finally to press, I am sorry to record that certain island stocks have recently suffered attack. In the absence of a positive policy of conservation, a law means little.

There is a fine colony of Atlantic seals on the skerries off Oronsay, south of Colonsay. They are well protected, and they breed in perfect surroundings—namely, a terrain of flat skerries rising gently from sea level to a height above the highest spring tides ; and this ground is intersected by numerous sheltered channels which give the seals sea ways. There is another good colony on the Treshnish Isles, now carefully protected by the proprietor, yet when I was there in 1937 it was possible for a so-called sportsman to come to one of the other islands, the Dutchman's Cap, and clear it of any young seals. I got there myself the day after and found no young seals in blue coat. I had had the party under observation through my glass at three miles range while the seals were being got into the launch. (Although the seals are protected by a special Act of Parliament, there has been only one prosecution, of two crofters in North Uist in 1921, and although the incident described above and the name of the party concerned were brought to the notice of the Procurator-Fiscal, no action was taken. We must be thankful that the Act does deter some people, but we may deplore the fact that the Act is ahead of the solid desire to implement it.) Grey seals also breed on Oidhsgeir and on the rocks at the west end of Canna. I believe they have bred on Glas Leac Beag of the Summer Isles, but I have never managed to get confirmation of this. Colonies of one or two cows and a bull are not enough to keep up a regular station.

The Atlantic seal varies greatly in colour. He has been called the grey seal for a hundred years or more, but this is not the general colour. The bulls are often olive brown, the same colour as seaweed, or they may be dark iron grey with little or no white markings on the throat and chest. Very rarely a pale slate-grey or a wholly black bull is to be seen. All tend to show a bright steel-grey cap on top of the head in high summer, but this fades in the breeding season when practically all bulls turn olive brown.

The most common colour for cows is pale slate-grey on the whole of the upper surface, though the skin itself has irregular black marks and spots on it which show through the slate-grey coat. The underside is white, irregularly splashed with black. Occasionally one of these normally-coloured cows will have chestnut shading on the throat which makes them handsomer still. Then there are light and dark mole-coloured cows not showing the black-and-white underside. I once saw a dark mole-coloured cow which did not seem to have even a sprinkling of white hairs. When the young cast their first coat and go to sea, they have a short blue-grey coat and a lighter underside not very different from the cows. But it fades to yellowish fawn, vaguely marked by spring. A coat like that of the adults is not gained until the young are two years old. Occasionally a youngster in its first sea-going coat will be jet black, velvety and beautiful, but it fades to a gingery brown by spring.

Many seals are migratory, some markedly so, such as the fur seal (*Callorhinus ursinus*) which gathers from its feeding grounds as far south as California, and moves to the Pribilov Islands, Alaska, in large herds —now accompanied by a U.S. patrol cruiser to prevent poaching on the way. The Newfoundland seal industry is also based on this absolutely regular movement of the hooded seal (*Cystophora cristata*) and of the Greenland or harp seal (*Phoca groenlandica*). The Atlantic seal is not generally considered as a migratory species, but in fact it is, though its migrations are short and not always concerted. For the rest of this chapter only the Atlantic seals resident off the West Highland and Hebridean coasts will be discussed.

A glance at the Distribution Map (p. 281) will convey the fact of insularity in breeding stations and their comparative fewness. Yet almost every visitor to the outer coasts of the West of Scotland will have

F. Fraser Darling

BASKING SHARKS cruising along open-mouthed ; female in front and male following close. Summer Isles, Wester Ross. June 1943

F. Fraser Darling

BLACK GUILLEMOTS. North Rona, Outer Hebrides August 1938

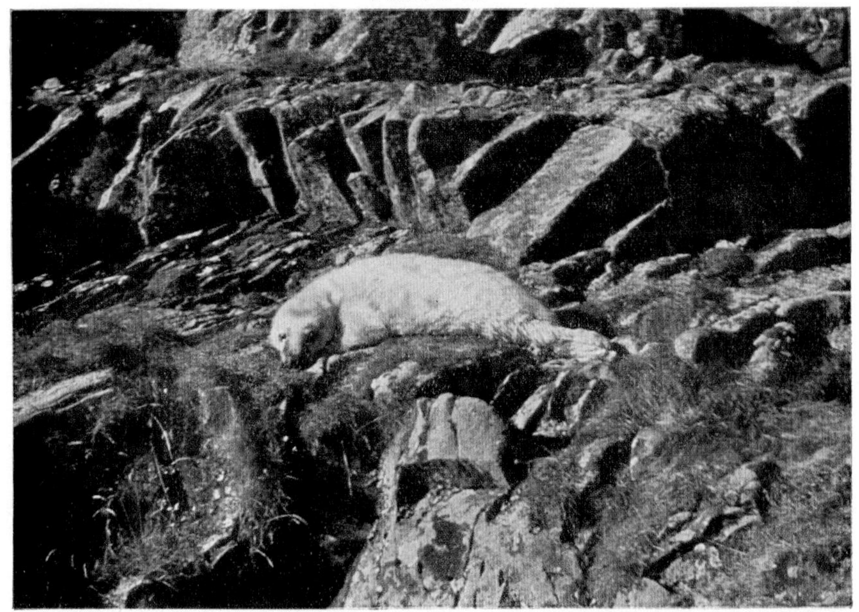

F. Fraser Darling

ATLANTIC SEAL, one week old. Oronsay, Inner Hebrides
September 1945

F. Fraser Darling

AN ATLANTIC SEAL takes a momentary look from the surf
North Rona, Outer Hebrides
June 1938

seen an Atlantic seal during spring or summer. It would seem there is a widely spread feeding distribution in summer ; the seals may not be seen in parties of more than two or three, and single bulls are common. The close observer will notice, however, that these summer residents disappear early in August and do not reappear until spring. They leave for the breeding grounds, quietly and without the fuss which is characteristic of the beginning of migration in many birds. We know little or nothing of the Atlantic seal's migrations, but it is reasonable to postulate that there is radial movement in definite sectors from the breeding grounds. As such movement is regular, the fact that it is radial as far as the particular stock is concerned does not warrant our calling it mere dispersal. What is not known is how far the animals go from each station and whether the areas of diffusion overlap. Concerted autumnal migration to the breeding ground is not to be ruled out because it is so rarely witnessed. In mid-September 1940, I was on the hill of Tanera looking out to sea and about the islands through a glass. The field changed till it showed the north-east side of Glas Leac Mor where there is a large shelving rock running up from the sea. On it were laid 54 Atlantic seals, mostly cows judging from their light bellies. They were quite motionless, obviously resting and not sparring and bickering as is so common among them when lying out in desultory fashion. There are not half a dozen Atlantic seals in the Summer Isles all summer. These seals were on passage, probably going north to Rona, for it is reasonable to think that some of Rona's seals will work down into the Minch for summer feeding.

This diffusion from the re-convergence to the breeding islands probably means that the social system of the seals concerned with reproduction is biologically isolating the several groups. It strengthens the geographical isolation of the stocks, so that they become more or less closed societies, but all this problem will take a lot of time and trouble to elucidate. If there is biological and geographical isolation, it would be natural that a highly variable character such as coat colour would be tending to show differentiation between the island stocks. This does seem to be happening, for there is a difference between the general olive-brown colour of the bulls of the Treshnish stock and those of North Rona, which are much greyer. The people of North Uist say they can distinguish the seals of Hasgeir from those of the Sound of Harris. There is also a common ring pattern on the throat of Shetland bull seals which I have not seen on those of the West Coast.

Again, the external ears of the bull seals are visible and when working on the Treshnish Isles I could first tell a bull from a cow in the water at a long distance by the prominence of the ears, before I looked at the other sexual differences of facial form. But the ears of the Rona bulls do not appear to be so prominent. Differentiation of races is going on before our eyes.

The Atlantic seal feeds largely on rock fish such as saithe, pollack or lythe and on some crustaceans. Therefore it is a coastal species, though not of the inner sheltered coasts as is *Phoca vitulina*. Wherever there are skerries round which the rock fishes live, there a seal takes his place for the summer, fishing diligently and eating far more fish than is needed to provide the energy he is using. This is the time when the animals are laying on fat underneath the skin, probably a hundred-weight and a half of soft fat. Lighthousemen report them from the Flannans, Dhu Artach and Skerryvore, from Cape Wrath, Stoer and Rudh' Re, from the Butt of Lewis and Barra Head, and all remark on the fact that they normally disappear in August.

If the observer is at a breeding station, say Rona or Treshnish, in June, he will not find the place deserted (see Pl. 28b, p. 221). Some seals, both young and adult, will be found feeding round the islands. My own estimate is that about 10 per cent of the population remains to harvest the fish of the immediate neighbourhood of the breeding ground. There is, perhaps, a disproportionate number of yearlings but it cannot be said at all that yearlings do not migrate, for the appearance of these about West Highland coasts farther inshore and in more sheltered waters than the adults, is a noticeable phenomenon in late spring. Their faded coats are yellowy-fawn in colour and they are not unlike the common seal in size and appearance. Their habits nearly approach these of the common seal at this time and it is mostly these yearlings (8–9 months old) which cause the trouble in the salmon bag nets.

Some or possibly all of these migrant yearlings do not come back to the breeding ground in the first season, a habit comparable with that of some birds that take more than one year to come to maturity. Different colonies vary in the number of yearlings to be seen in the breeding season. There were a few on Rona, none at Lunga of the Treshnish and many at Oronsay. It would appear that at each nursery there are conditions or traditions influencing movements and age-groupings to be seen during the autumn breeding season. These influences are not yet known. Exactly the same state of affairs may be observed at Britain's gannetries and the parallelism between sea birds and seals in this and other respects is a matter for the naturalist's wonder.

The observer on the nursery islands from July onwards sees the number of seals gradually increasing. They begin to spend more time out of the water in August, but not on the main mass of the island as yet. Both at the Treshnish Isles and at North Rona there are certain skerries favoured by the immigrant seals, and it is on these they gather, lying hauled out in close groups. The adult bulls tend to have a rock of their own where they almost overlap each other in their slumbers—and still there is no quarrelling. There are many bulls to be seen as well among the increasing numbers of cows on these resting rocks. Cows are more quarrelsome and more vocal than the bulls, but they pack close all the same. A certain number of yellow yearlings haul out on some rocks, but other skerries are frequented wholly by adults, and it is at these latter places that it is possible to make accurate counts of the increase of numbers through late summer. Here is a typical example from Rona, the counts being made during the afternoon each day, at which time lying-out is common:

August 14th—56; 15th—72; 16th—103; spell of rough weather during which the rocks were untenable; 26th—170.

The annual association of the seals with the land is their time of greatest danger. There is possible danger of predatory animals, including man, to an animal whose activity is much curtailed by being ashore; there is the danger of the licking surf and the equinoctial spring tides to the young calves, and the very massing of the beasts produces quarrelsome behaviour which may bring casualties. The social system of the seals, as well as their metabolism, has become finely adapted to lessening this danger—and the preliminary resting period on the outlying skerries observed at two widely-differing nurseries is in line with this axiom. The animals certainly quarrel on these rocks, but not seriously, and as no territorial behaviour is shown they are able to mass close together.

This resting period finishes at the end of August and now the adult bulls begin to come ashore to the breeding grounds. It is amazing to see the climbing power of these 9-foot and 6–7-cwt. animals. There is great gripping strength in their hands, which hold on while their belly muscles contract and expand as they heave themselves upward and forwards. The bulls take up their chosen places and lie quiet there. Preferably they lie by a shallow pool of water which becomes more or less the centre of their territory and is the place where coition occurs later. Now the Treshnish Isles are volcanic in origin, with sheer cliffs falling to erosion platforms at approximately sea level. These shelves of lava are the breeding ground of the seals. The animals cannot get far away from the sea and we find the territories of the bulls set in linear fashion along the coast. Rona is cliff-bound and an immense swell makes the sea's edge a dangerous place. The seals of Rona come farther inland and stay there without frequent return to the sea. The bulls come as far as 300–400 yards from the water and as high as 300 feet above it. The plan of the territories, therefore, is not linear as on the Treshnish, but like a honeycomb or draught-board.

Cows come into the territories from the sea 2–5 days before calving and the number of seals ashore increases throughout September. On one strip of shore on the Treshnish Isles where the first bull took up his territory on August 28, numbers grew from two on that date to 78 on September 15. The cows leave first for the sea as the breeding season declines, and once more the seals are found on the resting rocks, lying in close masses. There they lie like empty bags during late November and December, changing their coats, and it is not until this is completed that the seals return to the sea and leave the breeding islands for the feeding areas once more.

Let us look closer at the life of the seals on the breeding territories and nursery grounds. There are many more adult bulls on Rona than can immediately take up territories. These animals lie on the rocks at a place where there is most traffic up to the territories, and this traffic tends to be up accepted tracks which give easiest access. This bull rock may be called the reservoir, for 500 bulls can be seen there, and the cows stay among them a short time before going up to calve. No challenging behaviour is to be seen at the reservoir, which is strictly neutral ground.

The bulls inland in possession of territories will not trouble each other much either. Challenge comes from fresh bulls emerging from the sea and working their way up from the reservoir. Sometimes the sight of the possessor is enough to deter the new bull, but if not, the two will indulge in a primary display of weapons which, though so different, is comparable with the challenging display of stags described in an earlier chapter. The bull rolls over from side to side, turning his head sideways in the direction of the roll, opening his mouth and raising his hand. The canine teeth on each side and the powerful claws are thus shown to the opponent. An Atlantic bull seal has such a large development of muscle and foreface that the canines cannot be seen head on. The limit of challenging behaviour is when the bulls come muzzle to muzzle, heads raised. If that does not suffice there is a fight with teeth and claws. Great rips may be made in the hide and once started the fight goes on for some minutes until both appear seriously wounded. As mentioned in the chapter on the red deer, such biological wastage is unusual. Sabre-rattling is cheaper. Defeated bulls or spent ones return to the reservoir and there all challenging behaviour is set aside. Here again the comparison with the stags is close.

When a bull comes ashore for the breeding season he is very fat, extraordinarily fat, yet he looks what he is, as fit as a fiddle. He has now had his last meal for a month or two and I would not be surprised to find after further observation that he may go three months without a square meal, for he will not go to sea again permanently until he has changed his coat on the resting rocks. He now begins to live on his blubber and gradually loses condition. This is the position on Rona, but on the Treshnish where the animals are nearer the sea, the bull will spend many hours in the water opposite his territory, gently patrolling the length of it. All the same, I do not think the Treshnish bulls feed though they are in the water. The inland territories of Rona are not kept by the same bull from beginning to end of the breeding season ; there is always the traffic up of fresh bulls and down of spent ones, and it is probable that each territory has a succession of three or four bulls, between August 28 and October 15, though there is little change in the first fortnight. I cannot be certain that some of these spent bulls do not return to the territories again, just as a stag will come down from the resting neutral corrie, but I do not think they do.

Atlantic seals are polygamous, each bull having four or five cows. If the sex ratio is near equality at birth and there is a slightly heavier mortality in the males thereafter, the adult stock of a polygamous species still appears to have a large excess of males. But assuming a succession of three or four bulls in the territories and the normal harem as being four or five cows, almost all of the adult bull population will be in service some time or other during the season, and the apparent excess of males at any one time is no true indicator of the situation for the season as a whole.

The cows are free to go wherever they like. Sexually they belong to the bull in whose territory they may happen to be at any one moment. This is unlike the social system of the Alaskan fur seal and of the elephant seal (*Macrorhinus angustirostris*) each of which species collects a harem of up to sixty cows, and the harems are herded by the bulls. I am told that although quarrelsomeness is not common between the cows the actual crowding and dynamic activity of the bulls are responsible for casualties among the young, and two ardent bulls have been known to pull a cow in two. This type of rutting behaviour which makes for a large surplus of bulls hanging about on the outskirts of the breeding ground, and is associated with great disparity in size between bulls and cows, is biologically wasteful, especially so when the eager bulls reach the extreme of injuring cows. Bertram (1940) has drawn attention to this correlation between the size of bull and size of harem. In the Atlantic seal the harem number is low and the difference in size between the sexes, though marked, is not extraordinary. A big bull may measure nine feet and an adult cow is very generally six feet long. A cow weighs between three and four hundredweight. The Atlantic bull seal within his territory is not extraordinarily active among his few cows. They are within an area possibly ten yards square and the cows are jealous and quarrelsome. If they were crowded closer than this it is possible that injury to the calves would be serious and much commoner. The matings take place 11–14 days after the birth of the calf. Coition usually occurs ashore, preferably in a shallow pool but the bare rock or the open sea may be used. The bull, then, has been ashore at least three weeks without any cow having been in season. During all this time he has been ready to fight for his territory in which sexual satisfaction has not been obtainable. The north end of Rona is by this time, the latter end of September, completely invaded by the seals and some have climbed a very steep hillside to the top of the ridge. I once saw a cow seal heavy in calf half-way up the west cliffs of Rona where they were about 150 feet high and at an angle of 45°. Had it not been bare, rough, stable rock she could never have finished her climb. Another calf was successfully reared at the edge of the 300-foot sheer column of the western cliff. Professor D'Arcy Thompson has told me that he once came on an Alaskan fur seal bull at the summit of a hill about 2,000 feet high.

All these cows ashore in the territories of Rona were ones with a calf or about to calve, and all the bulls were adults with territories or seeking them. Now it was indicated a little earlier in this chapter that the social system of the seals was finely adapted for lessening the danger from their association with the land. In 1937, on the Treshnish Isles, I had been surprised to find that no maiden cows came ashore for breeding on the island where we were encamped, and there were no immature animals to be seen either. It was a puzzle circumstances did not allow me to solve at that time. But on Rona there is no maze of little islets and skerries ; the observer can see almost everything to do with the seals from the island itself. I found that the maiden cows collected on the large flat skerry, Loba Sgeir,[1] at the south-west corner of the island, and a few were to be seen among the reservoir of bulls on Leac Mor Fianuis. There was a large number of bulls on Loba Sgeir, mostly young adults, and that was where the mating of the maiden and the barren cows took place. This flat skerry is practically always safe for the seals because it is ringed by a very bad surf, but it would not serve as a place for the calf to be born on, for the sea washed right over it in really bad gales. It was observed that no breeding territories were apparent on Loba Sgeir. Bulls and cows lay cheek by jowl and matings occurred with comparatively little quarrelling. In fact 2–3-year-old seals are far more playful than those in any other age class. I saw frequent mock battles taking place on Loba Sgeir between young bulls, sometimes between a cow and a bull, but only rarely between young cows. Like their older sisters they were too apt to become seriously quarrelsome.

It is not desired to draw a teleological conclusion but one must point, all the same, to the value which the fully adult territorial behaviour has for the survival of the calves. It makes for sufficient room for each cow and calf during that fevered fortnight of maternal jealousy after the calf is born. At the same time, I do not wish to imply that unlimited room or solitariness is a good thing for cow and calf. The point will be mentioned again below.

There remains to be described the behaviour of mother and calf and to note the interesting metabolic processes which fit them for a period of life outside their chosen element. Birth is usually very rapid and the afterbirth is shed within half an hour. The calf when born is clad in a thick coat of fluffy hair, cream or ashen in colour. The head

[1] Note the name Loba Sgeir and the Portugese name for seal, *Lobito*.

appears large and discrete from the body, and the limbs look relatively long, for as yet the calf is thin. If a still-born calf is skinned a dense loofah-like layer of connective tissue is found immediately below the skin. This tissue opens up to accommodate fat in the same way as a new loofah opens up to take water. The new-born calf is about 30 inches long and weighs about 30 lbs.

The mother takes very little notice of the calf for the first quarter of an hour after birth ; then she offers it her two teats and within half an hour the calf is taking its first meal of milk which is ten times as rich in fat as cow's milk ; she does not lick it at all though she will smell it. The first two days of its life the seal calf is more active than it is for the next month. It is possible to tell a new calf at a glance because its two hind flippers tend to spread to the side and it half-uses them in scrambling about those journeys of a few yards hither and thither. After two days the flippers remain longitudinal and are not used. Here, presumably, is some measure of evolutional recapitulation, a half-successful use of the hind feet for a few hours. These small adventures of the calf are responsible for much trouble between the cows, and any calf is liable to be severely bitten by a cow not its mother. If a bull finds a calf in his way he will pick it up and shake it (30 lbs. is nothing to him) and put it down again quite unhurt.

The over-anxiousness and jealousy of the cows over their calves mean that the bull of a harem is sometimes attacked with great ferocity. The bull backs away quickly from the cow behaving in this fashion and makes as if to defend himself only when the cow is upon him and then he does her but little harm.

I have asked myself why, if the cows are so jealous, they should be so closely gregarious ? The limited number of suitable nursery sites might impose a density of population causing extreme quarrelsomeness, but after seeing two different nurseries, I think the seals could spread out more if they wished. There is a probable biological advantage, but again it is not suggested that the closely gregarious habit and constant fussiness are followed *because* of any end they may serve. I found that in places where the cows could get to and from the water easily—as on the Treshnish Isles—they spend much more time out of the water with their calves when they are closely gregarious than when they are isolated. If predatory animals were present there would be an obvious advantage in the cows remaining with the calves.

Immediately after the first feed the cow begins to show maternal

PLATE XXIX

Robert Atkinson

SOAY RAM. Hirta, St. Kilda
Boreray and the Stacks in the distance, across the sea
July 1938

F. Fraser Darling

ATLANTIC SEAL and calf. Treshnish Isles, Inner Hebrides
September 1937

F. Fraser Darling

YOUNG ATLANTIC SEAL, changing coat. North Rona
November 1938

affection, which increases in intensity during the following three or four days. She shuffles round in order to touch the calf with her muzzle and then to scratch it lightly with her fore paw. This scratching is a habit almost invariably practised after feeding has taken place, and after the first feed the calf comes itself towards the mother's head and is scratched from head to tail down the back.

The seals of Rona have their calves well up from the sea, so the danger from swell and spring tides is small. But on the Treshnish Isles the calves are never more than a few yards from the water's edge. One is accustomed to seeing carnivorous animals carrying their young in their mouths in the face of danger, but the Atlantic seal cannot do this. She has but one young, weighing 30 lbs. at birth, and the closeness of her head to the ground makes it almost impossible for her to carry the calf.

What the cow can do for her calf, then, is limited, but that little she does well. I have seen a cow move her newly-born calf 20–30 yards by shuffling it along between her paws. Where there is a heavy surf with ground swell at high tide, the cow lies below her calf at the water's edge and breaks the force of the waves to the calf. She curls herself almost half round it, and the calf is caught against her instead of being sucked back by the swell into the sea. If the calf is perverse, its mother will make as if to snap, and these threats are successful in helping to get the calf above the reach of the surf. I saw a cow on Rona holding her calf against the cliff edge with her paws at a place where it could climb on to a ledge. This type of behaviour is often conducted with perseverance and I have seen a cow maintain it for the six tides of a three-day, onshore gale at the time of a spring tide.

Young grey seal calves will play happily in the pools of an erosion platform or in the sea if it is quiet and there is an easy beach for them to climb ashore. But their long white coats are unsuitable for much swimming exercise and a calf would not seek escape into the sea. If they get there by accident such as by the lick of the swell at high spring tides, young calves will swim vigorously and make valiant efforts to get ashore. Sometimes, when they have been unsuccessful, I have examined the bodies. The claws have been worn away; the chin and palms of the hands have been raw. At these times the calf cries pitifully with almost exactly the sound of a human child.

The calf is fed (Pl. XXXa, p. 229) at about two-hourly intervals during the first few days and then at rather longer periods. Each meal appears to be a good one, for suckling takes from ten minutes to half an hour. The growth rate is very rapid (Pl. 28a, p. 221), for it reaches about 84 lbs. weight at a fortnight old, i.e. an average of 4 lbs. a day. This increase has been made on milk alone and wholly at the expense of the mother's body, for when she comes up from the sea before calving she starves until she returns after weaning the calf. An observer is soon able to tell to a day or two how long any cow has been out of the sea by her degree of fatness. Similarly, the age of a calf can be judged accurately by its increasing degree of fatness. A cow loses about 200 lbs. weight between calving time and her return to the sea after changing her coat, and a bull loses 300 lbs. or more in the same time.

The calf begins to shed the fluffy white coat at 13 days (Pl. XXXb, p. 229), beginning on the muzzle, the paws, and a patch on the belly ; it assumes a very beautiful blue coat within the next fortnight. This is a time when the calf moves very little at all. It is common to see an almost-blue calf lying in the middle of the old hair which it has been several days in casting and rubbing off its back by rolling this way and that.

The time when the white coat is shed is synchronous with weaning. In this species, as in many other mammals and birds, the birth coat of fluffy hair or down appears to have a highly valent quality for the mother. Once hard fur or feathers are showing, maternal care rapidly declines. There is variation in maternal care. Most calves are weaned at precisely a fortnight old, but a few are suckled to three weeks and I once saw one in full blue coat being fed by its mother. At weaning they are left absolutely by their mothers and have to find their own way to the sea—the same process as in the gannet, the puffin, and the petrels and shearwaters.

The calves have but a little way to go on the Treshnish Isles and they already have some experience of going in and out of the water in playful fashion ; but on North Rona where many are born high on the island or on the edges of the cliffs the journey is fraught with danger. Many make sheer drops of 50–75 feet into the sea. These calves, which have fed and prospered so richly on nothing but mother's milk, face a period of complete starvation from a fortnight old. They may get to the sea in a week but some take a month to do it and even then do not appear in an urgent hurry. From a telescoped infancy they enter a protracted childhood, for their live-weight increase from then to one year old is small. The calves of the season can be easily recognized by their extreme buoyancy. When they rise to the surface a good half of them comes into view like a bobbing cork. Conversely, if the adult animals are frightened into the sea when changing their coats, their lack of buoyancy is apparent.

I have been struck by the solitary nature of month-old calves which have newly taken to the sea. They find little crabs and molluscs and may sometimes be seen on the sea bottom from a cliff above turning over stones with their little hands. Gregariousness has to be re-established and at a year old, or rather nine months, it is obvious how they have formed a group of their own with favoured rocks for lying out.

The complex social system, the specialized metabolic processes, and the protracted gestation period of eleven and a half months which allows calving and mating within a short period ashore, all combine to lessen the whole time of association with the land. One thing remains for us to remember—the flocking of these seals to a very few breeding stations, and their comparative helplessness ashore at that time, lay them open to particular danger from exploiting mankind seeking commercial gain. It is for us all to protect the seals adequately, for of few other species have we such a rich heritage.

FRESH WATERS: LOCHS AND RIVER SYSTEMS

Physical and Chemical Factors

A GOOD DEAL is known about general fresh-water biology and of the varied botanical field associated with the banks, but I wish, if only for my own enlightenment, that someone would write a good book on the river systems of Scotland and their ecology. Look at a tracing of fresh-water lochs and river systems of the Highland area: here alone is material for a whole evening's imaginative thinking. First we can relate it to the orographical map which in effect it mirrors. Throughout the Highland region we are struck by the large numbers of large and small lochs, many of which act as reservoirs for the rivers running from them. The great ridge of Scotland, Drum Albyn, is much nearer the west coast than the east; in fact, at one point in Glen Dessary above Loch Nevis, the ridge comes to within four miles of the western sea. The general result of this conformation is that western-running rivers of the Highlands are short, and those going east much longer. The higher hills form Drum Albyn, except for the Cairngorm massif, so the western rivers have far to fall in a short distance. This means that their velocity is on the whole many times greater than that of the eastern rivers. Water is one of the great carriers of this earth, and the power of water to carry is governed by its velocity. A law of hydrodynamics says that the carrying power of a stream varies as the sixth power of its velocity. Thus, a stream able to move shingle of one ounce in weight would, if the velocity were doubled, be able to move boulders four pounds in weight. The scouring power of these western rivers is, therefore, very great; and if the waters are clear as we see them to-day, compared with the more turbid southern rivers, it is partly because all the smallest particles have been washed down long before.

There is another pleasant hour to be spent comparing the map of the fresh-water systems of the Highlands with the geological map. A river eventually reaches a base level of erosion, a curve which ideally differs in relation to height of head-waters above sea level and the length of the river. It means that the upper reaches of a river make for themselves a steeper gradient than the lower reaches, and if the whole country through which the river might pass were easily and uniformly erodable, the river would be straight and occupying a V-shaped valley, the V being closer-angled at the upper reaches than at the foot. Highland rivers follow no such ideal movements. The varying hardness of different rocks, of different complexes within the same formation, and the effects of faults and intrusions referable to cracks, slips and crinkles in the earth's surface, cause both obstacles and opportunities to the falling waters which we call rivers. Glaciation is an event in earlier time which has had a profound effect on the forms of fresh-water systems to-day.

Furthermore, the rain water which makes rivers does not fall as pure H_2O. It gathers atmospheric carbonic acid and ammonia which render it a powerful solvent, quite apart from its dynamic power when given velocity, and its abrasive power when charged with particles carried by virtue of velocity. When rain water seeps through a mass of decaying vegetation such as peat, as it often does in Highland country before it reaches the rivers, it has a definite influence on moulding the ultimate courses of rivers. To take a purely agricultural example of this differing solvent power of soil waters, it may be mentioned that rock phosphate is a highly satisfactory fertilizer for hill ground in Scotland because the acidity of the water (an acidity almost wholly referable to carbonic acid content) is sufficient to dissolve the particles. Rock phosphate does not do nearly so well on neutral soils.

Different rocks vary in resistance to the solvent power of river water charged with carbonic acid. The archaean gneiss is highly resistant; thus, if we look at the courses of rivers and burns in western Sutherland on a large-scale map we find them having to go round the rock and often not managing to get away again until a small loch has been formed and egress found at a new level. And if we walk that rugged country, the insolubility and hardness of the rock can be studied by the shapes of surfaces over which the water has been running. The same county of Sutherland will show us the other extreme in its limestone country. There are the caves of Smoo on the north coast, wholly water-worn, and the caves and disappearing burn in the limestone of the big corries east of the road between Stronchrubie and Inchnadamph. Water laden with carbonic acid can dissolve limestone so that it will hold one part in a thousand of limestone. This may not be much, but it must be remembered that there is a lot of time and a lot of water. Limestone-laden water is in turn an extremely potent factor in changing vegetational complexes and the incidences of small invertebrate animal forms wherever it touches.

The action of carbonic acid in the micro-habitat of a small loch on the limestone island of Lismore is responsible for summer cloudiness and winter clarity of the water, described by A. Scott in T. Scott (1890). In these conditions the water becomes charged with an unstable acid carbonate of lime, but as long as the water contains an excess of carbonic acid, the compound remains in solution and the water remains clear. There is abundant aquatic vegetation in the loch, which vegetation in the vigorous growth of spring and summer, in the presence of sunlight, will take up much of the carbonic acid needed to keep the calcium carbonate in solution. This action is more or less continuous in summer when there is little darkness and a higher temperature increases the rate of chemical action. The calcium carbonate is therefore precipitated in an extremely fine state of division, giving the milky appearance to the water. Scott gives the following descriptive equations :

$$H_2CO_3 + CaCO_3 = CaH_2(CO_3)_2$$

$$CaH_2(CO_3)_2 = CaCO_3 + H_2O + CO_2$$

It is a humbling thing to consider philosophically the vast field of action and interaction which a study of the physics, chemistry and dynamics of water reveal. This imaginary river of ours, gouging out its base level of erosion, has met obstacles which have changed its course and momentarily its velocity, it has gathered solvents and altered landscapes, it may have meandered and deposited alluvial flats, and ultimately it comes to the sea where it meets another body of water, its own element, but different ; because the sea is far more heavily charged with salts in solution. The chemistry and physics of sea water are a study in themselves, but this much most of us know, that the river and the sea have their lifeless, unconscious, swift-moving, rhythmical battle. Not only dynamics are concerned with the deposition of the bar, where the fight is fiercest, but chemistry as well. The sea water meeting the fresh causes the latter to precipitate some of its salts, and its particles to flocculate. Forms of life have evolved which can take advantage of these conditions and new chains of biological interactions are set in train.

The days of the ice sheet are past in Scotland, but its consequences are plain and some have been discussed in the early chapters of this book. Frost allowed the immense weight of water to accumulate, but as ice it was still fluid and could move mountains. Ice could also act as a mass, and dam water to make lakes. The Highlands have one fine example of such action which left a mark that puzzled man for centuries. The northward-flowing glacier from Ben Nevis dammed up the entrance to Glen Spean, Glen Roy and Glen Gloy. The waters flowing into these glens from the tops formed lakes over a thousand feet deep. The different levels of these lakes through time have left beaches high on the present-day hillsides, and are known as the Parallel Roads of Glen Roy. Just as the river brings down detritus to form a bar at its mouth, the glaciers did similar things and formed some of the lochs near the sea which we know to-day, such as Loch Coruisk in Skye. How the depths of some of these chasms were gouged out is not completely understood. There are some outstanding ones in the Highlands. Loch Morar, which is but a mile from the sea, reaches a depth of 1,077 feet; a depth which the ocean does not reach until the dip of the Continental Shelf outside Rockall. It is the deepest fresh water in Britain. Loch Ness, which forms the largest single mass of fresh water in the United Kingdom, is 754 feet deep and not much more than 50 feet above sea level. Loch Lomond is four miles from the sea at the nearest point and 20 feet above it, yet reaches a depth of 653 feet at the upper end. Loch Lomond, 27½ square miles, is the largest area of fresh water in the kingdom. The present great depth of these lochs has biological consequences which will be referred to later, and it is with these we are concerned here rather than with the puzzle of the origin of deep loch basins.

Temperature in water is an important factor in the biological chains concerned. These deep lochs are obviously more constant in temperature than the shallow ones. Their temperature does not rise above 60° F. in summer or fall below 42° F. in winter. The abyssal water of Loch Ness and Loch Morar remains at slightly above 42° F. permanently, not varying more than a degree in several years. Such water is but little aerated. Aeration in the shallow *dubhlochan* (Pl. XXXIIb, p. 237) may be slight because it is small and does not have chance to develop large waves, and there may be little inflow and outflow. Large lochs, set as they are between steep hills, are subject to extra wind pressure and develop very steep waves, and they all have large inflows and outflows ; though extreme aeration is confined to the upper layers of water.

The rainfall map is of interest in relation to the river systems of the Highlands. It will be seen that the short rivers of the West Highlands north of the Firth of Lorne and Loch Linnhe have to take a particularly heavy rainfall. Many of them provide a spectacle during the heavy spates, but their catchment areas are so small and the slopes so steep that these rivers may rise and fall within a few hours, and quite often in summer they may fall from a raging torrent to little more than a trickle in two or three days. Such quickly-changing conditions much affect the natural history both of the river and its banks. The rivers lack the stability of those on the eastern side of the hills.

Fast-running water holds little life. The scoured bed of such rivers has no mud and little sand to grow plants. Molluscs cannot endure such conditions and we know that brown trout rely on some species of fresh-water snails (*Pisidium* spp.) for their bread and butter. In a way, the lochs of the West Highlands may be looked on as sanctuaries for many forms of fresh-water life. Without these patches of quiet water they would scarcely have a chance to persist.

The river and loch systems of the Highlands are the lines of communication for much of the wild life of the area. Rivers if of any size and difficulty, and lochs, may be boundaries for some animals ; for example, the red deer tend to include both sides of a hill in their territory and make the rivers in the glens their boundaries, whereas man tends to make the watershed his boundary in the Highlands. The otter must know the river system intimately as it helps him to get about —even the tiniest burns being used, if only to wash away scent, and if we watch carefully enough it will be found that weasel and stoat are great travellers along river banks. Certain birds also follow the river faithfully, even to slight meanders and deviations. The dipper (*Cinclus c. gularis*) comes first to mind, moving but a few inches above the surface of the water, but the goosander (*Mergus merganser*) flying 20 feet above, is equally faithful to the course of the river.

The rivers of the Highlands are vital thoroughfares in the life history of the salmon and sea trout. These fish are comparable with those other sea creatures which have been studied already, the gannet

John Markham

RED-THROATED DIVER: nesting by freshwater loch and feeding in salt water
Hoy, Orkney. June 1939

Eric Hosking

SLAVONIAN GREBE (cock), a bird of the *dubhlochan* (see Plate XXXIIb)
Inverness-shire. June 1939

Robert Atkinson

RED-NECKED PHALAROPE, male. Outer Hebrides
July 1938

F. Fraser Darling

A *DUBHLOCHAN* : water-lilies and *Carex rostrata*. Sutherland
July 1939

and the Atlantic seal which had to come to land to breed. The salmon and the sea trout must come to fresh water to spawn and the young spend their life in fresh water for two or three or even four years.

The fresh-water lochs of Scotland are linked with the river systems, though in parts of Sutherland and Ross and in the Outer Isles it is sometimes hard to work out inlets and outlets from the hundreds of lochs which occupy a large proportion of the total area. The catchment areas of the many lochs vary enormously, from a few acres for a Sutherland *dubhlochan* to 686 square miles for Loch Ness. The character of the waters varies also : first the acidity, or to put it in present-day scientific form, the hydrogen-ion concentration, which is expressed by the symbol pH. The peaty lochans of the far north are very acid and give a pH value as low as 4·2. This I have found out for myself. Some of the larger lochs strike a stratum of basic rock in their depths and this immediately raises the pH reading to possibly 6·5 or 7·0. The water of a loch on limestone may read pH 8·0–9·0 if there is not a mass of decaying vegetable matter in the shallow parts. There are biological influences on pH also, so that the figure for a loch may change with the seasons. When I was on Priest Island, where there were eight lochs within 300 acres (Pl. 29, p. 244), I found sharp differences referable to the behaviour of sea birds, and in one instance possibly to a very slight dilution with spray from the sea. One loch was the favoured place for gulls of several species to bathe. Cormorants came as well, and grey lag geese. The accumulated effects of these birds defecating in the water raised the pH from 6·0 to 7·6 in spring and early summer. This loch alone appeared to have the fresh-water shrimp *Gammarus pulex* and it was very plentiful all summer. This was the only loch on the island which experienced the phenomenon of the swarming of the blue-green algae. The water was green for a while in July and then it would clear. And as the year waned the pH fell again. It has been said that *G. pulex* dies if the pH falls below 7·4 (i.e. if the acidity rises) but I think this should be questioned in some of the waters of the North-West Highlands.

Usually, however, pH is mostly referable to geological or physical causes and pH has a large influence on the fauna and flora which the loch supports. For example, in that part of Ross-shire where there are many rather shallow lochs of low pH, there is one, the Fionn Loch, in the depths of which the thin band of limestone runs which was mentioned in the early chapters. This so raises the pH, and consequently the quantity of fresh-water diatoms, the fresh-water copepods and the larger crustacean and insect life on which fish feed, that the trout of the Fionn Loch are famed for their size and there are plenty of them. Yet within a few hundred yards of the Fionn Loch are small *dubhlochain* with trout about three inches long. *Dubhlochan* means a small black loch ; it is usually shallow as far as clear water is concerned, but has a floor of peat which may be several feet thick. The roots of water lilies (Pl. XXXIIb, p. 237) may be in the peat and their flat leaves ornament the surface, usually just out of reach, because the deer are very fond of them and take such as may grow very near the edge. But the deer know the danger of the *dubhlochan* and are not so foolish as to step down into it.

There is still a lot of work to be done on the natural history of Highland lochs, for so much remains unknown. Why, for example, do the salmon and sea trout come up the Little Gruinard River for its five or six miles, but do not go into that Fionn Loch from which the Little Gruinard runs ? There are other lochs in the Highlands which salmon can reach quite easily but they do not enter them, Lochs Frisa and Uisg in Mull, for example. Not far from the Fionn Loch salmon and sea trout run up nearly six miles of rapid river with some very awkward rocky patches, through a mile of loch and up three miles more of a rough burn to another loch at 1,100 feet. That is the end of the system, 1,100 feet in ten miles. Perhaps these large and numerous trout of the Fionn Loch would gobble up the smolts if the salmon bred there. Perhaps they *have* done that and thus removed the race of salmon which went into the loch. Those which bred in the river, where the big trout do not come, would survive.

The Salmon Family (Salmonidae) in the Highlands

The members of this family hold an important position in the ecology of the river and loch systems of the Highlands. Some members are themselves no mean predators on a variety of animal forms and are the prey of many others. The brown trout (*Salmo trutta*) is so widely distributed throughout the area that it takes thought to remember which lochans and burns do *not* hold them. Man has been an important influence in this general distribution. He is one of the predators on the fish and in days long past there can be no doubt that he shifted stocks to empty waters and to burns above unscalable falls. Sportsmen of later years have done this on a large scale and have introduced new stocks to waters already tenanted. The spirit of interested fun and play in small boys is not to be disregarded either. Several high lochans and stretches of burn have been stocked in this way. The physiology of growth in fish allows an extraordinary latitude of alimental conditions, and the hydrogen-ion concentration of the water also affects the sex ratio of brown trout in small streams in the Highlands. A brown trout may reach no greater length in its life than three inches, or it may reach three feet. Many West Highland rivers subject to rapid rise and fall and carrying mossy water have very small trout, and may yet have a good reputation for salmon and sea trout. But the brown trout is the sedentary form dependent on what the river produces and what is attracted above its surface in the way of insects. If we let our minds play a little beyond the immediate environment of the trout, we see how much our human activities have influenced him to his detriment in the Highlands. Man's destruction of forest and scrub growth has greatly emphasized the swing between spate and trickle because the trees acted as a sponge and a reservoir of moisture. Spates scour a river's course and a long period of trickle is an impoverishment. Again, the trees shed leaves. The birch and alder leaves falling into the burn in a good length of their courses provided organic matter for food and cover for those invertebrate forms on which fish live. Putting so much of the gathering ground of Highland rivers to sheep farming, to the virtual exclusion of cattle, has also been a loss to the trout. Cattle are great makers of organic matter—plain muck—which raises the carrying power of both land and water for invertebrate life. If you watch with a seeing eye it will be evident that rivers are natural drains and that their banks are usually much drier than the ground farther away. Cattle are sharply alive to this fact and take advantage of the banks for a dry bed. Some of the dung is washed into the water fairly readily. The rest enriches the riparian vegetation. In the rivers of the Eastern Highlands where the ground is better wooded and where, from other reasons, spates are less excessive, and where the cattle-sheep ratio is narrower, the trout are much larger and the rivers give good angling.

The trout of the lochs of the Highlands give the extremes of size, a fact indicated by the comparison of the *dubhlochan* and the Fionn Loch. The presence of *Gammarus* is an important factor in the size of trout in lochs, and that is largely dependent on the pH. But there are nevertheless some large trout to be found in poor lochs. This is because the trout is not averse to becoming a cannibal, and when he can live on his fellows he does quite well. Sometimes a stock of trout will be put into a *dubhlochan* of fair size which has no gravelly burn running into it. The trout are then unable to breed and the end product of the experiment is one or two large fish which, once having attained their growth, live a sluggish life and can manage to exist on the produce of the loch.

Salmo trutta is not only an organism with an elasticity in size referable to environment, but also with great plasticity of form. The cannibal trout of large deep lochs take on an extremely ferocious and carnivorous appearance and lose the red spots so characteristic of the species. Such fish were once thought to be a separate species and were given the name of *Salmo ferox*. Again, where brown trout live in the estuary of a river, they gain the name of slob trout, being neither like river trout or sea trout in appearance, but something in between. Whether the slob is a sea trout become sedentary or a brown trout turned estuarine, we do not know. There is always a possibility that both forms contribute to the population of slobs. They are far commoner in the West of Ireland than in the Highlands. Lastly, there is the migratory form of *S. trutta*, known as the sea trout or salmon trout. This race is hatched in small burns (Pl. 30a, p. 245) where brown trout may also breed and the young of the two races are indistinguishable. But at the age of from two to four years the migratory form begins to move downstream towards the sea. These smolts develop a silvery quality of the skin before taking completely to the sea. After a year at sea, during which the young sea trout may travel far, he comes back to his own river or a neighbouring one as a finnock, but he is not yet a breeder. He may stay a few weeks or a few months, and then away to sea again until fully grown.

The sea trout of different rivers tend to vary in the time they run up to spawn, and the lack of absolute fixity in the migratory habit is shown by the behaviour of individuals which may not conform to the general procedure but hang about the river for several months, either before or after spawning ; and at the other extreme, some fish run up and down the river again in a few days. The sea trout have been landlocked from time to time by design or accident, whereupon they have adopted the habits of brown trout and have eventually become like them in appearance. Harvie-Brown (1888) mentions that those in a fresh-water loch above Loch Slapin, Skye, have been landlocked for a century, and his informant said the fish still silvered before spawning.

Research on the sea trout and salmon in Scotland is largely conducted by the naturalists and inspectors of the Fishery Board for Scotland, now incorporated with the Scottish Home Department. The reports of the Fishery Board should be studied, also the books of W. J. M. Menzies, the Senior Inspector of Salmon Fisheries in Scotland. A great deal of marking has been done, and scale examination as a matter of course.

The salmon which run up the Highland rivers show every sign of being closed societies and differentiations are well known to experts and enthusiasts. This view has been confirmed from marking as a routine procedure in various rivers (Menzies). Smolts marked in one river are never taken as grilse or salmon in any other river but their own. Each river has its own season for the run of its salmon and in some rivers there are two runs, which would indicate that two races are using one river. Once more, the salmon is comparable with the Atlantic seal, in that when it leaves the sea in fat condition to breed, it does not feed until it returns to the sea.

Salmon parr remain in the river of their birth for two or three years before moving down to the sea. The growth and behaviour of parr have been the subject of an interesting paper by Allen (1940–41). He shows that growth takes place from early April until late October, but does not continue through the winter months. There is a decrease in the rate of feeding as the summer passes, though the amount of food available remains constant. It is probable that temperature largely determines whether growth occurs or not. Below 7° C. (45·6° F.) the parr are inactive and lie in deep pools, but when the temperature exceeds this level they move to shallower water of moderate current and feed actively. This temperature is critical. Allen (1944) has also studied the behaviour of the young salmon when they migrate to the sea as smolts. He trapped at various points on the Thurso River system in Caithness from the middle of April onwards, and found that shortly after that date the activity of migration declined until May 16, when it was *nil* for a few days, but after May 20 the rate increased to a maximum on May 25, then it declined again to *nil* by the end of the first week of June. The smolts did not appear to travel in permanent shoals, for individuals released from one trap on the same day would arrive at the next trap over a considerable period of time. It appeared that rising water was a definite stimulus to migration, and temperature probably has its influence also. A most interesting observation was that the passing of other actively-migrating smolts seems to act as a stimulus to migration. Scale examination showed that the great majority of smolts migrated after two years and a very small proportion after one or three years. Migration began about eight days earlier in the upper reaches of the river than in the lower. Sometimes, parr which have become sexually mature will be found in West Highland rivers. I have caught such a male fish in the Dundonnell River ; it was between four and five inches long and was exuding milt. When opened, its sexual maturity was obvious. Fish of this kind will cross with brown trout and may produce grossly distorted sex ratios and a fair crop of monstrosities in the offspring (Howietoun Experiments Maitland, 1887).

Once these young salmon reach the sea they move away quickly to the marine feeding grounds which, for the British salmon stock, are not yet known, but which are probably in the North Atlantic or even in the Arctic Ocean. It is rather to be hoped that the feeding place will not be found until a more sensible world is ready to receive the knowledge. Such a discovery at present would see every old hulk that would hold together making its way there, and nations vying with each other for the bulk of the trade.

The grilse return to their river in a year or two, those of the East Coast in spring and those of the West Coast about the middle of July. As soon as there is a spate they drive into the fresh water of the river. They return fairly soon and go away to their feeding ground for a further period of growth before coming back again as fully mature salmon. Salmon spawn between September and January. How common it is in November in some of the western deer-forest country to find the small rivers far into the hill almost alive with spawning salmon ploughing up the gravel ! The early-running fish spawn in the lower reaches and the later ones go farther up. The intensity of netting is greater off the mouths of eastern Scottish rivers than off the western ones, and once clear of the nets the eastern salmon has much farther to go to the head waters. The run is an exhausting activity, and it is found that on the East Coast a salmon rarely runs more than once. West Highland salmon may breed four or five times.

Remark was made in the chapter on the summits of the hills that these were biological islands holding a flora of more northern habitat. Plants which we find on our summits are to be found at sea level in

Spitsbergen. The summits hold the relics of the last glacial age. Similarly, the depths of sea lochs are islands of another kind, possibly holding their own types of living arctic relics. The char (Genus *Salvelinus*) is the only animal of this kind. It is found in many Highland and some Hebridean lochs which are deep, and it lives near the bottom. Nowhere is it fished commercially as in Lake Windermere : in fact, it is surprising how few are taken at all, considering that there must be a fair population of char in some lochs. Probably a fresh-water mollusc such as *Pisidium conventus* forms one of its foods near the bottom, for this species has been found only in high, cold lakes, or at the depths of others ; it has been dredged from 400 feet in Loch Ness. If other deep lochs were dredged, the distribution of this snail might be found to be wider than it is at present. The char come to the surface of these deep lochs at night time and may be met with in considerable shoals. This time is probably its main feeding period. The Copepoda and Cladocera on which they feed are also nearest the surface in darkness.

Reference has been made already (p. 83) to the only migratory char we have, that of Loch Insh, Inverness-shire. Other races of char in the Highlands and Islands are as follows : Willoughby's char (*S. willoughbii*), in Loch Bruiach, Inverness-shire ; Loch Maree, Ross-shire ; Lochs Borollan, Loyal and Baden, Sutherland ; and Loch Fada, North Uist ; the Struan char (*S. struanensis*) in Loch Rannoch, Perthshire ; this race is brilliantly coloured and has a large, deep-water eye ; the " haddy " (*S. killinensis*) of Loch Killin, Inverness-shire —a very distinct form ; the large-mouthed char (*S. maxillaris*) in a small loch near Ben Hope, Sutherland ; Malloch's char (*S. mallochi*) in Loch Scourie, Sutherland—a short-faced face, small-mouthed race (Regan, 1911 ; Jenkins, 1942).

Invertebrate Biology

Apart from the char, however, the biology of the lochs of the Highlands shows no relict marine fauna or any peculiar abyssal fauna, or forms peculiar to certain lochs. Murray (1910) concludes, therefore, that though arctic forms are common, ordinary migration (which may be rapid) accounts for their presence quite satisfactorily. Such abyssal fauna as exists is of littoral origin and not modified. For example, the copepod *Cyclops viridis* is a constant abyssal form down to 750 feet.

They have functional eye spots which, though unused in the depths where light does not penetrate, are apparently used when the animal is dredged to the surface by the inquiring biologist.

The fresh-water hydrobiology of invertebrates in the loch and river systems of the Highlands is too large a subject for it to be usefully treated in this book. (To the shrewd reader, also, the fact will doubtless have emerged that the subject is rather outside the author's scope!) It should also be remembered that Scotland, and the Highlands particularly, are badly in need of a fresh-water biological station on the lines of that established at Wray Castle, Lake Windermere. There has not been a great deal of work done, even of a preliminary survey type, over much of the Highlands. The shapes of the basins of the lochs, their depths, their geology and the supra-littoral floral and topographic conditions are of very great importance. The initial survey work appears in the six volumes of the *Bathymetrical Survey of Scotland* (1910). If the Scottish Tourist Board wished to increase tourism by way of increasing facilities for fishing and the quantity and quality of fish, it could do no better than support a fresh-water station where the lowly Invertebrata could be studied. The amount of bad biology at present being acted upon in movements of trout of various kinds to this loch and that is quite fantastic, and very expensive. The smaller kinds of aquatic invertebrates are, as J. A. Thomson used to say, a most important factor in the circulation of matter. The smallest kinds are gatherers of diatoms, and many slightly larger are predatory. Fish are predatory on them.

Deep, narrow lochs, such as Loch Morar, do not hold a rich invertebrate fauna, though the forms present may be fairly abundant. Also, the plankton of such lochs tends to be uniform in quantity throughout the year because of the more equable water temperatures. There is a much-limited, shallow, sub-littoral zone owing to the sudden dip of the ground to the depths, and as one might expect, the Ostracod group is particularly poor. The depths of Loch Morar appear to be sterile and the bottom is covered with a fine peaty mud. The bottom fauna of Loch Ness, over 750 feet, is very sparse—one mollusc, three crustacea, three worms, one insect and several infusorians (Murray, 1910). Scott (1892) found in Loch Morar two or three species of Copepoda, five of Cladocera, in the pelagic Entomostraca; and on the bottom at the shallow east end there were eight species of Copepoda, five of Ostracoda and sixteen of Cladocera. The common fresh-water

Amphipod, *G. pulex*, was absent, conditions being doubtless too acid. Mollusca would obviously be poorly represented in a loch of this kind. Scott found only *Limnaea peregra* and that deep-water species *Pisidium pusillum*. How different are the conditions in one of the limestone lochs of Lismore, where five water snails were found ! The bottom consists of a greyish marl largely composed of the shells of dead molluscs. Crustacea in such a loch are abundant and varied, *G. pulex* being common, of course. The shallower lochs on good ground in the east of Scotland are richer again, the more varied vegetation of the water doubtless having an enriching effect.

A shallow, sub-littoral margin with plentiful vegetation, some coming above water, is an important factor in fresh-water ecology. Apart from the chemistry, the physical factor of temperature is so much affected. The temperature of these sheltered shallows tends to rise under such conditions. Growth of plankton, crustaceans and molluscs is favoured in the summer season, when these forms are active ; indeed, the water may become too warm for the molluscs.

Reference was made in Chapter 9 to the paper by Nicol on the brackish-water lochs of Uist : there is another paper by Humphries on the profoundal and sub-littoral fauna of Lake Windermere (1936). They are extremely helpful to anyone wishing to know how a habitat "works." I wish there were more papers of the kind and standard of these for the varied types of fresh-water lochs in the Highlands.

In Highland river systems the brown trout acts as the host for the early stage, the glochidia, of the fresh-water pearl mussel (*Unio margaritifer*) which is a common resident on the bottom of quick-flowing, clear rivers about three feet deep which have a bottom strewn with stones. The glochidia attach themselves to the gills of the fish. Boycott (1936) says this mussel may reach the great age of 70 years and remarks that destruction of the adults seriously diminishes the population. This is precisely what has happened in the Highlands. Certain rivers such as the Kerry in Wester Ross, the Laxford in Sutherland, and the Gruline in Mull, fulfil conditions for the mussel and also for their being easily fished. Pearl fishing is done by the tinkers. They stand in the bed of the river, slowly quartering it, bent double, a glass box in one hand in order to see the bottom clearly, and in the other a long stick notched at the end. They press this stick over the mussel, and pull it from the bed of the river and put it in a sack slung over the shoulder. The load of bivalves is brought ashore where they are opened with a knife. Certainly not more than one mussel in a hundred carries a pearl, and many of the pearls are too small to be of value. The wastefulness of the fishery is apparent and some of the rivers have become not worth fishing. It is a pity that the presence of a pearl cannot be detected from external examination of the mussel.

Highland waters are singularly devoid of those fresh-water fish so common in English rivers and canals. The pike is one of the few coarse fish to be found, and it has been introduced. It infests several Highland river systems now. A pike of 74 lbs. has been taken from Loch Lomond and other very big ones from Loch Awe. Where the pike is present it is responsible for heavy mortality among ducklings and the young of other waterfowl and, of course, it thins out the trout considerably. Pike are particularly unwanted in a salmon river where the parr of two seasons are always present.

The Avian Fauna of Highland River and Loch Systems

The Highlands are relatively poor in many forms of living things common in England and Lowland Scotland, but in the birds whose habitats call for reaches of fresh water the Highlands are rich. First, there is the osprey, an empty pride for the Highlands, for the present status of this bird is to the shame of the country as a whole. From being relatively common it has become extinct in the Highlands, but may yet return because one or two have been seen in summer in the North recently. The odds are heavy against the bird because of the fanaticism of collectors and the fact that it is a migratory species ; it has to run the gauntlet through England. The history of this fish-eating hawk is melancholy reading. Charles St. John in his *Tour in Sutherlandshire* says, " I walked on to look at the osprey's nest on the old castle, and an interesting sight it is, though I lamented the absence of the birds. Why the poor osprey should be persecuted I know not, as it is quite harmless, living wholly on fish, of which everyone knows there is too great an abundance in this country for the most rigid preserver to grudge this picturesque bird his share." A few pages later the same Charles St. John is shooting a hen osprey and taking her two eggs from the nest. He sentimentally describes the calling of the distraught male bird and finishes up, " I was really sorry I had shot her." A few pages further on still he is trying to get another shot at an osprey while his friend Dunbar swims out to the nest and comes back with a half-grown young and an addled egg. On this same afternoon they find another nest, the friend has another swim, and comes back with three young ospreys ; and to cap it all St. John stalks the male bird, " I am sorry to say that I shot him deliberately in cold blood as he sat." St. John and his friend make another journey to the loch where he shot the hen osprey and got the two eggs. They find the male bird has got another mate and they are able to lift two more eggs from her. St. John shot the last ospreys in Sutherland on Loch Assynt.

St. John and his friend Dunbar are the villains in the story of the osprey in the Highlands, for not content with finishing the Sutherland population (on their own confession) they were concerned with the harrying for several years in succession of the Loch an Eilean eyrie, for which we have a well-documented history (Cash, 1913, 1914). Dunbar did the swimming and St. John received the eggs. It was not until the fifth year that Dunbar got cramp, and even then his cousin managed to haul him out ! The ospreys were unlucky throughout.

There is reason to believe that the osprey has bred in the Highlands more recently than the last recorded instance on Loch Arkaig in 1908, but secrecy must prevail as to the whereabouts. The average person, therefore, who sees beauty in the flight of a bird, cannot be allowed to see the plunge of an osprey. In 1808, Elizabeth Grant was able to pass Loch an Eilean (Pl. 30b, p. 245) in her decorous journeyings : " Often the birds rose as we were watching their eyrie, and wheeled skimming over the loch in search of the food required by the young eaglets, who could be seen peeping over the pile of sticks that formed their home." (*Memoirs of a Highland Lady.*)

The osprey is a social bird in North America, nesting in colonies, and though the European race does not seem to have the habit well developed, there is a tendency for the birds to be sociable in Germany. It is possible that the Scottish ospreys suffered in their last days from the lack of opportunity for a limited sociability.

The birds of the fresh-water systems of the Highlands divide up fairly easily into those of lochs and those of rivers. Dippers are regular inhabitants of most rivers and burns in that area, and ascend to considerable elevations. I remember often hearing the song of the dipper in deep winter at Loch Toll an Lochan, 1,750 feet, in Dundonnell Forest. And once, at another high lochan, 1,650 feet, in the same forest, I saw a pair of dippers go through an elaborate display of bowings and steppings accompanied by long peals of song. This was on the shortest day, December 21, 1934. Kingfishers (*Alcedo atthis*) occur and breed in the southern half of the West Highlands, but the bird is rare and chancy in its appearance from year to year. Occasionally the bird may be seen on passage on the outer coasts. The common sandpiper (*Actitis hypoleucos*) (Pl. XIIa, p. 97) is one of the commonest river and loch-side birds in the Highlands. It comes during the last week in April, and after much show and sound during the breeding season it becomes a silent and almost furtive bird of the coasts in August and until it leaves. The grey wagtail (*Motacilla cinerea*) is the last of this small group : it nests freely in the Highlands, preferably on quite small but tumultuous burns that have a bit of cover of birch scrub, fern and long heather. The display of grey wagtails is particularly ardent, varied and beautiful, and I have seen it take place at the nest. As British bird literature has no consecutive, detailed, objective account of this, it remains for someone so to enjoy a leisurely week or two in late May. Goosanders are also birds of the rivers rather than of the lochs. They are probably extending their range in the Highlands and increasing their numbers also. At one time the wilds of Sutherland and Ross were their last breeding stronghold, but they are now breeding down into Argyll. These large, handsome birds will continue to have a more or less perilous time as their food is largely fish, including salmon parr, got from fresh water. The goosander is much less a marine species than the red-breasted merganser (*Mergus serrator*) which is by far the most common sea duck on West Highland coasts in winter. I have seen as large a flock as 123 birds in Little Loch Broom. They go up the rivers to breed as they take up a nest site very close to the water, usually approached by a tunnel in the undergrowth on the bank. The mergansers indulge in a fast-moving communal display in April, which includes tilting, hydroplaning and opening wide the beak, ending in what appears to be promiscuous coition.

The mallard (*Anas platyrhyncha*) is found on fresh-water systems throughout the Highlands but is much commoner as an estuarine species. Nowhere in the Highlands proper does it occur in those large concentrations found on the East Coast and in the south-west of Scotland. The teal (*Anas crecea*) is widely distributed, but in my experience is a rare duck over the whole West Coast region, especially in the north. Considered all round, it is a decreasing species in the

Highlands. The wigeon (*Anas penelope*) is now a well-established breeder in the Highland region. This bird is one of our gains in the last 150 years, having spread from an original colonization in Sutherland. It breeds in all the mainland Highland counties, in the Uists and in Coll, but not in the Inner Hebrides. The wigeon becomes estuarine in winter and its numbers are augmented by birds presumed to come from Iceland. The shoveler (*Spatula clypeata*) is resident in the southern part of the Outer Hebrides and in the Moray Basin. Its possible habitats are limited by its need for shallow, muddy conditions of water. Reed beds form a favourite nesting site in the Outer Isles. The pochard (*Nyroca ferina*) used to breed in Tiree, but has now gone. It is also doubtful whether it has continued to breed in Ross-shire. The tufted duck (*N. fuligula*) has vastly increased in the Highlands except in the north-west where it remains scarce. It breeds regularly in the Outer Hebrides north of the Sound of Harris, and in some of the Inner Hebrides.

The reed bunting (*Emberiza schoeniclus*) is found throughout the Highlands and Islands, but is, of course, restricted to habitats of reed beds (*Phragmites communis*), for the fresh-water systems do not carry the growth of osiers and such other plants as the reed bunting would frequent. It is remarkable what a small area of reeds will satisfy the simple needs of this bird and how widely distributed it is. *Phragmites* is a plant which will help to fill a lochan, so that these habitats are constantly though slowly changing.

The sedge warbler (*Acrocephalus schoenobaenus*) is also a bird of the sluggish portions of fresh-water systems, but it is not common anywhere in the Highlands. It needs a richer habitat than the generally acid conditions provide, a place of rank vegetation. Nevertheless the sedge warbler does occur as a breeding bird in every Highland county and is reckoned to be common in Islay. It is breeding in very small numbers in the southern half of the Outer Hebrides.

The lesser redpoll (*Carduelis flammea cabaret*) is not really a bird of the fresh-water systems so much as of the sallow willow, alder and birch scrub associated with them. In the North-West Highlands the lesser redpoll seems to be particularly inclined to a habitat of sallow willows and has been known to disappear from a district when an area of sallow was burnt. This brings to mind the boreal quality of this section of the Highlands, for in Greenland, the Greenland redpoll (*C. f. rostrata*) nests only where the sallow is found.

The heron (*Ardea cinera*) in the Highlands finds so much more food on the innumerable miles of sheltered coasts that it is not the river bird which one considers it farther inland. There are heronries on islands in fresh-water lochs, though many have been extirpated ; there are some in high trees on the edge of sea lochs ; and some herons in the Highlands have taken to an almost completely marine existence, nesting in the rocks of small treeless islands offshore, e.g. the Summer Isles and those at the mouth of Loch Laxford. A communal prancing display is to be seen at a heronry if the ground near allows this to take place ; or such a display may occur at a considerable distance from the nests. I once counted 21 herons prancing (not all together) to and fro along a flat stretch about the length of a cricket pitch. Legs were lifted high and wings held away from the body.

The cormorant (*Phalocrocorax carbo*) is a marine cliff-nesting species which spends a good deal of time on fresh water in the Highlands, except in the central region. Many lochs have " cormorant rocks " where the birds may be seen sunning their wings in summer. The cormorant is not a common nesting species on the west side of the Highlands, but there are a few quite large colonies, e.g. that of the Summer Isles, which has a total of nearly a hundred pairs. What impressed me about their behaviour at that place was their annual or biennial change of nesting station among the islands, involving a move of perhaps two miles each time—one year on the north and south of Priest Island, next at Carn an Iar, then on the north cliff of Tanera Beag, and back to Priest Island again. The move involved about 80 per cent of the whole colony, about 10 per cent remaining at or near the previous year's site and the others going still farther ahead to perhaps another locus on Priest Island. Although quite common on the fresh-water systems, it rarely nests on them.

The oystercatcher is almost entirely a shore-nesting and shore-living bird in the West Highlands, but in the Central Highlands it is a river bird. Oystercatchers are a feature of the shingle beds and barely-grassed islands and banks of the Spey, and are sometimes found on upland grazings at over 1,500 feet.

Coming to the birds more characteristic of the lochs, the status of the divers may be mentioned. The black-throated diver (*Colymbus arcticus*) is commoner in the Sutherland and Ross-shire area, and the red-throated diver (*C. stellatus*) (Pl. XXXIa, p. 236) is commoner in Argyll and Inverness-shire. The habitats and preferences of these two birds are very similar. The red-throat will inhabit a small lochan but the black-throat is shyer, and perhaps because it is much more a feeder in the loch by which it nests it needs more water. The red-throated diver gains most of its food from the sea even when nesting several miles inland. The observer will see and hear it coming down to the sea in the very early morning of summer. It flies high, the wing movement is quicker than that of a duck and it looks more streamlined; the call is also sharper than a duck's quack and uttered in rapid staccato succession.

The common gull (*Larus canus*) breeds on the banks of shallow lochans in the hill country, especially on the west side of the Highlands. It is very common and its daily passage from the hill lochs down to the estuaries and sea lochs is a characteristic sight. The lesser black-backed gull follows a somewhat similar habit, but is nothing like so land-minded as the common gull.

The status of the grebes in the Highlands is interesting; the little grebe (*Podiceps ruficollis*) is of general distribution, choosing small lochans with sedge and reed cover for breeding, and going to the coast for the winter. The great-crested grebe (*Podiceps cristatus*) is not generally considered as a Highland nesting species except for the few on the eastern and northern frontier zones of Perthshire, Angus, Aberdeen and Loch Spynie, Moray. But in fact it is found in the north-west as well. It has bred on Loch Maree for about the last fifteen years. The Slavonian grebe (*P. auritus*) (Pl. XXXIb, p. 236) is a well-established breeding species in the far north-west and a few are found in Inverness-shire. I have also seen the black-necked grebe on a sedgey, water-lilied *dubhlochan* (Pl. XXXIIb, p. 237) in Sutherland, but was not able to make sure that the two birds were breeding. The coot (*Fulica atra*) is of far more general distribution in the Highlands than the moorhen (*Gallinula chloropus*); the coot is found in quite remote islands such as Colonsay and Coll and North Uist. Moorhens need better land round their lochan which need be no more than a tiny pond surrounded with sufficient cover. The moorhen finds the bulk of its food ashore, and the barren moor round a hill loch is not good enough. It is much commoner in the wider valleys of the Central and Eastern Highlands than it is on the West, where a strath may contain no more than one pair.

Then there is a group of rare birds of the loch and bog country. First, the whooper swan (*Cygnus cygnus*) which is such a common winter visitor. Two or three pairs breed in the Highlands most years but their whereabouts have to be kept quiet. There is little reason why they should not be regular breeders. Highlanders do not kill swans and the tameness of these birds as compared with the grey lag geese is remarkable. The grey lag goose (*Anser anser*) is becoming scarcer every year as a breeder, though it is still fairly evenly distributed over the Outer Hebrides. The Summer Isles race suffers from English sportsmen visiting hotels in the district, and the fact that Lord Tarbat made Priest Island a sanctuary in 1937 has had little or no effect on the depredations. We got up to two pairs and young on Tanera in 1943, and by that time we were managing to get them feeding on our ground in winter, but they were always much wilder than the barnacle geese, which would come into the garden. The Loch Maree stock has now quite gone. The tangle of lochs and land in North and South Uist will probably be the last stronghold of the species in Scotland. The few nesting in Caithness are fairly well protected, and as this bird has been widely bred in semi-captivity, there is always the chance that we shall manage to keep it with us. Along with the raven, the grey lag must surely be Britain's most intelligent bird, or the world's for that matter. There still remains a lot of good work on animal behaviour to be done through watching the grey lag goose, both in the wild and by rearing them as close friends as Lorenz did. One of my happiest bird-watching moments was on Tanera, when, with a friend, we lay hidden in a clump of bracken by the edge of a lochan on which swam the two pairs of adults and their fledgling broods. They all came ashore near us for a few minutes and we were struck by their gentleness among themselves, and their small, quiet conversation. One felt the existence of a definite community.

The greenshank (Pl. XIIb, p. 97) is a rare bird but probably commoner than is thought. Speyside and the surrounding region is one famous haunt. The ground, being relatively near to a main-line railway, is regularly quartered by collectors. The greenshanks of the north-west are remote and live in one-mile-an-hour country. They are fairly safe, even in this day of the motor car.

This abbreviated mention of the fresh-water group of birds may close with the scarcest of them, the red-necked phalarope (*Phalaropus lobatus*) (Pl. XXXIIa, p. 237) which breeds in one place in the wide area of the Highlands, a station in the Outer Isles. It is doubtful whether it now breeds in Tiree. The breeding lochs are always near the sea.

This species is one of those waders in which the female has taken on the characteristics usually assumed by the male. She wears the brighter colours and does the courting—and lays the eggs. He incubates them alone and tends the young.

No mention is made of the large winter immigration of ducks and waders to the estuarine end of the fresh-water systems. It is not a striking phenomenon in the Highland area proper. Had we included the Beauly Firth and the coasts of the Moray Firth, then another chapter could well have been devoted to them. The eastern side of the Highlands is much richer in immigrant waders, and ducks and geese. Waders like good mud which the western estuaries have not got. They are gravelly. The estuary by which I live has many acres of tidal flats, but its total winter stock is less than a score of curlews, two or three pairs of oystercatchers, a few herons, a few resident mallard, and two score of wigeon. The sound of a redshank is an occasion for remark.

One is left with the impression that the birds of the fresh-water systems are too few in total numbers to have any considerable effect on the remainder of the eco-system. The rest of the life of this habitat would continue very much as it is if they were not there. The pike would lose a source of food in mallard ducklings, but otherwise birds are at the summit of the pyramid of fresh-water life. The spiritual loss to humanity of the water birds would be crushing. As a group they are the subject of a good deal of pressure from man, and the extinction of one species has already been accomplished.

The Botanical Complex of Highland Fresh Waters

The botanical complexes of the fresh-water systems of the Highlands are of great interest when studying distribution in relation to rate of flow, altitude, depths of lochs and chemical nature of the water and the soil of the floor. The observer is constantly encountering surprises and points to make him think. The burns carry plants and seeds from their sources, so that alpine plants may be found far below their normal habitat on the banks of rivers. The very presence of water is necessary to the fertilization of many Cryptogams. Alexander Macdonald (1904) made the interesting remark that the seeds and fruits of river-side plants are usually buoyant, at least for a time. He mentioned a singular exception in the toad rush (*Juncus bufonis*).

The banks of burns in the Highlands are often sanctuaries bearing a woodland flora. Immediately the banks come within reach of the questing, destructive muzzles of sheep, they are woodland no longer, but sedgey moor and bracken. In these cleughs are birches, hazels, rowans, oaks, willows, ashes and hollies—and sometimes pines—with an undergrowth of shade-loving grasses, garlic, wood sorrel, stitchwort, hawkweeds, wild hyacinth, primroses, polypody and scented fern. If the grazed and burnt ground of the hillside close by is examined, it will be found to be full of young trees cut by the incisors of the sheep. The trees of the cleughs are acting as mother trees and the situation in their vicinity shows how soon there could be regeneration of and reversion to forest to an altitude of almost 2,000 feet. Wherever it gets a chance on the lower reaches, alder is common. This tree has considerable value for the surrounding country where it is allowed to grow, for it has considerable leaf-fall and its roots fix nitrogen by means of symbiotic nodule bacteria. The timber (often called Scotch mahogany, from its redness) is excellent firewood and is suitable for matchmaking.

The lochs of the Highlands vary so much in size, slope of shore, depth, type of shore and floor, acidity, exposure and so on that a whole body of ecological work is waiting to be linked up with a similar study of the rivers for which the lochs are " breathers." Islands in lochs tend to be like the cleughs just described. In Lewis the islands of the fresh-water lochs are covered with dwarfed, but fruiting, rowans, but on the mainland a full forest growth is found on them. The flora of part of the Outer Hebrides has recently been well described and explained in a small volume edited by Miss M. Campbell (1945). The chapter by A. J. Wilmott is particularly enlightening in its account of the several habitats and associations, including that of the flora of the rivers and lochs in that region.

The truly lacustrine flora calls for some study of physical conditions of the environment. Access to light is a very important factor in the life of submerged plants. If a loch is shallow and clear, a rich variety of water-growing plants is possible, to an ultimate depth of between 40 and 50 feet. (The red seaweeds of the ocean, the Rhodophyceae, thrive to a depth of 250 feet.) The peaty lochs of the Highlands, however, allow sufficient light to much shallower depths than 40–50 feet. West (1910) has suggested the following rough rule : " The extreme depth to which such plants as *Nitella opaca* (a charad) and

Fontinalis antipyretica (a moss) will flourish in peaty water may roughly be estimated by multiplying by four the greatest depth at which one can see the gravel at the bottom, when looking over the shaded side of a boat about midday in the summer, when the sun is shining brilliantly, the water being perfectly calm and the boat still. Such a depth in Loch Ness and others is from 7 to 8 feet; in many peaty lochs, however, the depth is considerably less."

It is possible to divide any loch into: *a*, a photic zone, in which the higher flora can develop; *b*, a dysphotic zone, normally carrying a cryptogamic flora of charads and mosses, but still supporting a few attentuated members of the higher zone; and *c*, an aphotic zone, where organisms needing light cannot exist. As indicated above, these zones not only vary in actual depth depending on the clarity or lack of it in the water, but in extent with the slope and depth of the loch basin. Taking Loch Ness as an example of the deep, narrow loch with water of intermediate clarity and with gravelly shores, it is obvious how poor the flora must be. The great mass of the floor of the loch is without plants because the fall from the shore is so steep (opposite Invermoriston a depth of 652 feet is reached only 120 yards from the shore). Furthermore, wave action can be so great on the loose gravelly shores that no higher Phanerogamic vegetation can get a hold. It is only on fixed rocks that the low Cryptogamic plants grow without being eroded away. The action of wind is a considerable ecological factor in the vegetation of these larger lochs. Finally in Loch Ness, there is the fairly deep range of water level, which is inimical to the growth of a waterside vegetation. Urquhart Bay is the only place with a considerable water-edge flora, including an alder swamp.

The shallow limestone lochs of Lismore have the richest flora of any Highland lochs and they are not large enough for wave action to have any considerable effect on their shores. The following list is typical for these lochs:

Water crowfoot	*Ranunculus aquatilis*
Lesser spearwort	*R. flammula*
Marsh marigold	*Caltha palustris*
White water-lily	*Nymphaea alba*
Yellow water-lily	*N. lutea*
Cuckoo flower, lady's smock	*Cardamine pratensis*
Bog stitchwort	*Stellaria uliginosa*

Meadowsweet	*Filipendula ulmaria*
Purple loosestrife	*Lythrum salicaria*
Mare's tail	*Hippuris vulgaris*
Spiked milfoil	*Myriophyllum spicatum*
Water chickweed	*Montia fontana*
Marsh pennywort	*Hydrocotyle vulgaris*
Marsh ragwort	*Senecio aquaticus*
Buckbean	*Menyanthes trifoliata*
Common bladderwort	*Utricularia vulgaris*
Shoreweed	*Littorella uniflora* (=*L. lacustris*)
Amphibious polygonum	*Polygonum amphibium*
Iris	*Iris pseudacorus*
Common rush	*Juncus communis* & *J. articulatus*
Branched burweed	*Sparganium erectum*
Broad pondweed	*Potamogeton natans*
Shining pondweed	*P. lucens*
Perfoliate pondweed	*P. perfoliatus*
Slender pondweed	*P. pusillus*
Obtuse pondweed	*P. obtusifolius*
Slender pondweed	*P. filiformis*
Cotton grass	*Eriophorum polystachion*
Tufted sedge	*Carex aquatilis*
Bottle sedge	*C. rostrata*
Common reed	*Phragmites communis*
Flote grass	*Glyceria fluitans*
Horsetail	*Equisetum limosum*

A typical *dubhlochan* of the Sutherland gneiss country has the following group of plants :

Lesser spearwort	*Ranunculus flammula*
White water-lily	*Nymphaea alba*
Water milfoil	*Myriophyllum alterniflorum*
Water starwort	*Callitriche hammulata*
Water lobelia	*Lobelia dortmanna*
Buckbean	*Menyanthes trifoliata*
Shoreweed	*Littorella uniflora* (=*L. lacustris*)
Small burweed	*Sparganium affine*
Broad pondweed	*Potamogeton natans*
Cotton grass	*Eriophorum vaginatum*
Bottle sedge	*Carex rostrata*
Reed	*Phragmites communis*
Horsetail	*Equisetum limosum*
Quillwort	*Isoetes lacustris*

F. Fraser Darling

FLAGS AND ROYAL FERN. Wester Ross
July 1943

F. Fraser Darling

THE LOCHAN of the flags and royal fern, Priest Island, Wester Ross
The loch is the haunt of sea-feeding otters
July 1943

John Markham

A Highland Trout Stream in its upper reaches. Rothiemurchus, Inverness-shire
September 1944

John Markham

Where Ospreys Bred : the castle on Loch an Eilean
Rothiemurchus, Inverness-shire
September 1944

Sometimes the reed *Phragmites*, tolerant as it is of a wide range of conditions between acid and basic, finds the *dubhlochan* too sour, and in such places *Carex rostrata* takes its place as a provider of cover to some of the animal life of the loch. Both species are loch fillers and land makers, but *C. rostrata* is particularly active in this direction. It can make a shallow loch into *terra firma* in comparatively few years and then the plants of the moor creep in, or the colonization of *Eriophorum* may be so marked as to make the *quondam* loch a firm cotton sedge flat to which, as has been said earlier in this book, the sheep and deer repair in late winter and early spring. By that time *C. rostrata* will have gone and the *Phragmites* as well, though it is surprising how a few much-shortened plants of the latter will persist. The treading and the dunging by the animals bring about other changes, and so the great cycle goes on.

CONCLUSION

THE END of this book is in sight, and the writer of it left with a sense of the inadequacy of his own knowledge, which is a different thing from the inevitable feeling a man has that his skill has not equalled his inspiration. This book has been written with sustained enthusiasm and yet at the end of it the craftsman feels a brooding disappointment which is not quite pessimism. As he has written, the vast pageant, the beauty and the tragedy have filled his mind's eye and passed in noble and awful array. The loved country of the Highlands and Islands with its power, colour, variety and movement ; the diversity of living forms and the delicacy of their inter-relations ; then the regret that one man cannot compass the whole natural history of a region, and finally the realization of what the Highlands have suffered, the extent of their despoliation.

We are apt to view with pleasure a rugged Highland landscape and think we are here away from the works of the mind and hand of man, that here is wild nature. But more often than not we are looking at a man-made desert : the summits of the hills and the inaccessible sea cliffs alone are as time and evolution made them. The bare hillside, kept bare by burning and the grazing of an artificially large stock of sheep are not wild nature. The last consequences, the hundreds of thousands of acres of bracken and wastes of deer's-hair sedge are not nature but the results of ill treatment of nature. Wild birch, oak and pine woods without joyous young growth, bereft of their rightful offspring by the all-consuming mouths of sheep and too-numerous deer, these are not nature. In the sedge at our feet are the crippled children of the trees, trying each year to get on to their feet but kept low by fire and tooth. Where the woods have gone, there are gashes and landslips on many a hillside, wounds in the earth which are not nature.

Man is an indigenous animal in the countryside. Living for himself and not for the export of his natural resources, his alteration of the landscape is not great and the changes he does bring about are not necessarily—or by any means—all loss. His cultivations bring song birds, new growths and forms and colours which are beautiful in themselves. A landscape of growing corn, clover ley and the varied greens of root crops is beautiful to the eye of man and a satisfying habitat to many mammals, birds and plants. The traditional English scene, a large part of the Scottish Lowlands and the borderlands of the Highlands in Perthshire, Angus, the valleys of the Don and Dee and that lovely country of Banff, Moray and Nairn that runs from the hills to the sea, all these have a rich wild life which will persist while men work their land, grow their trees, and are given room, leave and leisure enough to fashion a small landscape not purely for commercial ends. In such places man is making many positive additions to the wealth of the soil which is the basis of wild life just as it is of our own food. The Highlands have not much rich soil, but time and climate had between them established this great area of park-like woodlands in which there was still plenty of grazing and lush valley vegetation, and there were the naturally bare grazings above 2,000 feet for the summer. The Highlanders of the past lived with this environment, growing and exporting a stock of cattle quite equal to what goes away to-day in the form of sheep. The people took to the hills themselves in summer so that their stock should use the high pastures, and in this way the low ground was conserved for the winter season. In that environment dwelt not only a larger human population than at present, but a more varied wild life as well. Golden eagle and white-tailed sea eagle, kite and osprey, were all relatively common ; so was the pine marten, and the range of presently scarce woodland birds such as the crested tit and the Scottish crossbill was wider than it is to-day. The capercaillie is with us through reintroduction ; the blackcock and greyhen get scarcer as the years pass ; even the red grouse is growing fewer every year on the western hillsides that have had a century and a half of misuse.

Two revolutions struck the Highlands—the coming of the sheep from the Southern Uplands following the destruction of the forests, and the delight in game preservation which meant an almost automatic fixation of mind on killing any carnivorous mammal or raptorial or fish-eating bird without reference to its whole life history. Even dippers were shot because they worked on the floors of gravelly streams where it was known that salmon and trout laid their spawn. These two foreign pursuits of sheep farming and game preservation have held the Highlands in their grip and the one still wears a cloak almost of sanctity, although the whole industry has to be bolstered by a generous subsidy on every ewe. Only in the Central and Eastern Highlands has there developed a more gracious style of husbandry which is not both destructive and extractive. The drier climate of the valleys of the Spey and Dee and the country to the north coincides with the fact of large tracts of glacial silt, and timber has never lost its place as a crop. This means coniferous timber, but throughout the area a large amount of birch and alder is tolerated which beautifies and fertilizes the countryside. The cattle-sheep ratio is much narrower and the density of sheep over all is less, though on the ground used as sheep farms it is greater than in the West.

The farther west one goes the poorer is the ground, and the more liable it is to erosion and leaching if the cover is removed ; which is precisely what has happened. The sheep also become poorer in type the farther west, but they receive the same subsidy as the grand Blackface and Cheviot stocks of the Southern Uplands. Even the very flowers diminish in numbers and variety until certain sheep-free *machairs* are reached, where the flowers of July are one of the joys of the Highlands.

The Forestry Commission has purchased large tracts of ground in the Highlands and nowhere has the antagonism been so great as in the West, where planting (Pl. 31, p. 252) is most needed as a buffer in the natural economy of the region. As soon as a West Highland sheep farm is bought for re-afforestation (employing perhaps one shepherd for each 600 ewes and each ewe occupying between 4 and 10 acres, with a Highlands-wide average of 5) then we hear that it was the finest sheep farm in the West. Unfortunately, the Forestry Commission has not shown itself in the past to be an enlightened authority sociologically or ecologically in the Highlands. Planting has for the most part been done on principles which have been obsolete for half a century on the Continent and there has been little attempt to forge the idea and fact of community among the forest workers. Many of us have hopes of this authority for the future and will not hold up the past against it. The Commission's initial remit was far too narrow. Now it is heartening to know that the Commission has an ecological committee and is already doing some mixed planting. All of us who see the necessity for a much extended forestry programme in the West should give the Commission earnest support and good will, for the interests working against it are very great. As the Commission develops and widens its outlook it will be solving part of the human problem of the Highlands and part of the problem of caring for the wild life of the area. Already the Forestry Commission has done more towards the establishment of national parks and more or less effective reserves than any other body. (But I wish it would not snare roe deer, and shoot the last few blackgame in the country. There is room for both.)

There is not the same threat to wild life in the Central and East Highlands as there is in the West. Many estates in the West which were formerly kept with care are now going completely out of control. The crofting population of the West Highlands is not yet conscious of any desirability to maintain wild life and its environment, and wherever there is a natural resource left which can be drained easily it is being depleted. This applies to woodlands and rivers directly; and indirectly through the overgrazing of the common pasture, and in some places through cutting the superficial turf from the commons. There was strict control of these activities in the past by the factors and ground officers of the estates and particularly by the township constables, these last officials being elected by the crofters themselves. These controls have slipped, civic sense in the townships is not well developed and far too commonly there is heard that phrase of despair, "It will serve our time."

There is no definite, direct set against the wild life by the human population of the West Highlands, none at all, for the folk are kindly to wild animals, but there is the marked tendency thoughtlessly to kill the environment. The time of heather burning, done in an irresponsible and uncontrolled manner, is one of excitement and enjoyment. Heather burnings are the beltane fires of this age. On the whole, the Celtic ethos—and the Scandinavian for that matter—has never been remarkable for its sense of conservation or for its active care for a stock of wild animals. Norse influence has generally been towards positive destruction. Even now, with Rona proclaimed a sanctuary, the annual or biennial visit to the island is an occasion for a battue. Seals are shot and not recovered, and any of the birds are fair game. It is an occasion, the banging of shotguns makes an impressive sound and you might as well aim at something rather than at nothing, especially when there are so many living things swimming and flying around. Highlanders are not alone to blame. The yachtsmen in the West Highlands have a very bad reputation which is well deserved. I have been astounded to read in yachting journals open boasts of robbing tern colonies for eggs—and finding them half incubated—what a lark!

How can we blame the West Highland crofters (or rather, those few of them) when we remember that they have no football matches or organized sporting amusements, and they see people with more wealth and leisure being plain vandals ? When a crofter once told me that there were nothing like the number of geese there used to be, that he remembered running a brood of seven over the cliff and getting six of them (" They kept us in meat for a week "), I felt no anger ; one could understand ; but when an hotel launch with guests wanting sport on the cheap comes shooting shags and gulls as they fly from the cliffs—and this in June and July—hope dies. Donald is indifferent on the whole, not consciously indifferent, but unconscious of ultimate consequences, and he always desires to please. Who exterminated the ospreys in Sutherland ? Not Donald, but St. John the educated, aristocratic Englishman. St. John failed his class.

Education in civics and a consequent realization of the place of wild life in Highland economy are reasonable possibilities in the townships throughout the West ; a far more ponderous quantity is the *apathy* of the British public at large ; this is a stiffer problem to tackle even than the slow-timing by certain interests which do not want national parks. Apathy is the greatest danger to the wild life of the country as a whole, let alone that of the Highlands.

National parks alone are no guarantee of the biotic complex of the Highlands being held together. What is meant by a national park ? There is every reason to believe that, in the minds of many who will have a large say as to whether they will or will not be, they are considered largely as lungs for urban industrial populations. So they should be, and let none of us who live in easier surroundings be one little bit scornful of this tremendous necessity, or of the almost pathetic hope that is in the minds of millions of young people. Travel the road from the head of Loch Lomond to Balloch at Easter time, and see the lads and lasses from the poorer parts of Glasgow trudging along with their packs. Their clothes may be weird and their paraphernalia ridiculous (if one sees things that way) but you will be deeply moved by what it all means. If you stop and talk or walk along with these youngsters you will find their earnestness, their wonder and their desire to know. National parks are a necessity as lungs and as an educative force leading to the care of wild life in the rest of the Highlands.

Supposing that in addition to the parks being lungs, our legislators wish wild life to be conserved in the areas ; what reason is behind the wish and how is it to be done? Wild life does not exist for man's delectation. Man may find it beautiful, edifying, amusing, useful and all the rest of it, but that is not why it is there, nor is that a good enough reason for our allowing it to remain. Let us give beast and bird and flower the place to live *in its own right*, unless pest or obnoxious parasite. If we can admit that right and desire to accord it, we are well on the way to taking a holistic view of wild life in the economy of the nation. It is interesting and gladdening to find that the Secretary of State for Scotland, in his remit to the Committee he has appointed to advise on the establishment and administration of national parks, has asked that special attention should be given to the conservation of wild life in Scotland as a whole, and recommends that a sub-committee should be formed to deal with the subject. This has now been done and the committee is at work. But when all is said and done, wild life in the Highlands and the rehabilitation and preservation of environments will not be successfully cared for by the deliberations of a committee. It will depend on the active wish of ordinary folk, of people who visit the Highlands and of those who live there ; and with all this good will, finally on a trained wild-life service, a corps of men working on natural history, studying phenomena and forecasting consequences and gaining a knowledge of the dynamics of natural populations. (Actuaries are needed for animals as well as for human beings !)

The crofting population will have an integral part to play in the scheme of national parks, and in the ultimate conservation of wild life. Their way of life at its best has great value for the nation, for it is unhurried, unselfish and kindly. From the point of view of logistics, any accommodation the crofts can offer will be needed, and all the fresh food, in the shape of milk, eggs, soft fruit and vegetables will find a ready market in the visitors to the parks. And if the crofter can come to say about the wild life and its environment, " This is part of my heritage and I want to take care of it," the battle will be won. It will have meant a change from an alien, destructive, extractive husbandry of the wild lands to their constructive management and a concentration on the productive power of the small area of arable ground. The mild climate and the fact that much of the arable land is at sea level make possible a very high productivity of land which is well drained, limed, given phosphates and properly cultivated.

Forestry, national parks and crofting agriculture have been mentioned as important factors in the existence of wild life in the

Highlands. Hydro-electric power schemes might well be added. At the moment all these interests are separate, going their own way in their own way, and it seems to me that wild life is going to be squeezed and buffeted between the lot of them unless special steps are taken. National parks alone will not preserve wild life, nor even the plain establishment of special nature reserves for particular species and habitats. Some co-ordination is needed as well.

The British Ecological Society recently issued a Memorandum entitled *Nature Conservation and Nature Reserves* in which it was recommended that a new council should be constituted under the Lord President of the Council, parallel with the Agricultural and Medical Research Councils. Under this council would serve the research and advisory staff concerned with the wild life problems of the whole country, and it is suggested that the Ecological Research Council might be the controlling body for the several nature reserves throughout the country. The subject is further discussed by Professor Tansley in his book *Our Heritage of Wild Nature*. The idea is obviously a sound one and in a modified form will probably become fact.

But the final word must be concerned with the attitudes and thoughts of our own minds : it is not enough to delegate our individual responsibilities to " them." " They," as someone other than one's self, can so easily be nobody. The Highlands and Islands are the only large mass of very rugged country in Britain, where land values are still low. A wild life second to none in the kingdom still exists there. We may wish to preserve it for sentimental reasons ; it will be found necessary to conserve it for economic reasons ; it may be valuable because it is beautiful.

These reasons are not enough ; we need to conserve because we love and see wild life as part of the same whole as ourselves. Man is the only living creature with the divine gift of freedom. He alone is conscious, with the power to reflect, able to choose whether he will act for good or ill. The search for accurate knowledge, surely, is a cornerstone of morality ; and with knowledge in our minds and methods in our hands, how shall we use our freedom ?

THE END

BIBLIOGRAPHY

AINSLIE, J. A. & ATKINSON, R. (1937). On the breeding habits of Leach's fork-tailed petrel. *Brit. Birds 30* : 234–48.

(1937). Summer bird notes from North Rona. *Scot. Nat.* 1937 : 7–13.

ALLEN, K. R. (1940–43). Studies on the biology of the early stages of the salmon (*Salmo salar*). 1. Growth on the River Eden. *J. Anim. Ecol. 9* : 1–23.

2. Feeding Habits. *J. Anim. Ecol. 10* : 47–76.

3. Growth in the Thurso River system, Caithness. *J. Anim. Ecol. 10* : 273–95.

4. The smolt migration in the Thurso River. *J. Anim. Ecol. 13* : 63–85.

ALSTON, C. H. (1913). A list of Gaelic names of British mammals. *Scot. Nat.* 1913 : 145–53.

ATKINSON, R. (1938). Natural history notes from certain Scottish islands—North Rona, the Flannan Isles, Handa Island. *Scot. Nat.* 1938 : 145–47.

(1940). Notes on the botany of North Rona and Sula Sgeir. *Trans. Proc. Bot. Soc. Edin. 33* : 52–60.

BADEN-POWELL, D. & ELTON, C. (1936–37). On the relation between a raised beach and an iron age midden on the Island of Lewis, Outer Hebrides. *Proc. Soc. Antiq. Scot. 71* : 347–65.

Balfour Report on Hill Sheep Farming. 1944. London, H.M.S.O.

BALFOUR-BROWN, F. (1911). The aquatic coleoptera of the North Ebudes. *Ann. Scot. Nat. Hist.* 1911 : 149–57.

BARRINGTON, R. M. (1885). (In "Further notes on North Rona," J. A. Harvie-Brown.) *Proc. Roy. Phys. Soc. 9* : 289.

BEARE, T. HUDSON (1913). *Thanasimus rufipes*, Brahm, a beetle new to the British fauna, and its life-history. *Proc. Roy. Phys. Soc. 19* : 60–62.

BEDFORD, DUCHESS OF (1914). Spring bird-notes from various Scottish islands. *Scot. Nat.* 1914 : 3–8.

BENNET, A. (1907). The plants of the Flannan Islands. *Ann. Scot. Nat. Hist.* 1907 : 187.

Bentham, G. & Hooker, J. D. (1937). Handbook of the British Flora (7th edition). Ashford, Reeve.

Berry, J. (1939). The status and distribution of wild geese and wild duck in Scotland. Cambridge, University Press.

Bertram, D. S. (Ed.) (1939). The natural history of Canna and Sanday, Inner Hebrides: a report upon the Glasgow University Canna Expeditions, 1936 & 1937. *Proc. Roy. Phys. Soc. 23*: 1–71.

Bertram, G. C. L. (1940). The biology of the Weddell and crabeater seals with a study of the comparative behaviour of the Pinnipeda. *Brit. Graham Land Exped., 1934–37 Sci. Reps.* London, Brit. Mus. (Nat. Hist.).

Beveridge, F. S. (1918). The birds of North Uist. *Scot. Nat.* 1918: 245–54.

Booth, F. (1913). Molluscan investigation in West Ross. *Scot. Nat.* 1913: 56–59.

Boycott, A. E. (1936). The habitats of fresh-water mollusca in Britain. *J. Anim. Ecol. 5*: 116–86.

Boyd Watt, H. (1937). On the wild goat in Scotland. With supplement: Habits of wild goats in Scotland, by F. Fraser Darling. *J. Anim. Ecol. 6*: 15–22.

Breadalbane, Marchioness of (1935). The High Tops of Blackmount (2nd edition). Edinburgh, Blackwood.

Bristowe, W. S. (1927). The spider fauna of the Western Islands of Scotland. *Scot. Nat.* 1927: 88–94, 117–22.

British Ecological Society (1943). Nature conservation and nature reserves. *J. Anim. Ecol. 13*: 1–25.

Brögger, A. W. (1929). Ancient emigrants: a history of the north settlements of Scotland. Oxford, Clarendon Press.

Buchanan, J. H. (1882). Distribution of the chough in Scotland. *Proc. Roy. Phys. Soc. 7*: 99.

Bullough, W. S. (1942). The reproductive cycles of the British and Continental races of the starling (*Sturnus vulgaris* L.). *Phil. Trans. Roy. Soc. Lond., B.* 231: 165-246.

Calderwood, W. L. (1907). The life of the salmon. London, Edward Arnold.

Cameron, A. G. (1923). The wild red deer of Scotland. London, Blackwood.

Campbell, J. L. (1938). The Macrolepidoptera of the parish of Barra. *Scot. Nat.* 1938: 153–63.

CAMPBELL, M. (1945). The flora of Uig (Lewis). Arbroath, Buncle.

CASH, C. G. (1914). History of the Loch an Eilean ospreys. *Scot. Nat.* 1914 : 149–58.

CHITTY, D. (1938). A laboratory study of pellet formation in the short-eared owl (*Asio flammeus*). *Proc. Zool. Soc. Lond. 108* : 267–87.

CLARKE, W. E. (1912). Studies in Bird Migration. 2 vols. London, Gurney & Jackson.

(1914). Notes on the mice of St. Kilda. *Scot. Nat.* 1914: 124–28.

(1915). The wren of St. Kilda : its status, plumages and habits. *Scot Nat.* 1915 : 291–96.

(1917–18). Wild life in a West Highland deer forest. *Scot. Nat.* 1917 : 255–64, 279–88 ; 1918 : 1–10.

COCKBURN, A. M. (1936). The geology of St. Kilda. *Trans. Roy. Soc. Edin. 58* : 511–47.

COLLETT, R. (1881). On *Halichoerus gripus* and its breeding on the Fro Islands off Throndhjems-fjord in Norway. *Proc. Zool. Soc. Lond.* 1881 : 380–87.

CRAMPTON, C. B. (1911). The Vegetation of Caithness considered in Relation to the Geology. Cambridge.

CUNNINGTON, W. A. (1910). On the nature and origin of fresh-water organisms. *Bathymetrical Surveys of the Scottish Fresh-water Lochs, 1* : 354–73.

DARLING, F. (1937). A Herd of Red Deer. Oxford, University Press

(1938). Wild life conservation. *J. Soc. Preserv. Faun. Empire*, n. ser., pt. 34 : 31–40.

(1938). Bird Flocks and the Breeding Cycle. Cambridge, University Press.

(1939). A Naturalist on Rona. Oxford, Clarendon Press.

(1943). Wild Life in Britain. London, Collins.

DAY, F. (1887). British and Irish Salmonidae. London, Williams & Norgate.

Department of Health for Scotland (1946). Control of Midges. Interim Rept. Sub. Comm. Sci. Advisory Comm. Edinburgh, H.M.S.O.

DONISTHORPE, H. ST. J. K. (1927). British ants. London, Routledge.

DRUCE, G. C. (1930). The comital flora of the British Isles. Arbroath, Buncle.

ELMHIRST, R. (1935). The occurrence of *Gammarus* in Scottish waters. *Scot. Nat.* 1935 : 17–21.

ELTON, C. (1936). Notes on freshwater animals in the Isle of Lewis. *Proc. Zool. Soc. Lond.* 1936 : 939–44.

(1938). Notes on the ecological and natural history of Pabbay. *J. Ecol. 26* : 275–97.

(1939). On the nature of cover. *J. Wildlife Manag. 3* : 332-38.

ELWES, H. J. (1912). Notes on the primitive breeds of sheep in Scotland. *Scot. Nat.* 1912 : 49–52.

EWING, P. (1910). On some Scottish alpine forms of *Carex*. *Ann. Scot. Nat. Hist.* 1910 : 174–81.

FENTON, E. W. (1937). The influence of sheep on the vegetation of hill grazings in Scotland. *J. Ecol. 25* : 424–30.

FERGUSON, E. M. (1945). Wild life notes from Scotland. *J. Soc. Preserv. Faun. Empire*, n. ser., pt. 52 : 46–49.

FISHER, J. (1941). The birds of Rockall as shown by photographs taken by the Royal Air Force. *Bull. Brit. Orn. Cl. 62* : 5–13.

FISHER, J. & VEVERS, H. G. (1943–44). The breeding distribution, history and population of the North Atlantic gannet (*Sula bassana*). *J. Anim. Ecol. 12* : 173–213 ; *13* : 49–62.

FISHER, J. & WATERSTON, G. (1941). The breeding distribution, history and population of the fulmar (*Fulmarus glacialis*) in the British Isles. *J. Anim. Ecol. 10* : 204–72.

FITCH, W. H. & SMITH, W. G. (1939). Illustrations of the British Flora (5th edition). Ashford, Reeve.

FORD, E. B. (1945). Butterflies. London, Collins.

FORREST, J. E., WATERSTON, A. R. & WATSON, E. V. (Ed.) (1936). The natural history of Barra, Outer Hebrides. *J. Roy. Phys. Soc. 22* : 241–96.

FRASER, G. K. (1933). Studies of Scottish moorlands in relation to tree growth. *Bull. Forest. Comm.* No. 15.

(1943). Peat deposits of Scotland. Pt. I. (Mimeographed). London, Geol. Surv. Gt. Britain and Dept. Sci. & Indust. Res.

FRASER, J. H. (1935). An experiment on the powers of survival of animals and plants from a pool above high-water mark. *J. Anim. Ecol. 4* : 229–30.

(1936). The distribution of rock pool Copepoda according to tide level. *J. Anim. Ecol. 5* : 23–28.

GEIKIE, A. (1887). The Scenery of Scotland (2nd edition). London, Macmillan.

GORDON, S. (1944). A Highland year. London, Eyre & Spottiswoode.

GORDON, W. S. (1933). Studies in tick-borne fever of sheep. 1. Transmission by the tick, *Ixodes ricinus*, with a description of the disease produced. *Parasitology*, *25* : 273–83.

GRANT, E. (1899). Memoirs of a Highland lady, 1797–1830. London, Murray.

GRIMSHAW, P. (1910). The insect fauna of grouse moors. *Ann. Scot. Nat. Hist.* 1910 : 149–62.

HALDANE, R. C. (1905). Notes on whaling in Shetland, 1904. *Ann. Scot. Nat. Hist.* 1905 : 65–72.

(1906). Whaling in Scotland. *Ann. Scot. Nat. Hist.* 1906 : 130–37.

(1907). Whaling in Scotland. *Ann. Scot. Nat. Hist.* 1907 : 10–15.

(1908). Whaling in Scotland for 1907. *Ann. Scot. Nat. Hist.* 1908 : 65–72.

(1909). Whaling in Scotland for 1908. *Ann. Scot. Nat. Hist.* 1909 : 65–69.

(1910). Whaling in Scotland for 1909. *Ann. Scot. Nat. Hist.* 1910 : 1–2.

HARDY, M. (1906). Botanical survey of Scotland : a general map of the Highlands with a sketch of the history and methods. *Scot. Geogr. Mag.* *22* : 229–41.

(1931). Afforestation in Lewis and Harris. *Scot. Forestry J.* *45* : 1–11.

HARKER, A. (1941). The West Highlands and the Hebrides. Cambridge, University Press.

HARRISON, J. W. H. (1938). A contribution to our knowledge of the Lepidoptera of the islands of Coll, Canna, Sanday, Rhum, Eigg, Soay and Pabbay (Inner Hebrides), and of Barra, Mingulay and Berneray (Outer Hebrides). *Proc. Univ. Durham Phil. Soc.* *11* : 10–23.

HARRISON, J. W. H. *et al.* (1936). The natural history of the Isle of Raasay and of the adjacent islands of South Rona, Scalpay, Fladday and Longay. *Proc. Univ. Durham Phil. Soc.* *10* : 246–351.

HARRISSON, T. H. & BUCHAN, J. N. S. (1934). A field study of the St. Kilda wren (*Troglodytes troglodytes hirtensis*), with especial reference to its numbers, territory and food habits. *J. Anim. Ecol.* *3* : 133–45.

(1936). Further notes on a field study of the St. Kilda wren (*Troglodytes troglodytes hirtensis* Seeb.), with especial reference to its nest habits and song. *Scot. Nat.* 1936 : 9–21.

HARRISSON, T. H. & LACK, D. (1934). The breeding birds of St. Kilda. *Scot. Nat.* 1934 : 59–60, 61–69.

HARRISSON, T. H. & MOY-THOMAS, J. A. (1932). St. Kilda house mouse. *Nature, 129* : 131.

(1933). The mice of St. Kilda, with especial reference to their prospects of extinction and present status. *J. Anim. Ecol. 2*: 109–15.

HARTING, J. E. (1880). British Animals Extinct within Modern Times. London, Trübner.

HARTLEY, C. H. & FISHER, J. (1936). The marine foods of birds in an inland fjord region in West Spitsbergen. Pt. 2 Birds. *J. Anim. Ecol.* 5 : 370–89.

HARVIE-BROWN, J. A. (1880–81). The history of the squirrel in Great Britain. *Proc. Roy. Phys. Soc.* 5 : 182 *et seq.*

(1892). The great spotted woodpecker (*Picus major* L.) in Scotland. *Ann. Scot. Nat. Hist.* 1892 : 4–17.

(1895). The starling in Scotland, its increase and distribution. *Ann. Scot. Nat. Hist.* 1895 : 2–22.

(1906). A Fauna of the Tay Basin and Strathmore. Edinburgh, David Douglas.

HARVIE-BROWN, J. A. & BARRINGTON, R. M. (1897). On the ornithology of Rockall. *Trans. Roy. Irish Acad. 31* : 66–75.

HARVIE-BROWN, J. A. & BUCKLEY, T. E. (1887). A Vertebrate Fauna of Sutherland, Caithness and West Cromarty. Edinburgh, Douglas.

(1888). A Vertebrate Fauna of the Outer Hebrides. Edinburgh, Douglas.

(1892). A Vertebrate Fauna of Argyll and the Inner Hebrides. Edinburgh, Douglas.

(1895). A Vertebrate Fauna of the Moray Basin. 2 vols. Edinburgh, Douglas.

HARVIE-BROWN, J. A. & MACPHERSON, H. A. (1904). A Fauna of the North-West Highlands and Skye. Edinburgh, Douglas.

HEWITT, G. (1907). A contribution to a flora of St. Kilda. *Ann. Scot. Nat. Hist.* 1907 : 239–41.

HEWITT, J. (1910). Some distinctive characters in the fresh-water plankton from various islands off the north and west coasts of Scotland. *Bathymetrical Survey of the Scottish Fresh-water Lochs, 1* : 335–53.

HINTON, M. A. C. (1924). Rivers and Lakes. London, Sheldon Press.

HOLMES, A. (1944). Principles of physical geology. London, Nelson & Sons Ltd.

HUMPHRIES, C. F. (1936). An investigation of the profundal and sublittoral fauna of Windermere. *J. Anim. Ecol.* *5* : 29–52.

HUXLEY, J. S. (1931). The relative size of antlers in deer. *Proc. Zool. Soc. Lond.* 1931 : 819–64.

(1938). Species formation and geographical isolation. *Proc. Linn. Soc. Lond.* *150* : 253–64.

HYDROGRAPHIC DEPARTMENT, ADMIRALTY, LONDON (1934). West Coast of Scotland Pilot (8th edition). London.

JENKINS, J. T. (1925). The Fishes of the British Isles. London, F. Warne & Co.

KITCHING, J. A. (1935). An introduction to the ecology of intertidal rock surfaces on the coast of Argyll. *Trans. Roy. Soc. Edin.* *18* : 351–74.

LACK, D. (1931). Coleoptera on St. Kilda in 1931. *Entomol. Mon. Mag.* *67* : 276–79.

(1932). Further notes on insects from St. Kilda ; including the orders Thysanura, Dermaptera, Hemiptera, Trichoptera, Lepidoptera, Coleoptera (Supplement) and Hymenoptera. *Ibid.* *68* : 137–45.

(1933). Notes on the Diptera of St. Kilda. *Ibid.* *68* : 262–66.

(1942). Ecological features of the bird faunas of British small islands. *J. Anim. Ecol.* *10* : 9–36.

LANKESTER, E. (1855). Notes on the Deer of Scotland. Appendix to Wm. MacGillivray's " Natural History of Deeside and Braemar." London.

LEWIS, F. J. (1906). The history of the Scottish peat mosses and their relation to the Glacial Period. *Scot. Geogr. Mag.* *22* : 241–52.

LODER, J. DE V. (1935). Colonsay and Oronsay in the Isles of Argyll. Edinburgh, Oliver & Boyd.

LUCAS, W. J. (1900). British Dragonflies. London, L. U. Gill.

MACAULAY, K. (1764). The history of St. Kilda. London.

MACCULLOCH, J. (1824). The Highlands and Western Isles of Scotland. London.

MACDONALD, A. (1904). Water-borne seeds. *Ann. Scot. Nat. Hist.* 1904 : 34–36.

MACGILLIVRAY, J. (1839). A History of British Birds. London. Vol. 2 : 367.

M'Intosh, W. C. (1866). Observations on the marine zoology of North Uist. *Proc. Roy. Soc. Edin.* 5 : 600–14.

Mackenzie, O. H. (1918). Vanishing birds, and birds that have already vanished, on the West Coast of Ross-shire. *Scot. Nat.* 1918 : 31–34.

(1924). A Hundred Years in the Highlands. (Popular edition.) London, Edward Arnold.

Macleod, J. (1932). The bionomics of *Ixodes ricinus* L., the "sheep tick" of Scotland. *Parasitology*, 24 : 382–400.

(1932). Preliminary studies in the tick transmission of louping-ill. *Vet. J. 88* : 276–84.

Macnair, P. (1893–98). The geological factors in the distribution of the alpine plants of Perthshire. *Trans. Perthsh. Soc. Nat. Sci.* 2 : 240–49.

Maitland, J. R. G. (1887). "The History of Howietoun . . ." Stirling, J. R. Guy.

Martin, M. (1934). A Description of the Western Islands of Scotland. (First publ. 1703.) Stirling, Eneas Mackay.

Matthews, J. R. (1937). Geographical relationships of the British Flora. *J. Ecol.* 25 : 1–90.

(1939). The ecological approach to land utilisation. *Scot. Forestry J.* 53 : 23–34.

Menzies, W. J. M. (1931). The Salmon. Edinburgh & London, Blackwood.

(1936). Sea Trout and Trout. London, Edward Arnold.

Middleton, A. D. (1930). Cycles in the numbers of British voles (*Microtus*). *J. Ecol.* 18 : 156–65.

Millais, J. G. (1904–06). The Mammals of Great Britain and Ireland. London, Longmans & Co.

Monro, Sir D. (1934). A Description of the Western Isles of Scotland called Hybrides. (First publ. 1549.) Stirling, Eneas Mackay.

Morley, A. (1943). Sexual behaviour in British birds from October to January. *Ibis*, 85 : 132–58.

Munro, J. W. (1916). *Hylastes cunicularius* Er., and its relation to the forest. *Scot Nat.* 1916 : 275–81.

Murray, J. (1905). Microscopic life of St. Kilda. *Ann. Scot. Nat. Hist.* 1905 : 94–96.

(1906). Scottish alpine Tardigrada. *Ann. Scot. Nat. Hist.* 1906 : 26–30.

PLATE 31

Loch Shiel from Glenfinnan. The Forestry Commission is planting the hillsides. Argyll–Inverness-shire border

J. Jenson

F. Fraser Darling

MODERN WEST HIGHLAND CROFT with unenclosed inbyeland. Sunart, North Argyll. August 1945

(1910). Biology of the Scottish lochs. *Bathymetrical Survey of the Scottish Fresh-water Lochs, 1* : 275–334.

NAIRN, D. (1890). Notes on Highland woods, ancient and modern. *Trans. Gaelic Soc. Inverness, 18* : 170–221.

NALL, G. H. (1930). The life of the sea trout. London, Seeley & Co.

NEWBIGIN, M. I. (1906). The Kingussie district : a geographical study. *Scot. Geogr. Mag. 22* : 285–315.

(1931). Life by the seashore. (R. Elmhirst's revised edition.) London, G. Allen & Unwin.

NEW STATISTICAL ACCOUNT OF SCOTLAND (1845). 15 vols. Edinburgh.

NICHOLSON, E. M. & FISHER, J. (1940). A bird census of St. Kilda. *Brit. Birds, London, 34* : 29–35.

NICOL, E. A. T. (1936). The brackish-water lochs of North Uist. *Proc. Roy. Soc. Edin. 56* : 169–95.

(1939). Three rare crabs from the Inner Hebrides. *Scot. Nat.* 1939 : 1–4.

NIVEN, W. N. (1902). On the distribution of certain forest trees in Scotland, as shown by the investigation of post-glacial deposits. *Scot. Geogr. Mag. 18* : 24–29.

OMOND, R. T. (1905). Zoological notes from the log-book of the Ben Nevis Observatory. *Ann. Scot. Nat. Hist.* 1905 : 129–41.

PALMER, L. J. (1926). Progress of reindeer grazing investigations in Alaska. *Bull. U.S. Dept. Agric.* No. 1423.

PEACH, B. N. & HORNE, J. (1914). Guide to the geological model of the Assynt mountains. Edinburgh, H.M.S.O.

PENNANT, T. (1774). A tour in Scotland and voyage to the Hebrides : 1772. Chester.

PETCH, C. P. (1933). The vegetation of St. Kilda. *J. Ecol. 21* : 92–100.

PHEMISTER, J. (1936). Scotland : the Northern Highlands. Edinburgh, H.M.S.O. (Geological Survey).

PICKARD-CAMBRIDGE, O. (1905). Spiders of St. Kilda. *Ann. Scot. Nat. Hist.* 1905 : 220–23.

PORTLAND, DUKE OF (1933). Fifty years and more of sport in Scotland. London, Faber.

REGAN, C. TATE (1911). The freshwater fishes of the British Isles. London, Methuen & Co.

REID, D. M. (1935). The range of the sea-urchin *Echinus esculentus*. *J. Anim. Ecol. 4* : 7–16.

Ritchie, J. (1918). Cave-hunting in Scotland. *Scot. Nat.* 1918: 97–102
(1919). The influence of man on animal life in Scotland. Cambridge, University Press.

Roebuck, W. D. (1904). *Limax tenellus* in Scotland. *Ann. Scot. Nat. Hist.* 1904 : 218–21.
(1918). The molluscan fauna of the Outer Hebrides. *Scot. Nat.* 1918 : 275–336.

St. John, C. (1884). A tour in Sutherlandshire. 2 vols. (2nd edition). Edinburgh, Douglas.
(1893). Short sketches of the wild sports and natural history of the Highlands (9th edition). London, J. Murray.

Salmon, H. M. (1935). Seals on the West Coast. *Trans. Cardiff Nat. Soc. 48* : 13–36.

Scott, T. (1890). The Invertebrate fauna of the inland waters of Scotland. *Rep. Fish. Bd. Scot. 8* : 269–96.
(1895). Invertebrate fauna of the freshwater lochs of the Outer Hebrides. *Rep. Fish. Bd. Scot.* 1895 : 237–57.

Scrope, W. (1894). Days of deer stalking. London, Hamilton Adams.

Seebohm, H. (1884). On a new species of British wren. *Zoologist, 8* : 333–35.

Service, R. (1905). Japanese larch *v.* hares and rabbits. *Ann. Scot. Nat. Hist.* 1905 : 121–22.

Sinclair, Sir J. (ed.) (1799). The statistical account of Scotland. 21 vols. Edinburgh.

Smith, R. (1900). On the seed dispersal of *Pinus sylvestris* and *Betula alba*. *Ann. Scot. Nat. Hist.* 1900 : 43–46.
(1900). Botanical survey of Scotland. II. North Perthshire district. *Scot. Geogr. Mag. 16* : 441–67.

Smith, W. G. (1911). Grass moor association. In " Types of British vegetation," ed. Tansley. Cambridge, University Press.
(1918). The distribution of *Nardus stricta* in relation to peat. *J. Ecol. 6* : 1–13.

South, R. (1909). The moths of the British Isles. 2 vols. London, F. Warne & Co.

Southern, H. N. (1938). Distribution of the bridled form of the common guillemot (*Uria aalge*). *Nature, London, 142* : 951.

Southern, H. N. & Reeve, E. C. R. (1941). Quantitative studies in the geographical variation of birds.—The common guillemot (*Uria aalge* Pont.). *Proc. Zool. Soc. Lond. 111* : 255–76.

SOUTHWELL, T. (1904). On the whale fishery from Scotland, with some account of the changes in that industry and of the species hunted. *Ann. Scot. Nat. Hist.* 1904 : 77–94.

STEPHEN, A. C. (1935). Notes on the intertidal fauna of North Uist. *Scot. Nat.* 1935 : 137–42.

STEWART, M. (1933). Ronay. Oxford, University Press.

(Ed.) (1937). St. Kilda Papers. Oxford ; collection of offprints publ. University Press.

(1938). Natural history notes on certain Scottish islands. *Scot. Nat.* 1938 : 107–14.

(1938). Notes on the gannetries of Sule Stack and Sula Sgeir. *Brit. Birds, 31* : 282–94.

STIRTON, J. (1907). West Highland mosses and problems they suggest. *Ann. Scot. Nat. Hist.* 1907 : 42–45.

STUART, J. S. & STUART, C. E. (1848). Lays of the deer forest. Edinburgh.

SUMMERHAYES, V. S. (1941). The effect of voles (*Microtus agrestis*) on vegetation. *J. Ecol. 29* : 14–48.

TANSLEY, A. G. (1939). The British Islands and their vegetation. Cambridge, University Press.

(1945). Our heritage of wild nature. Cambridge, University Press.

TARR, R. S. (1908). Glacial erosion in the Scottish Highlands. *Scot. Geogr. Mag. 24* : 575–87.

TAYLOR, W. L. (1946). The wild cat (*Felis silvestris*) in Great Britain. *J. Anim. Ecol. 15* : 130–33.

TEMPERLEY, G. W. (1938). The birds of Raasay. *Scot. Nat.* 1938 : 11–27.

THOMPSON, D'ARCY W. (1918). On whales landed at the Scottish whaling stations, especially during the years 1890–1914. Pt. I. The nordcaper. *Scot. Nat.* 1918 : 197–208. Pts. II & III. The sperm whale and the blue whale. *Ibid.* 1918 : 221–37.

TRAIL, J. W. H. (1905). The plants of the Flannan Islands. *Ann. Scot. Nat. Hist. 1905* : 187.

WALKER, J. (1812). The economical history of the Hebrides. 2 vols. London & Edinburgh.

(1812). Essays on natural history. London & Edinburgh.

WALLACE, R. (1917). Heather and moor burning for grouse and sheep. Edinburgh, Oliver & Boyd.

WALTON, G. A. (1942). The aquatic Hemiptera of the Hebrides. *Trans. Entomol. Soc. Lond. 92* : 417–52.

WARWICK, T. (1938). Notes on the mammals of the Isles of Barra, Mingulay and Berneray, Outer Hebrides. *Scot. Nat.* 1938 : 57–59

(1939). A list of the reptiles and land mammals of the Isle of Colonsay, Inner Hebrides. *Scot. Nat.* 1939 : 75–76.

(1939). Animal life on Mingulay, Outer Hebrides. *Scot. Nat.* 1939 : 127.

WATERSTON, A. R. (1939). Insects from Colonsay, South Ebudes. *Scot. Nat.* 1939 : 128–31.

WATERSTON, J. & TAYLOR, J. W. (1905). Land and freshwater molluscs of St. Kilda. *Ann. Scot. Nat. Hist.* 1905 : 21–24.

WEDDERBURN, E. M. (1910). Temperature of Scottish lakes. *Bathymetrical Survey of the Scottish Fresh-water Lochs, 1* : 91–144.

WESENBURG, L. C. (1910). Summary of our knowledge regarding various limnological problems. *Bathymetrical Survey of the Scottish Fresh-water Lochs, 1* : 374–438.

WEST, G. (1910). An epitome of a comparative study of the dominant Phanerogamic and higher Cryptogamic flora of aquatic habit, in seven lake areas in Scotland. *Bathymetrical Survey of the Scottish Fresh-water Lochs, 1* : 156–260.

WILLIAMS, F. N. (1908). The high alpine flora of Britain. *Ann. Scot. Nat. Hist.* 1908 : 163–69.

WILMOTT, A. J. (1945). Vegetation of Uig. Flora of Uig (Lewis). Ed. M. Campbell (q.v.) : 20–43.

(1946). Interesting plants found in Lewis. *Stornoway Gazette*, Nov. 8.

WILSON, R. (1915). Grey seals at Skerryvore. *Scot. Nat.* 1915 : 282.

WOOLDRIDGE, S. W. & MORGAN, R. S. (1937). The physical basis of geography. London, Longmans & Co.

MAPS SHOWING THE DISTRIBUTION OF CERTAIN ANIMALS IN THE HIGHLANDS

The fifteen maps that follow have been drawn by James Fisher specially for this book. The fundamental information is derived from notes and maps collected in the field, and from the literature, mostly by the writer ; the actual responsibility is as follows :—

For badger, red squirrel, capercaillie, wild cat, grey seal in the Highlands, red deer, golden eagle, dotterel and ptarmigan : F. Fraser Darling.
For great spotted woodpecker, pine marten and snow bunting : F. F. Darling mostly, James Fisher for northern limit of range.
For grey seal in Orkney and Shetland, J. G. Millais (1904–06).
For gannet, Leach's fork-tailed petrel and fulmar : James Fisher.

On the maps of the distribution of the grey seal, and of the three sea-birds, the dots represent the actual positions of the known breeding-stations. On the other maps each dot represents the intersection of two 10-km. lines of the National Grid, nearest to each place known to be inhabited by the species in the breeding-season. The radius of the dot-circles was chosen to represent about 7 km., so that for a land area of continuous distribution there is just enough overlap between the dots to make a continuously black area on the map. The National Grid is marked round the edge of the map.

Though involving considerably more research, this method gives a better approximation to reality than for instance, a crude blocking-in of vice-counties (which would, at the scale chosen, give a quite false impression of the distribution). In the cases of the eagle and dotterel the ranges may be somewhat exaggerated, as it is not possible (or indeed desirable) to indicate just what breeding-stations are inhabited each year. Otherwise the maps represent a first approximation to the position at the present time. Doubtless there will be changes in the future, and the amateur naturalist's help is always needed to keep such maps up to date and in correcting errors.

The dotted line on the maps represents the Highland Border Fault (see p. 2), the southern limit of the area under particular review. Maps 1–4 are of four animals which live to at least some extent in woodland. Maps 5–7 are of what many regard as the three most interesting British carnivores. Map 8 is of Britain's biggest wild land animal. Maps 9–12 are of four mountain animals, and maps 13–15 are of three sea-birds.

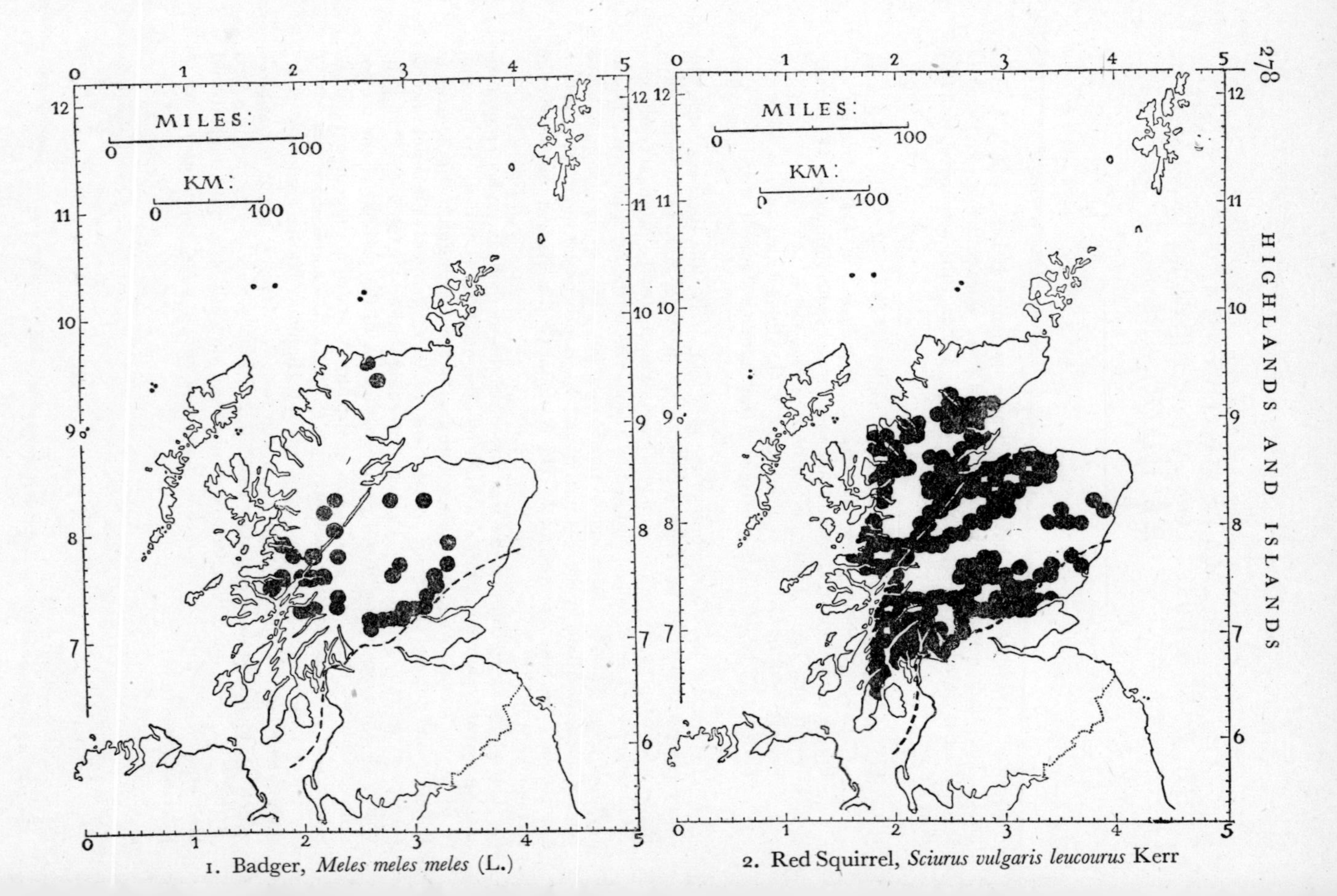

1. Badger, *Meles meles meles* (L.)

2. Red Squirrel, *Sciurus vulgaris leucourus* Kerr

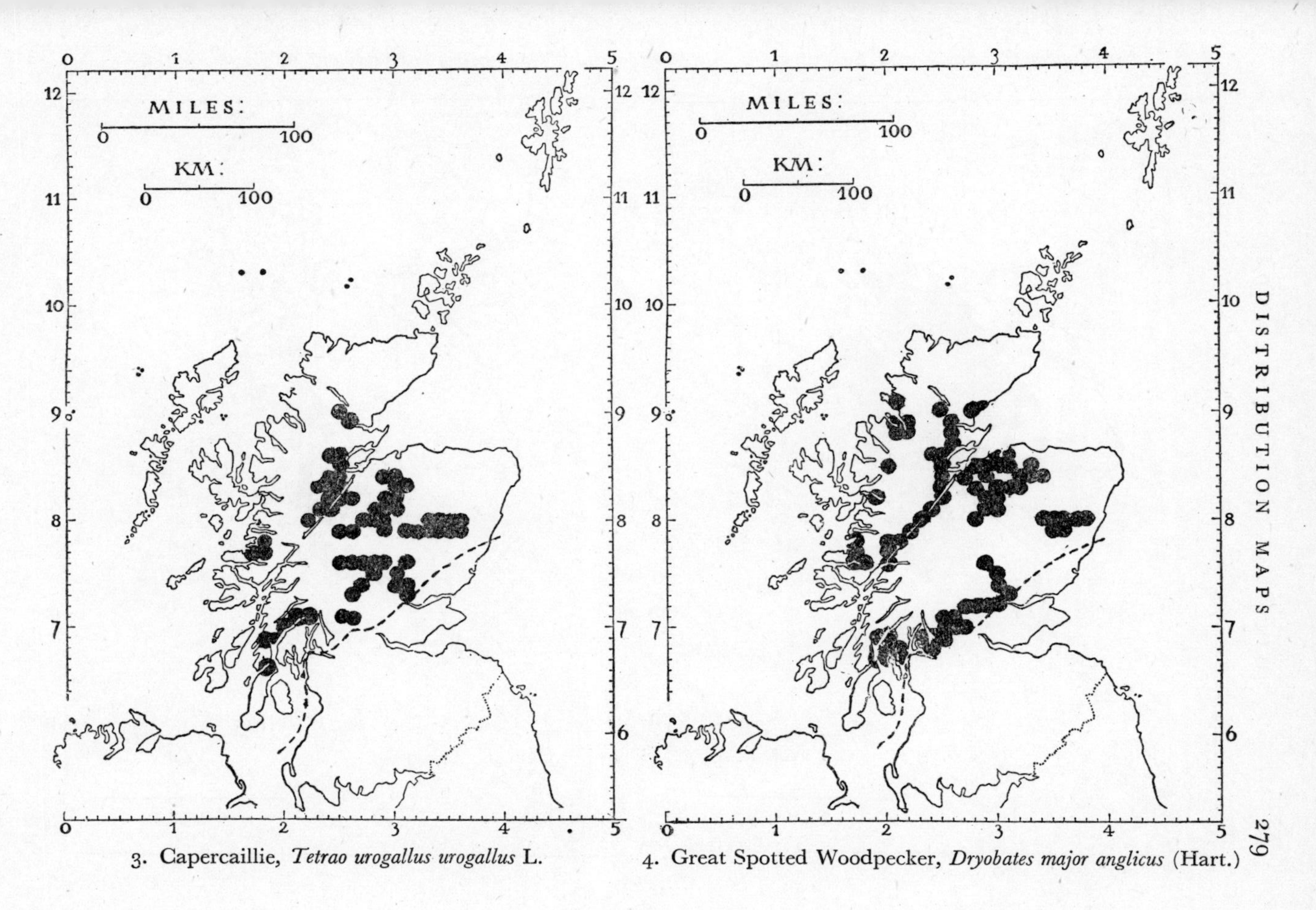

3. Capercaillie, *Tetrao urogallus urogallus* L.

4. Great Spotted Woodpecker, *Dryobates major anglicus* (Hart.)

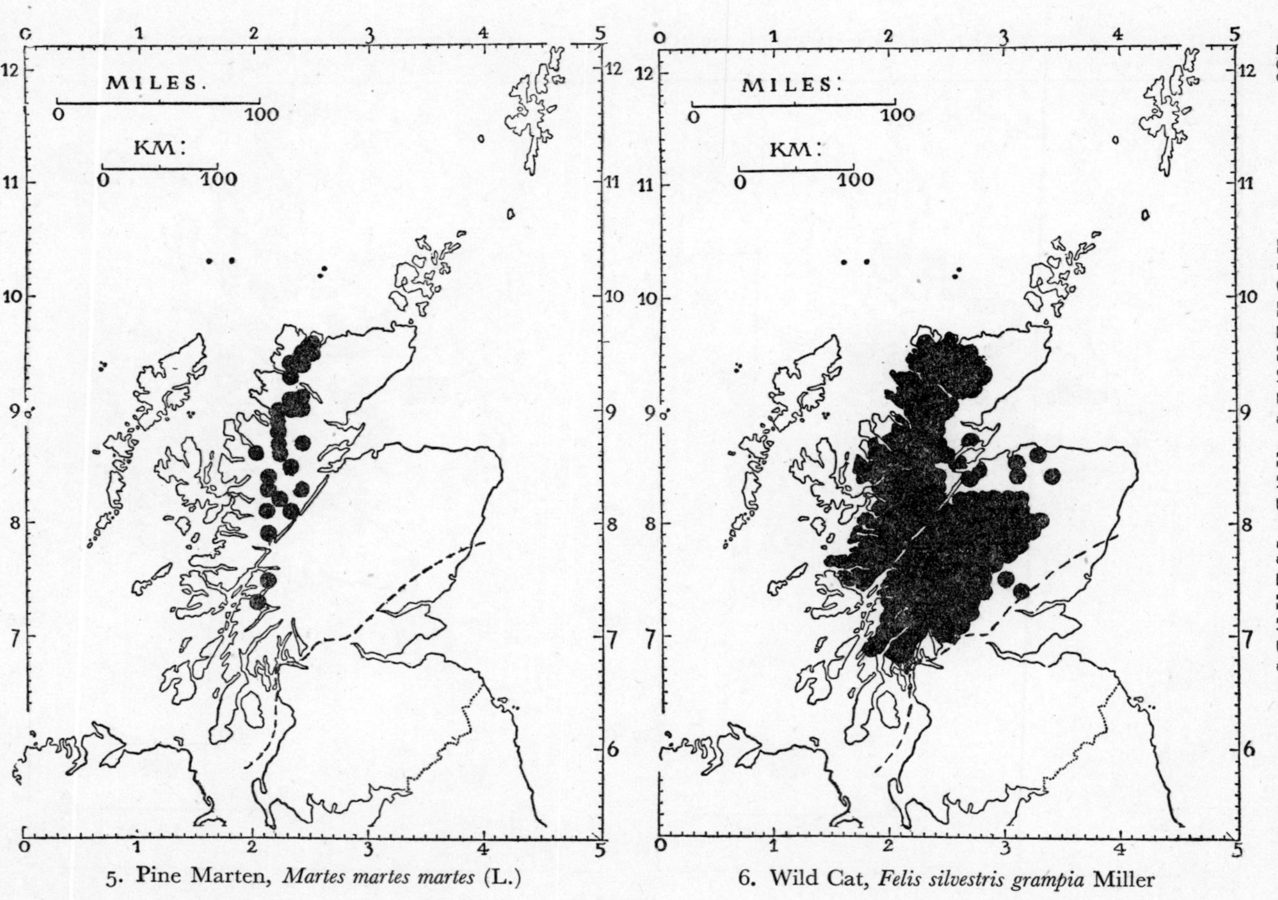

5. Pine Marten, *Martes martes martes* (L.)

6. Wild Cat, *Felis silvestris grampia* Miller

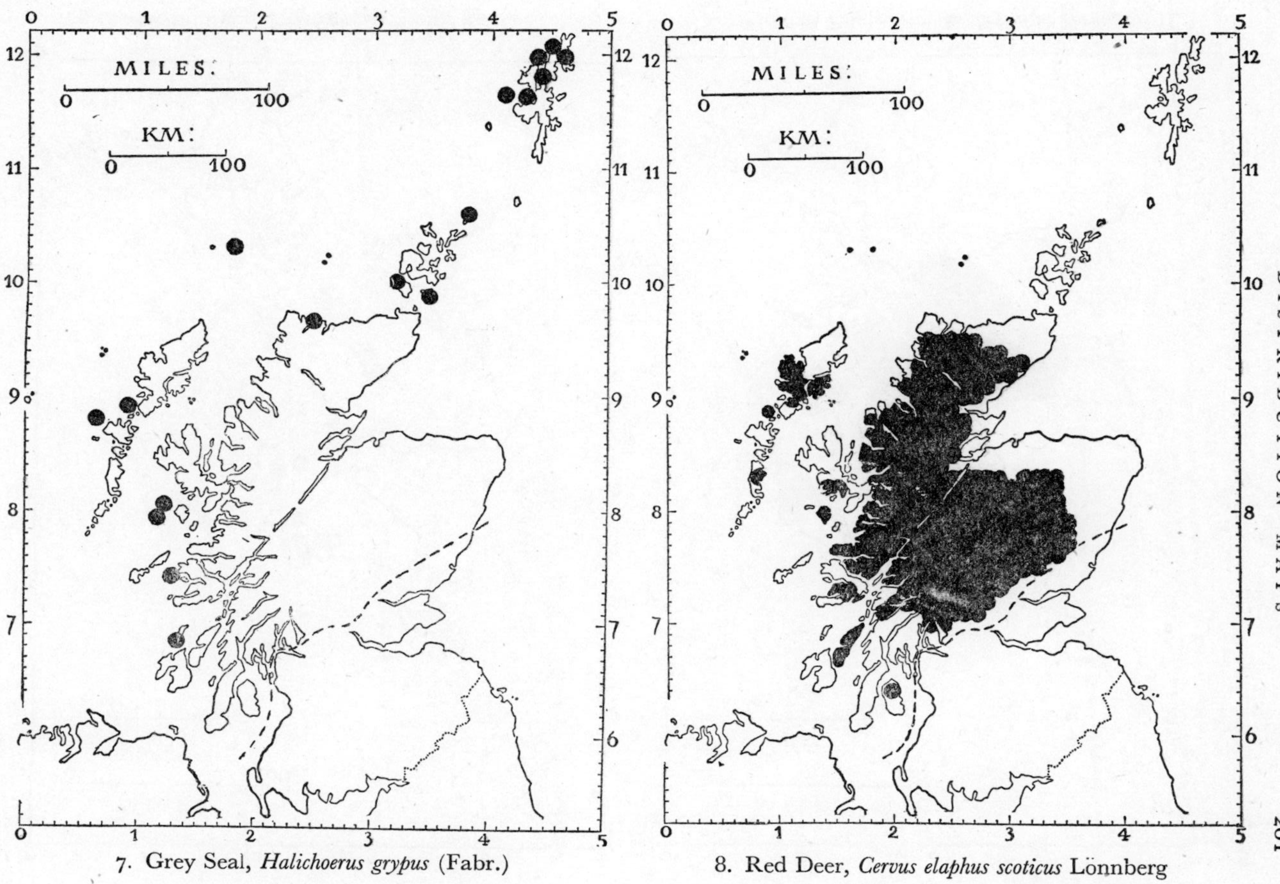

7. Grey Seal, *Halichoerus grypus* (Fabr.)

8. Red Deer, *Cervus elaphus scoticus* Lönnberg

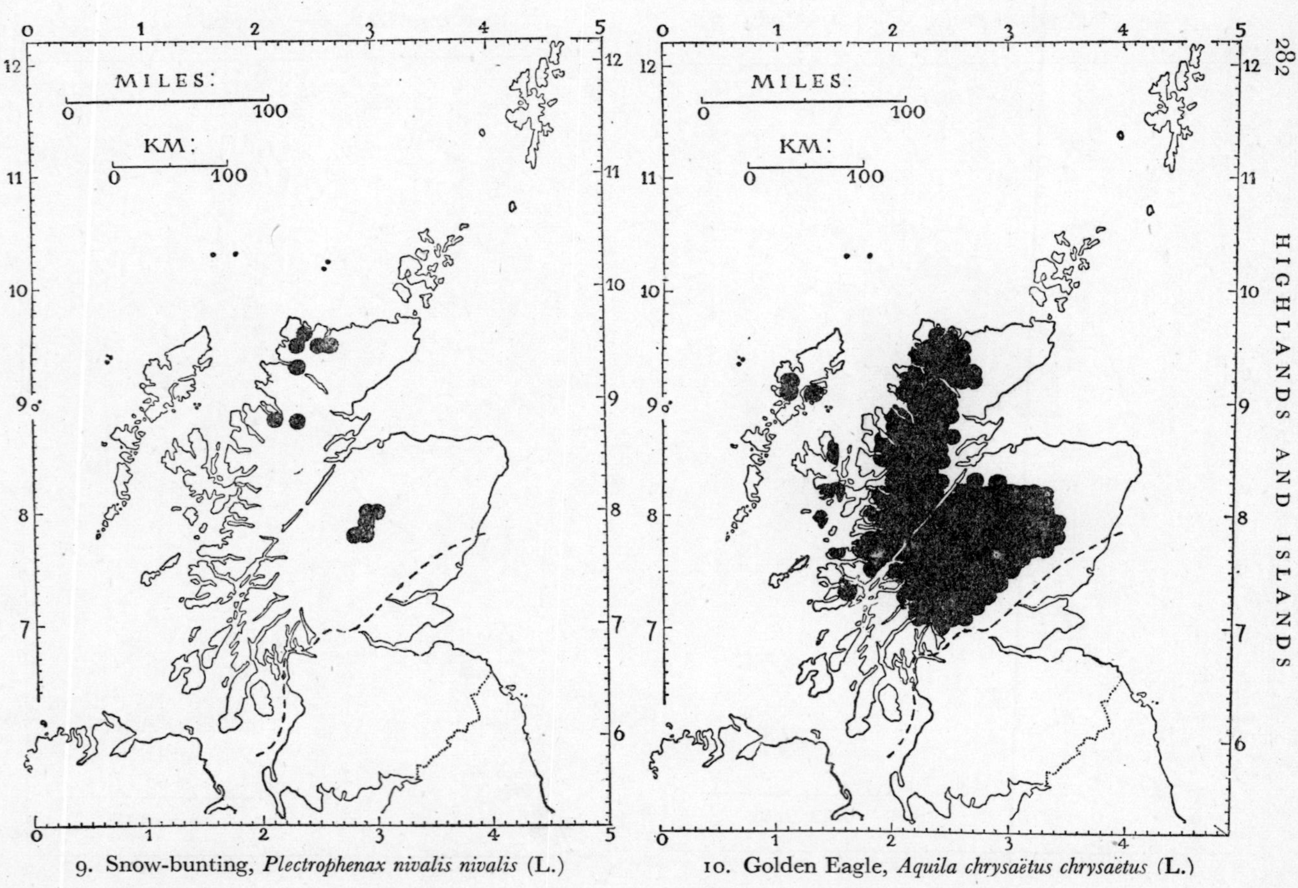

9. Snow-bunting, *Plectrophenax nivalis nivalis* (L.)

10. Golden Eagle, *Aquila chrysaëtus chrysaëtus* (L.)

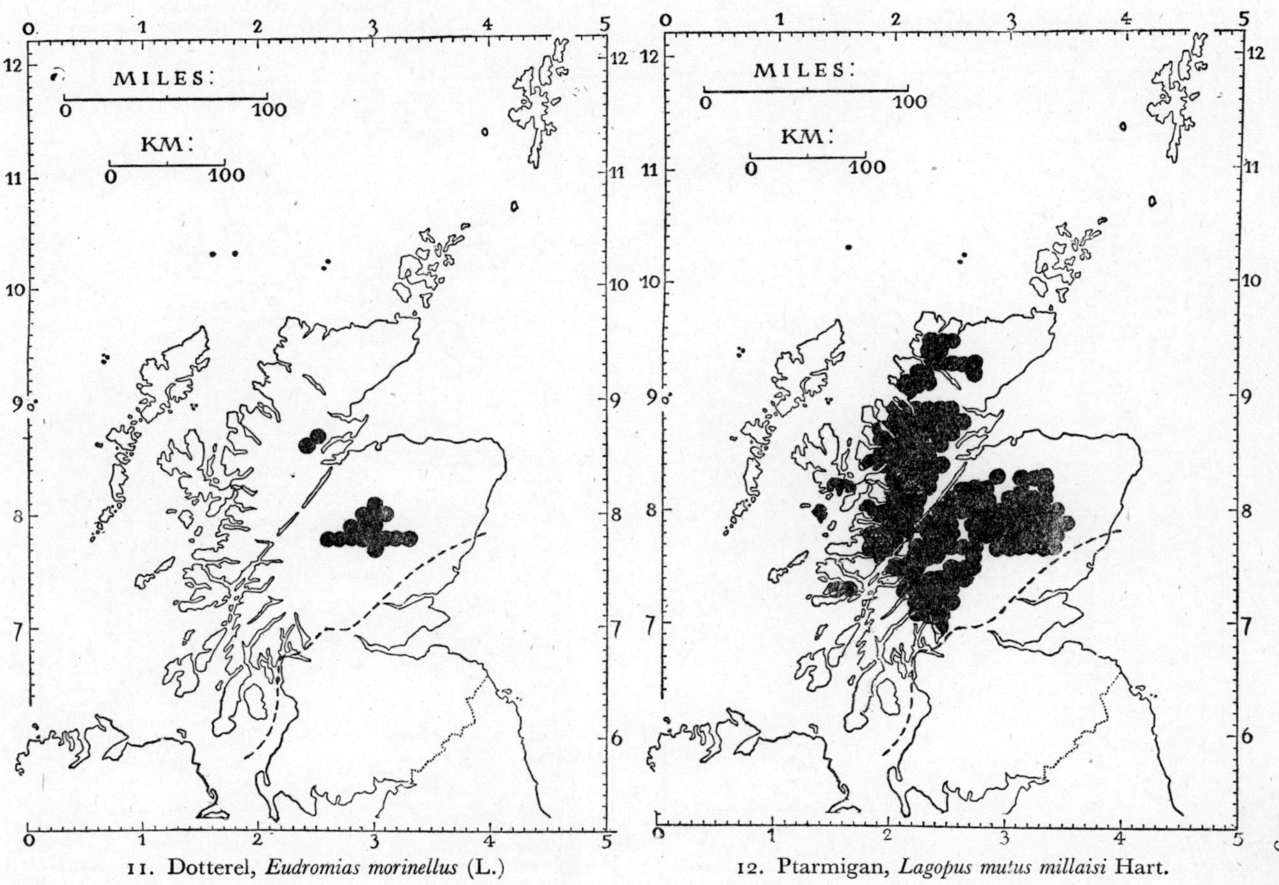

11. Dotterel, *Eudromias morinellus* (L.)

12. Ptarmigan, *Lagopus mutus millaisi* Hart.

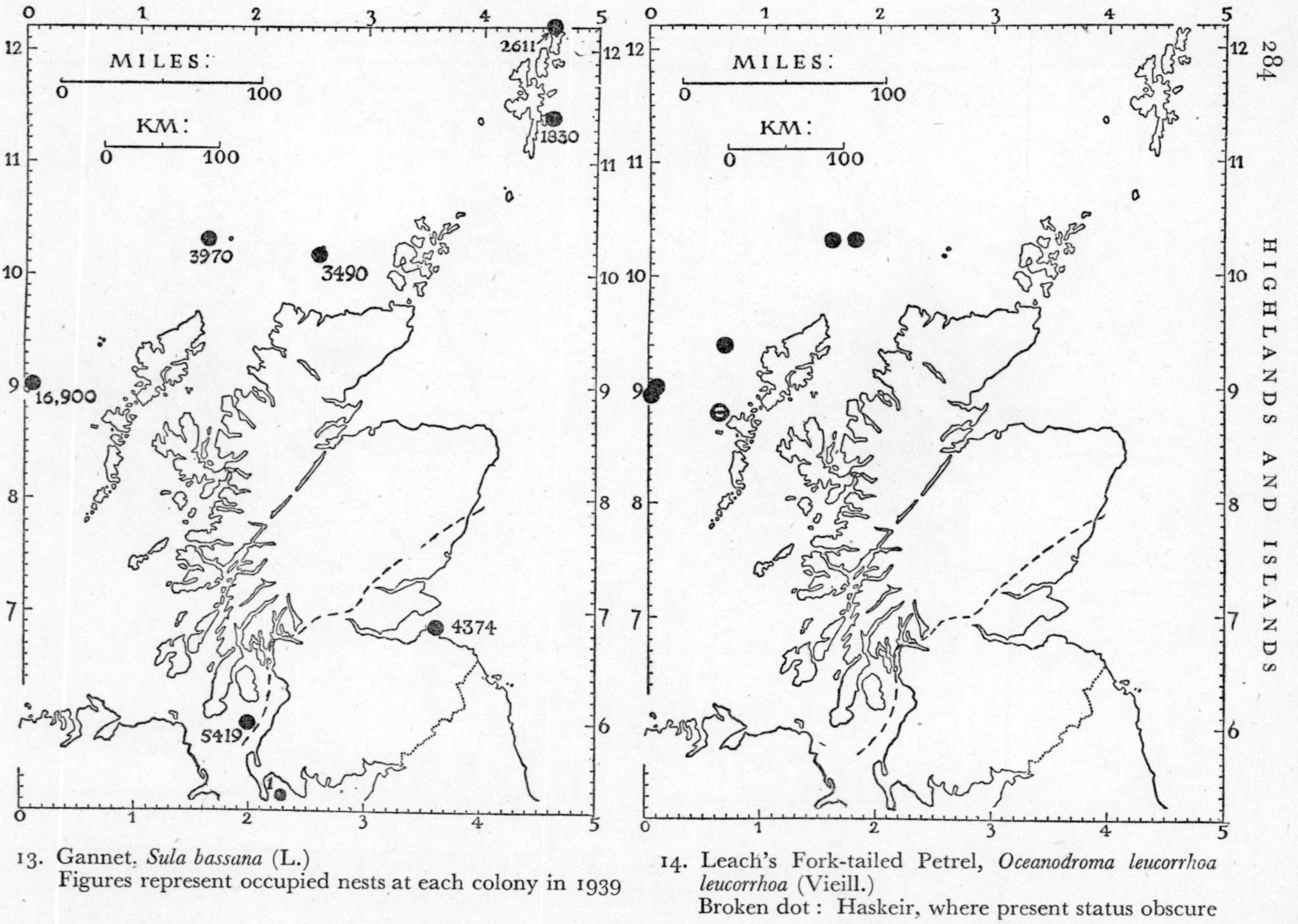

13. Gannet. *Sula bassana* (L.)
Figures represent occupied nests at each colony in 1939

14. Leach's Fork-tailed Petrel, *Oceanodroma leucorrhoa leucorrhoa* (Vieill.)
Broken dot: Haskeir, where present status obscure

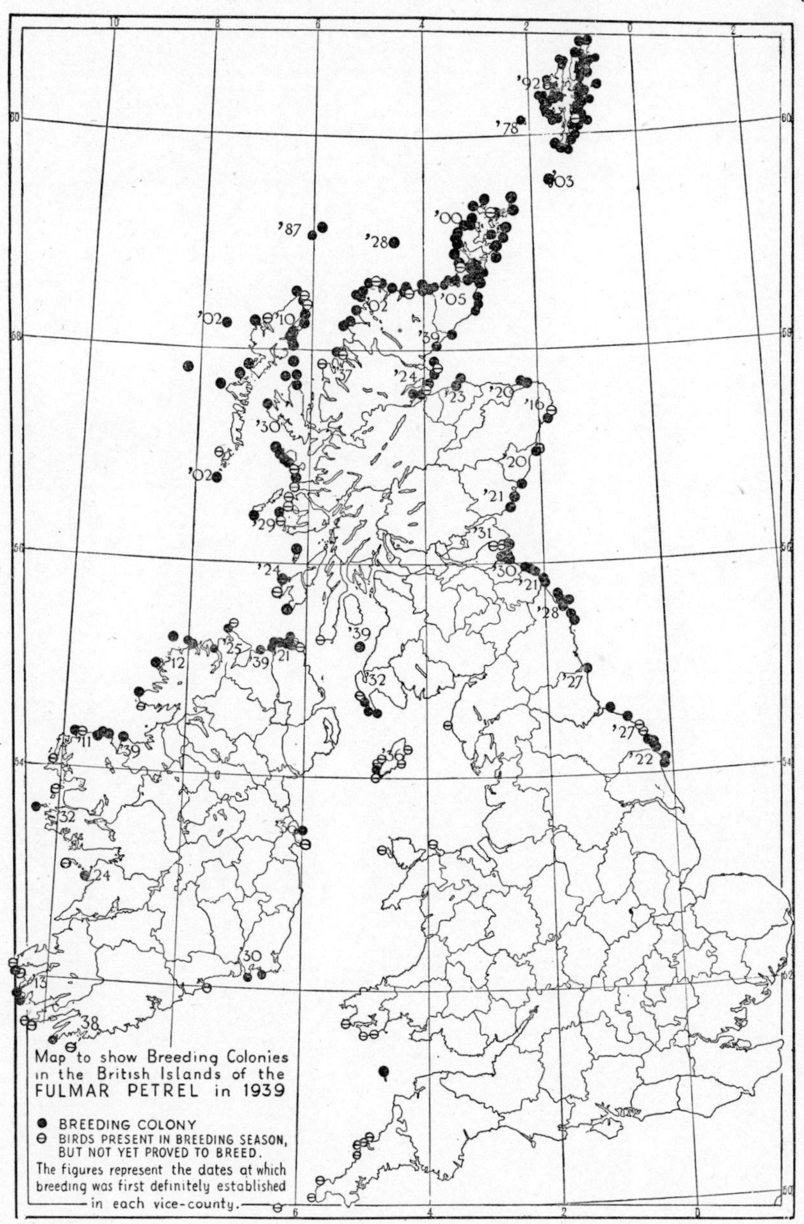

15. Fulmar, *Fulmarus glacialis glacialis* (L.)

INDEX

Arabic numerals in heavy type indicate Colour Plates; roman numerals refer to Black-and-White Plates.